teacher's handbook

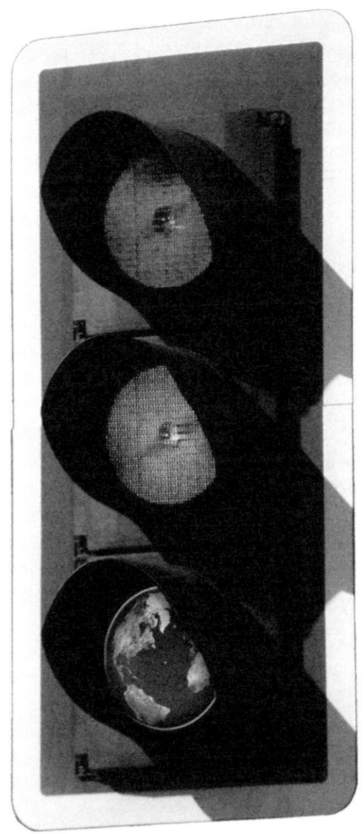

◆ starters ◆ plenaries ◆ objectives and outcomes
◆ answers ◆ further suggestions for class and homework

< rosemarie gallagher >

OXFORD

Great Clarendon Street, Oxford OX2 6DP

Oxford University Press is a department of the University of Oxford. It furthers the University's objective of excellence in research, scholarship, and education by publishing worldwide in

Oxford New York

Auckland Cape Town Dar es Salaam Hong Kong Karachi Kuala Lumpur Madrid Melbourne Mexico City Nairobi New Delhi Shanghai Taipei Toronto

With offices in

Argentina Austria Brazil Chile Czech Republic France Greece Guatemala Hungary Italy Japan Poland Portugal Singapore South Korea Switzerland Thailand Turkey Ukraine Vietnam

First published 2000

Second Edition 2005

Third Edition 2008

British Library Cataloguing in Publication Data

Data available

ISBN 978-0-19-913499-1

10 9 8 7 6 5 4 3 2 1

Printed by Bell and Bain Ltd., Glasgow

Paper used in the production of this book is a natural, recyclable product made from wood grown in sustainable forests. The manufacturing process conforms to the environmental regulations of the country of origin.

The publisher and author would like to thank the following for their excellent contribution to this book: Richard Farmer, Margaret Hunter, Katherine James, and Anna King.

Contents

About this course

geog.1 is the first book of *geog.123* – the complete geography course for KS3. The course covers the KS3 Programme of Study, and provides excellent support for Assessment for Learning.

The course components

The course consists of:

For pupils
- three pupils' books
- three workbooks

For teachers
- three handbooks
- three assessment files, each with an OxBox CD-ROM
- three resources and planning OxBox CD-ROMs

Find out more about the course components by looking at these panels.

The pupils' books
- Three books for the course
- Chapters divided into two-page units
- Chapter openers give the big picture – the big ideas behind the chapter – and the goals for the chapter
- Aims of unit given in pupil-friendly language at the start of each unit
- 'Your turn' questions at the end of each unit

The teacher's handbooks
- One for each pupils' book
- Chapter overviews
- Help at a glance for each unit
- Ideas for starters and plenaries for each unit
- Outcomes for each unit
- Answers for 'Your turn' questions
- Further suggestions for class and homework
- Glossary

The workbooks
- One for each pupils' book
- Support for each unit in the pupils' book
- Fill-in activities
- Ideal for homework and independent study

For more information, see page 18.

geog.123 provides a wide range of materials. The pupils' books are the core of the course. They combine a rigorous approach to content with a uniquely engaging style.

You can decide how to use the wealth of support materials, but notes in the teacher's handbooks will point you towards appropriate material in the assessment files and the resources and planning OxBox CD-ROMs. The result is a truly comprehensive and flexible geography course – which we hope you will enjoy using.

OxBox technology

OxBox CD-ROMs are bought individually. The software then allows the content to be tipped together to create a single resource on your network.

They are customisable – you can add your own resources. There are easy-to-follow guidelines on how to do this.

The resources and planning OxBox CD-ROMs

- One for each pupils' book
- Video clips and photo movies with run-times of between one and four minutes
- PowerPoint presentations
- All the photos, maps, and diagrams from the students' book
- Interactive activities for each chapter
- Editable and photocopiable worksheets, with answers
- Editable and photocopiable enquiries, decision-making exercises, role-plays, fieldwork, games, and thinking skills activities – with opportunities for pair and group work
- Editable 'Your turn' questions
- Ready-made and customisable course and lesson plans; the lesson player helps you arrange and launch the resources you want to use in sequence
- User management facility that allows you to easily import class registers and create user accounts for all your students

For more information, see pages 12-15.

The assessment file & OxBox CD-ROMs

- One for each pupils' book
- Assessment overviews
- Level-marked assessments with success criteria and feedback forms – photocopiable and editable
- Scored tests, with mark schemes – photocopiable and editable
- Interactive formative assessments answered on-screen, with feedback after every question and auto-marked results
- Interactive summative assessments answered on-screen, with auto-marking and levelled feedback
- You can create your own formative and summative assessment questions
- Self-assessment forms – photocopiable and editable

For more information, see pages 16-17.

Using this book

This book aims to save you time and effort! It offers full support for *geog.1* students' book, and will help you prepare detailed course and lesson plans.

What it provides

For each chapter of the students' book, this book provides:

1 a chapter overview
2 help at a glance for each unit, including answers for 'Your turn'
3 further suggestions for class and homework.

It also has a glossary at the back, covering the geographical terms the students will meet.

Please turn to the contents list on page 3 now, to see how this book is structured.
Then find out more about the three main components, below.

1 The chapter overview

This is your introduction to the corresponding students' chapter. Look at its sections.

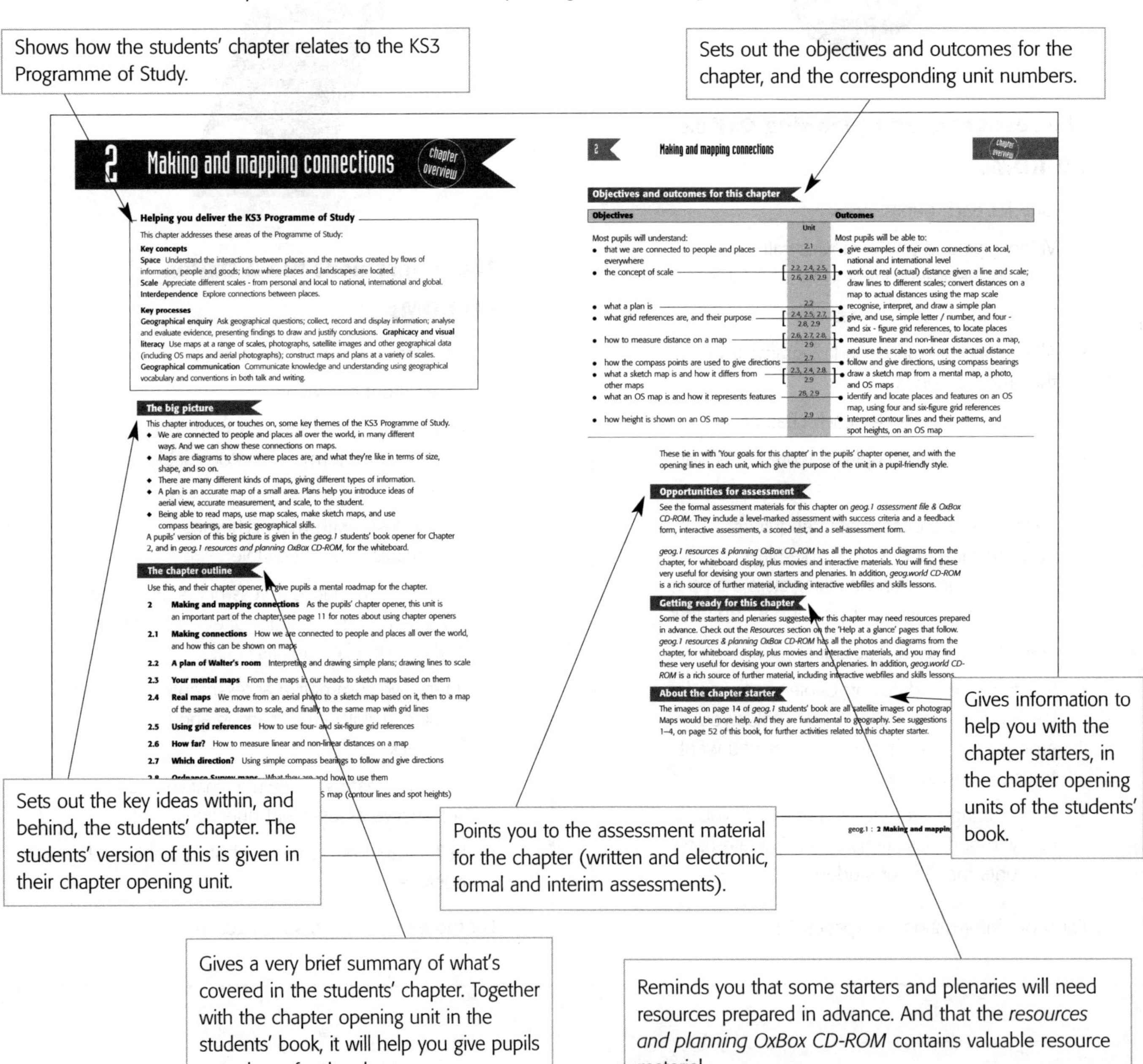

Shows how the students' chapter relates to the KS3 Programme of Study.
Sets out the objectives and outcomes for the chapter, and the corresponding unit numbers.
Sets out the key ideas within, and behind, the students' chapter. The students' version of this is given in their chapter opening unit.
Points you to the assessment material for the chapter (written and electronic, formal and interim assessments).
Gives information to help you with the chapter starters, in the chapter opening units of the students' book.
Gives a very brief summary of what's covered in the students' chapter. Together with the chapter opening unit in the students' book, it will help you give pupils a roadmap for the chapter.
Reminds you that some starters and plenaries will need resources prepared in advance. And that the *resources and planning OxBox CD-ROM* contains valuable resource material.

2 Help at a glance for each unit

These pages give comprehensive help for each unit of *geog.1* students' book.

Starts with a brief walk through the unit, to show you how it develops.

Summarises ideas covered in the unit, plus underlying ideas where appropriate.

Suggests plenaries for throughout the lesson, not just at the end.

New vocabulary introduced in the unit. See the glossary at the back of this book.

A breakdown of the skills practised. It will help you identify where pupils may need extra support.

Expected outcomes for the unit. They tie in with the expected outcomes for the chapter.

2.8 **Ordnance Survey maps** *help at a glance*

About this unit

This unit presents the first OS map of the course. It's a fairly simple map that includes Warkworth, which also appeared in the photo on page 22. 'Your turn' gives pupils practice in identifying OS symbols and using grid references.

Key ideas

- Ordnance Survey (OS) maps are always to scale and show a lot of detail.
- The OS maps that pupils meet in *geog.1* are at scales of 1:25 000 and 1:50 000 (or 1 cm to 250 m and 1 cm to 500 m).
- OS maps use numbered grid lines, and standard symbols to represent different features. (See the key for the symbols on page 138 of the student's book.)

Key vocabulary

Ordnance Survey, symbols

Skills practised in 'Your turn'

- Geography skills: reading an OS map and identifying OS map symbols; using four- and six-figure grid references for an OS map; comparing an OS map with a photo; measuring distance on an OS map using the 1:25 000 scale; drawing a sketch map from an OS map
- Thinking skills: drawing conclusions about population, tourism, and coastal dangers, from information shown on the OS map

Unit outcomes

By the end of this unit, most pupils should be able to:

- explain what Ordnance Survey maps are, and what kinds of features they show
- interpret OS symbols using a key
- use four- and six-figure grid references, for an OS map
- use an OS map to look for clues and gather information about a place
- draw a sketch map from an OS map, to show a route

Resources

For starter **2**: a set of flash cards with OS symbols on
For starters **3** and **4** and plenaries **1**, **2**, and **4**: all images from the book are on *geog.1 resources and planning OxBox CD-ROM*
Note: your pupils will find rulers helpful for working out grid references

Ideas for a starter

1 You are a map designer. How would you show a forest on a map? a river? a school? a church? a bridge? a phone box? a picnic area? (A short list of items could be written on the board.) Work with a partner to design symbols to use. Swap these (no labels!) with another pair of pupils and see if they can guess which is which.
2 With the books closed, hold up some flash cards with OS symbols on (or draw them on the board). Ask pupils to guess what the symbols mean.
3 Look at the OS map from page 31. (You can display it on the whiteboard, with the books closed.) What does the large blue area represent? What about the yellow area? What is the wide blue squiggle? What are the little beige rectangles? (and so on). Pupils try to guess without looking at the key.
4 The place in the photo on page 22 is shown on the OS map on page 31. Where? (You can display the photo.) What features from the photo are shown on the map?

48 geog.1 : **2 Making and mapping connections**

help at a glance

Ideas for plenaries

Plan plenaries for strategic points throughout the lesson, as well as at the end.

1 Look at the scale on the OS map. (You can display the map and scale on the whiteboard.) How far apart are the grid lines, in cm? What distance does that represent on the ground? What distance does 1 cm represent?
2 What clues can you find on the OS map, about how people in the area earn a living?
3 When might you find an OS map useful, outside school? For example would it be useful on holiday? If you were a walker or camper?
4 I spy with my little eye ... a public phone box (or Birling golf links, or Hermitage Farm, or similar). A pupil calls out something he or she sees on the OS map on page 31. Other pupils must quickly give a four-figure grid reference. Have a timekeeper, and see how many things can be found in five minutes. Or allow only so many seconds for each one. (You could display the map on the whiteboard for this.)
5 OS bingo: pupils choose any nine symbols from the key on page 30 and draw them into a 3 X 3 grid. The teacher calls out a list of features and pupils cross them off. The first to cross odd all nine symbols wins.
6 How do you think OS maps get made? (This could become a homework project. See suggestion 34 on page 53.)

Further class and homework activities

Worksheet 2G on *geog.1 resources and planning OxBox CD-ROM*
Police chase! and *OS Lotto* on *geog.1 resources and planning OxBox CD-ROM*
Suggestions 31 – 34 on page 53 of this book

Answers to 'Your turn'

1 The river is the River Coquet. It flows into the North Sea at Amble.
2 a 2407 **b** 2504 **c** 2705
3 a New Barns **b** a caravan park **c** Warkworth Castle
d Hermitage Farm **e** a cemetery **f** a lighthouse
4 4 cm on the OS map represents 1 km in real life. (So 1 cm on the map represents a quarter of a kilometre, or 0.25 km, or 250 metres.)
5 The top of the photo is north.
6 Violet lives in the house on the corner at 248056.
7 The population of Amble is 5600 (or 3.5 times the population of Warkworth). The map shows that Amble has a larger built-up area; it has 3 or 4 times as many buildings as Warkworth (but not 5 or 6 times as many). You can also tell that Amble is larger because it has five schools, while Warkworth has just one.
8 a five (one in 2503, one on 2603, one in 2604, two in 2704)
b four (all in 2604)
c two (one in 2504, the other in 2704)
9 a post office: 247060 (or 267046) **b** club house: 254066
c phone box: 275042 (or 234067) **d** mast: 266039 (or 265041)
For **c**, leader lines point to the exact location. Students may have difficulty with a grid reference for the second phone box in **c**, since only part of the square is shown.
10 campsite in 2506 and caravan sites in 2704 and 2506; caravan park in 2505; two parking areas in 2704; information centre in 2604; picnic sites in 2506 and 2604
11 These are some of the things visitors can do:
visit some historic spots – the ruins of the castle and hermitage, the old bridge in Warkworth, and the marked rock in 2303; explore Warkworth and Amble; explore the National Trust area in 2508; lie on the beach, or swim; play golf; take boat trips out to sea; go sailing in the sea in their own boats; go fishing in the river or sea; take long walks by the river; clamber about on the rocks by the sea, looking in rock pools; have picnics; enjoy camping or caravanning.
12 the lighthouse in 2705; the beacons in 2704 and 2705; the lifeboat station at 266047
13 a It's just about 3 km from Violet's home to the school in 2503.
b Pupils' sketch maps could look like this one (but larger):

My journey to school

WARKWORTH
North Sea
weir on river
my house
A1068
AMBLE
school
B6345
I don't see the sea on my journey
I see the river and a weir, and a muddy area, and shingle
I see lots of open land
We turn of the A1068 here
Key
built-up area
river/sea
open land
mud
beach
shingle

geog.1 : **2 Making and mapping connections** 49

Resources needed for some of the suggested starters and plenaries.

Suggestions for starters.

Full answers to the 'Your turn' questions in the students' book, to save you time.

Points you to related material, including interactive activities, worksheets, homework ideas, and assessment opportunities.

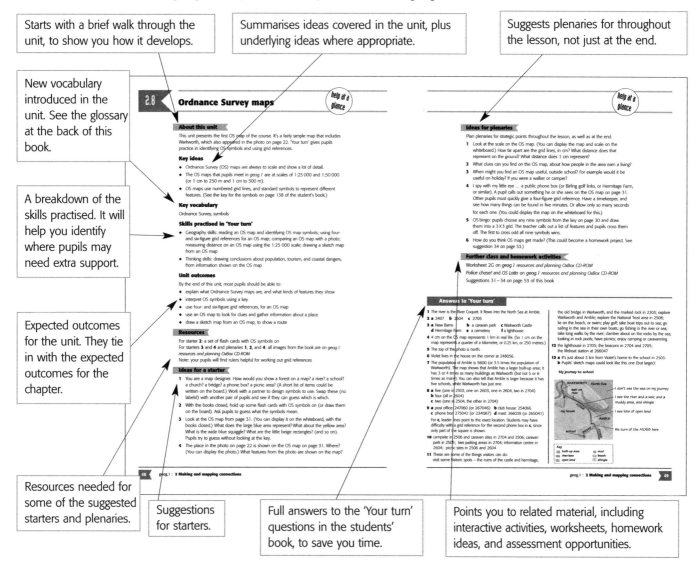

3 Further suggestions for class and homework

These pages give a wealth of further suggestions for class and homework. They have been graded *****, ****** or ******* according to level of difficulty. Some are suitable for all levels, and differentiated by outcome.

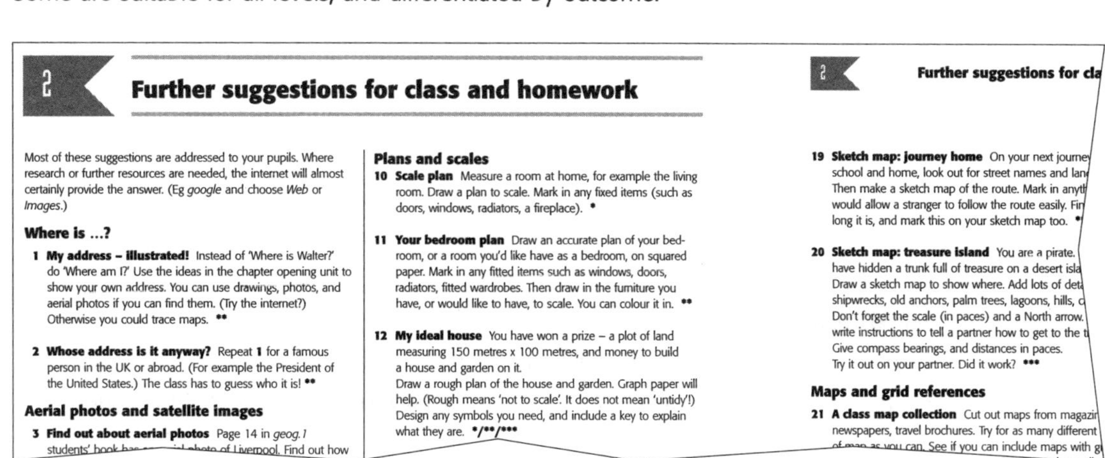

2 **Further suggestions for class and homework**

Most of these suggestions are addressed to your pupils. Where research or further resources are needed, the internet will almost certainly provide the answer. (Eg *google* and choose *Web* or *Images*.)

Where is ...?

1 My address – illustrated! Instead of 'Where is Walter?' do 'Where am I?' Use the ideas in the chapter opening unit to show your own address. You can use drawings, photos, and aerial photos if you can find them. (Try the internet?) Otherwise you could trace maps. **

2 Whose address is it anyway? Repeat **1** for a famous person in the UK or abroad. (For example the President of the United States.) The class has to guess who it is! **

Aerial photos and satellite images

3 Find out about aerial photos Page 14 in *geog.1* students' book has ... of Liverpool. Find out how

Plans and scales

10 Scale plan Measure a room at home, for example the living room. Draw a plan to scale. Mark in any fixed items (such as doors, windows, radiators, a fireplace). *

11 Your bedroom plan Draw an accurate plan of your bedroom, or a room you'd like have as a bedroom, on squared paper. Mark in any fitted items such as windows, doors, radiators, fitted wardrobes. Then draw in the furniture you have, or would like to have, to scale. You can colour it in. **

12 My ideal house You have won a prize – a plot of land measuring 150 metres x 100 metres, and money to build a house and garden on it.
Draw a rough plan of the house and garden. Graph paper will help. (Rough means 'not to scale'. It does not mean 'untidy'!) Design any symbols you need, and include a key to explain what they are. */**/***

2 **Further suggestions for cla**

19 Sketch map: journey home On your next journey school and home, look out for street names and lan Then make a sketch map of the route. Mark in anyth would allow a stranger to follow the route easily. Fir long it is, and mark this on your sketch map too. *

20 Sketch map: treasure island You are a pirate. have hidden a trunk full of treasure on a desert isla Draw a sketch map to show where. Add lots of det shipwrecks, old anchors, palm trees, lagoons, hills, c Don't forget the scale (in paces) and a North arrow. write instructions to tell a partner how to get to the t Give compass bearings, and distances in paces. Try it out on your partner. Did it work? ***

Maps and grid references

21 A class map collection Cut out maps from magazi newspapers, travel brochures. Try for as many different of map as you can. See if you can include maps with g

Planning your lessons around *geog.1*

Planning for high-quality lessons

Well-planned and well-structured lessons are a key requirement, for delivering high-quality teaching and learning in any subject, at any level. The *geog.123* course aims to make it easy to plan, structure, and deliver, high-quality lessons for KS3 geography.

Structure of a typical lesson

You will already be familiar with guidelines on structuring lessons. This shows a typical lesson structure.

STARTER

Purpose: To capture pupils' attention and focus the class. Use it as the lesson hook, or to find out what pupils know already about a new topic, or for quick revision of earlier work.

INTRODUCTION

Purpose: To prepare pupils for the activities ahead.

- If this is a new topic, tell pupils the topic objectives. Write these on the board.
- If it's a continuation of a topic, you can refer back to an objective as appropriate.

ACTIVITIES

This is the main body of the lesson.

Purpose: To achieve one or more of the topic objectives.

- Emphasis on exploration and investigation.
- Provide for practice in different types of skill: geographical, literacy, numeracy, thinking, listening, speaking, teamworking, and ICT skills.
- Choose from a variety of activities: reading, answering questions, enquiries, role play, game playing, fieldwork, and ICT.

Plenaries: note that plenaries can be used as staging posts throughout the activities, to gain feedback, check understanding, link to earlier work, and encourage reflection on what is being learnt, and how.

FINAL PLENARY

Purpose: To round off and review what has been done, and to assess what has been achieved against the topic objectives. This is where you help pupils to:

- check, and crystallise, their understanding
- generalise, for example from an individual case study
- set work in context, and make links to work already done, or to be done in the future
- reflect on how they have learned, as well as what
- check how well they have achieved the topic objectives (self-assessment).

HOMEWORK

Purpose: To confirm, give practice in, and extend, what has been learnt in the lesson.

- The homework can lead on from the final plenary, and be the basis for a starter for the next lesson.

Planning around *geog.1*

Now see how the components of *geog.1* provide material for each part of your lesson.

STARTERS

- The 'Help at a glance' pages in this book have suggestions for lesson starters.
- See further notes about starters, and resources for them, in this book.

OBJECTIVES

- The opening lines of each unit in the students' book give the purpose of the unit, in pupil-friendly language. The goals for each chapter are given in its opening unit.
- See also the objectives and outcomes given in this book.

ACTIVITIES

Using the students' book

- The text in the students' book provides the core information students need. Some lends itself to reading aloud, but try 'quiet time' too.
- You can let pupils work through the text uninterrupted, or break it up with 'Your turn' questions. (These generally follow the order of the text.)
- The questions give practice in literacy, numeracy, thinking, and geography skills.
- Some are ideal as whole-class questions with verbal response. Others can be worked through by pupils working alone, in pairs or in small groups. The final 'Your turn' questions are usually open questions that challenge pupils to show what they can do.
- For pupils who finish early, check out 'Further suggestions for class and homework' at the end of each chapter in this book. Or select a worksheet from the *resources and planning OxBox CD-ROM.*

Using the resources and planning OxBox CD-ROM

- The *resources and planning OxBox CD-ROM* gives you an extensive bank of material you can use in lessons – video clips, PowerPoint presentations, interactive activities, worksheets, enquiries, and editable 'Your turn' questions.
- Much of the material is suitable for whole-class teaching using an interactive whiteboard or projector, and offers scope for vibrant and effective lessons.

Using *geog.world*

- The *geog.world CD-ROM* has many activities you can base lessons on. These include interactive lessons with scored questions, skills lessons, and webfiles with on-screen worksheets.

PLENARIES

- The 'Help at a glance' pages in the this book give suggestions for plenaries, for throughout the lesson as well as at the end.
- See further notes about plenaries, and resources for them, in the this book.

HOMEWORK

- 'Further suggestions for class and homework' at the end of each chapter in this book offer lots of ideas.
- Select a worksheet from the *resources and planning OxBox CD-ROM*.
- The *workbook* provides support for every unit in the students' book.

More about starters and plenaries

Planning your starters and plenaries

Effective starters and plenaries need to be planned for. With planning, you can ensure that they'll help you to meet your lesson objectives, and that you won't have to rely on sudden inspiration in the classroom. But even where they are planned, you may want and need to modify them as you go along, in response to your pupils.

Our suggestions for starters and plenaries

The kinds of activities you feel comfortable with, for starters and plenaries, will depend on your teaching style, and the individual class. So the suggestions for starters and plenaries in this book are just that: suggestions! You may want to use some as described, or adapt them. Or they may provide inspiration for new ideas of your own.

The starters

- Most of these are intended for use with the students' books closed, before pupils have looked at the new unit. But they lead seamlessly into the work in the students' book.
- In some cases you may want to combine two starters to give a more extended one.
- A number of starters require the use of an atlas, and can be an excellent way of giving your pupils atlas practice that's fun.
- Other starters require both physical and mental activity – for example creating a graffiti wall on the board. This is a good way to get everyone involved.

The plenaries

- There are suggestions for plenaries for throughout the lesson, not just at the end.
- They have been chosen for a variety of purposes: to encourage feedback; assess understanding; promote reflection; build bridges with material already covered (or still to be covered), with other subjects, and with the real world; help crystallise what has been learnt; and see whether it applies to other situations.
- Some of the plenaries are single questions. You will find that you can readily combine some to make more extended plenaries.
- Some need more preparation than others. You might not want to choose these for every class, but it's a good idea to ring the changes, and keep your pupils surprised.
- Together with 'Your turn', the *Ideas for plenaries* section is a rich resource to help you deliver fresh, exciting and effective lessons.

Resources for starters and plenaries

Images

Many of the starters, and some plenaries, require images – mostly photos. All the photos, maps, and diagrams from the students' book are provided on the *resources and planning OxBox CD-ROM*. You could use some of these to design your own starters or plenaries. (For example have pupils make up their own captions for strip cartoons.)

The movies and interactive activities on the *resources and planning OxBox CD-ROM* also make great starters and plenaries.

The internet is an excellent source for other geographical photos and images. Please check with the appropriate people in your school regarding copyright issues.

Building a resource library

Some resources, such as photos, can be used over and over. You may want to create your own resource library. Laminating printed photos, and other resources (such as the True/False cards) will extend their lives and save you time and effort in the future.

The chapter openers

The chapter openers in the students' book are in effect the starters for new topics – and you can return to them as an end-of-topic plenary.

Below is a typical chapter opener.

Large photo to hook your pupils' attention (we hope!). The opening photos usually relate to specific material within the chapter, and are referred back to, at different points.

Gives the big underlying ideas for the chapter. These provide the context for new learning.
At the end of the chapter they can be reviewed, to help crystallise the learning.

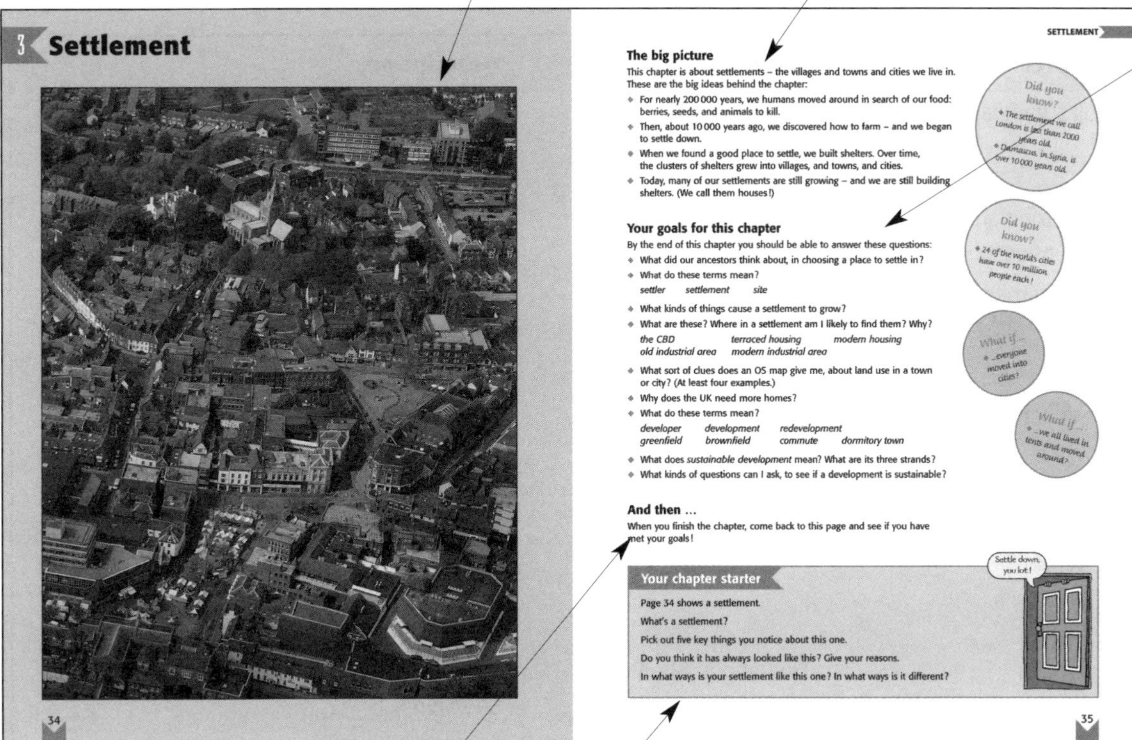
3 Settlement

SETTLEMENT

The big picture

This chapter is about settlements – the villages and towns and cities we live in. These are the big ideas behind the chapter:

- For nearly 200 000 years, we humans moved around in search of our food: berries, seeds, and animals to kill.
- Then, about 10 000 years ago, we discovered how to farm – and we began to settle down.
- When we found a good place to settle, we built shelters. Over time, the clusters of shelters grew into villages, and towns, and cities.
- Today, many of our settlements are still growing – and we are still building shelters. (We call them houses!)

Your goals for this chapter

By the end of this chapter you should be able to answer these questions:

- What did our ancestors think about, in choosing a place to settle in?
- What do these terms mean?
  settler *settlement* *site*
- What kinds of things cause a settlement to grow?
- What are these? Where in a settlement am I likely to find them? Why?
  the CBD *terraced housing* *modern housing*
  old industrial area *modern industrial area*
- What sort of clues does an OS map give me, about land use in a town or city? (At least four examples.)
- Why does the UK need more homes?
- What do these terms mean?
  developer *development* *redevelopment*
  greenfield *brownfield* *commute* *dormitory town*
- What does *sustainable development* mean? What are its three strands?
- What kinds of questions can I ask, to see if a development is sustainable?

And then …

When you finish the chapter, come back to this page and see if you have met your goals!

Did you know?
- The settlement we call London is less than 2000 years old.
- Damascus, in Syria, is over 10 000 years old.

Did you know?
- 24 of the world's cities have over 10 million people each!

What if …
- …everyone moved into cities?

What if …
- …we all lived in tents and moved around?

Your chapter starter

Page 34 shows a settlement.

What's a settlement?

Pick out five key things you notice about this one.

Do you think it has always looked like this? Give your reasons.

In what ways is your settlement like this one? In what ways is it different?

34

35

Sets goals for the pupils, in the form of questions they should be able to answer by the end of the chapter.

Invites pupils to revisit the goals at the end of the chapter. Note that the *assessment file & OxBox CD-ROM* has a pupils' self-assessment form for each chapter, which refers to these goals.

Chapter starter questions, to get your pupils thinking. The 'Chapter overviews' in this book give information about the photos (where available), and some background for the starter questions.

Using the chapter openers

As you can see, the chapter openers can do quite a lot of useful work, so it's worth spending some time on them.

- 'The big picture' can be read aloud, and discussed.
- You can work through 'Your goals for this chapter' in advance, to find out what pupils know already. Most will probably be able to answer at least a couple of questions.
- The chapter openers are supported by PowerPoint presentations in the *resources and planning OxBox CD-ROM*.
- For some of the chapter starters (but not all) there are suggestions for related work, in the 'Further suggestions for class and homework' pages in this book.
- Then the next step is to give pupils a mental roadmap for the chapter, using the corresponding 'Chapter overviews' in this book.

About the *geog.1* resources and planning OxBox CD-ROM

The *resources and planning OxBox CD-ROM* gives you an extensive bank of highly visual interactive whiteboard activities, resources, and homework support for the students' book. It will help you plan and deliver an exciting and vibrant geography course.

Movies

- The value of short video clips in the classroom is well known. We have put together a collection of photo movies and video clips that were either specially-commissioned or sourced from news and documentary footage.
- They have run-times of between one and four minutes, and will engage and interest your pupils.

Chapter	Movie title	Description
1 It's geography	Our world	People, places, and activities from around the world, showing the scope of Geography.
2 Making and mapping connections	Maps	The story of maps and map-making.
3 Settlement	The story of Totnes	How and why the town of Totnes has changed over the last 1100 years.
4 Let's go shopping!	Shops	How the location of shops has changed.
5 Exploring Britain	Images of Britain	People and places around Britain.
6 Rivers	A river's journey	The journey of the River Dart from source to mouth.
7 Floods	Flooding in Sheffield, 2007	News footage of flooding in and around Sheffield.
8 Sport	The London Olympics: are people pleased?	What people feel about the Olympic Games coming to London in 2012; vox-pop interviews.
	The London Olympics: how will people be affected?	How people have been and might be affected by the Olympic Games coming to London in 2012; vox-pop interviews.
9 Our restless planet	Earthquakes	Earthquakes explained, including footage of earthquake activity.
	Earthquake in Italy	News footage of the Puglia earthquake.
	Red hot lava	Erupting, flowing lava.
	Underwater volcano	An underwater volcano, erupting.
	Pyroclastic flow	Pyroclastic flows, Mount Merapi, Indonesia.
	Montserrat volcano	Views of erupting Soufriere Hills volcano and devastated Montserrat, 1997.

PowerPoint presentations

- There are two PowerPoint presentations to support each chapter opening unit in the students' book.
- One uses the large opening photo and the 'Your chapter starter' questions, the other uses the text headed 'The big picture'.
- They make colourful and engaging whole-class material.

Photos, maps, and diagrams

- All the photos, maps, and diagrams from the students' book are provided – each image can be obtained individually.
- You can display the images on whiteboards, use them in your own worksheets, or give them to pupils to use in class or homework activities.

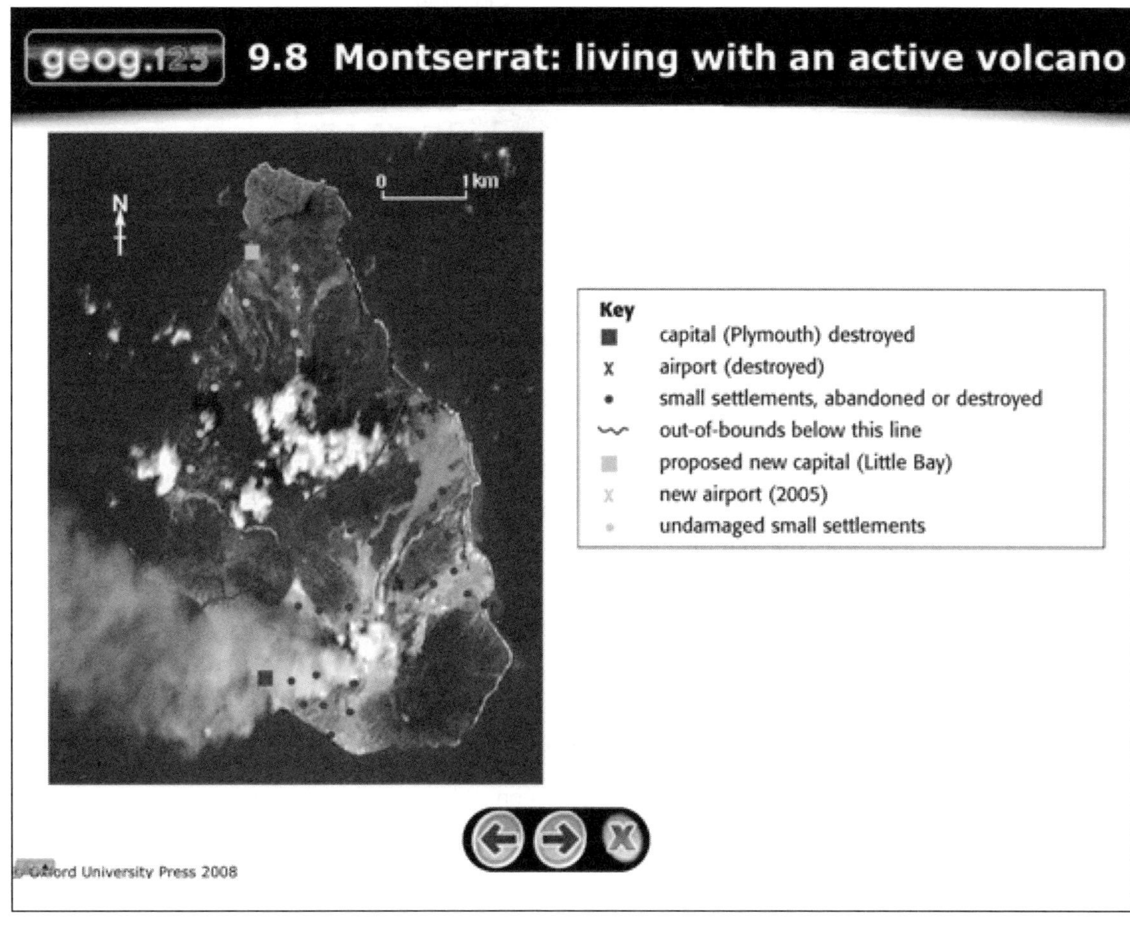

Interactive activities

- There's a collection of interactive activities for each chapter.
- They make motivating whole-class starters, plenaries, or main activities.
- They can also be used for independent study.

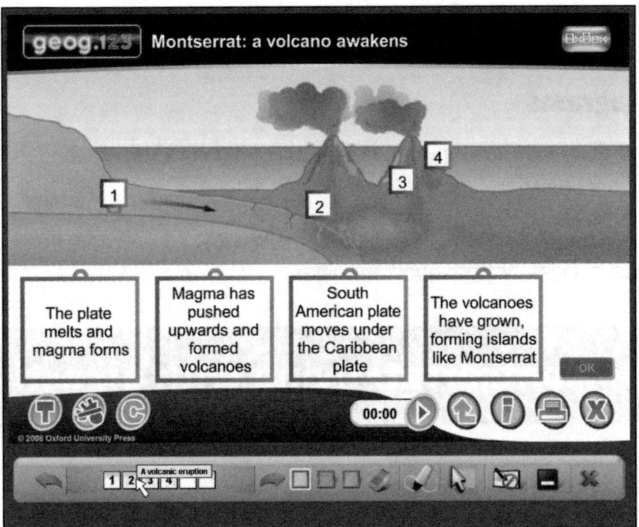

Worksheets

- There are worksheets for each chapter.
- Some provide revision, and some are extension material.
- They have been graded *, **, or *** according to level of difficulty (* is easiest).
- Answers are given where appropriate.
- They are provided as PDFs, so that you can print them off and photocopy them, and as editable Word files, so that you can amend them to suit your needs and those of your pupils.

Longer learning activities

- There's a collection of longer learning activities for each chapter – enquiries, decision-making exercises, role-plays, fieldwork, games, and thinking skills activities.
- Some of these activities are quite short. Others will take pupils several hours to complete.
- Some are for individual work, while others provide opportunities for pupils to work in pairs or small groups.
- Like the worksheets, they have been graded *, **, or *** according to level of difficulty (* is easiest).
- There are teacher's notes for each activity, giving the aims of the activity, and advice on how to set up and run it.
- They offer opportunities for interim assessments, outside the formal assessment package provided in the *assessment file & OxBox CD-ROM*.
- They are provided as PDFs, so that you can print them off and photocopy them, and as editable Word files, so that you can amend them to suit your needs and those of your pupils.

Editable 'Your turn' questions

- The 'Your turn' questions from the students' book are provided as editable Word files, so that you can amend them to suit your needs and those of your pupils.

Course and lesson planning

- We have provided a long-term plan covering the students' book, medium term plans for each chapter, and lesson plans for every unit (double-page spread).
- OxBox technology allows you to edit and adapt these plans to suit your needs, or to write your own plans.
- You can save your existing plans into the Planning section of OxBox.
- You can save your own resources – such as worksheets, photos, videos, and so on – into OxBox.
- The lesson player helps you run your lessons with ease: the resources you want to use can be arranged and launched in sequence.

User management

- The User management facility allows you to easily import class registers and create user accounts for all your students – perfect for personalised learning.

About the *geog.1 assessment file & OxBox CD-ROM*

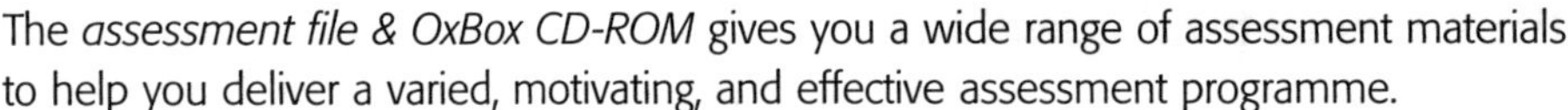

The *assessment file & OxBox CD-ROM* gives you a wide range of assessment materials to help you deliver a varied, motivating, and effective assessment programme.

Assessment overviews

- The formal assessment material for each chapter begins with an assessment overview – useful notes about the level-marked assessment, and suggestions for 'interim assessments' using other materials and activities from the *resources and planning OxBox CD-ROM* and this teacher's book.

Level-marked assessments

- There's a level-marked assessment for each chapter (except for the introductory chapter 1), with easy-to-use success criteria written in pupil-friendly language.
- You can discuss with each pupil their target level for the assessment, and there's space to record this at the start of the assessment. So each pupil sets out with a clear idea of what he or she is aiming for, and why.
- Because the success criteria are included in the level-marked assessment, pupils can check what they have to do to achieve – and improve upon – their target level.
- The assessments are varied and interesting, and cover a range of activity types and skills.
- Most pupils should be able to complete the assessments in under two hours although some may need a little longer.
- Each level-marked assessment has a feedback form, designed to be used with individual pupils. It allows you to record the level achieved, and to identify areas for improvement. It also allows the pupil to take part in this process.
- The feedback form can then form part of the pupil's assessment portfolio.
- They are provided as PDFs, so that you can print them off and photocopy them, and as editable Word files, so that you can amend them to suit your needs and those of your pupils. You could amend the success criteria and feedback form so that they could be used in peer assessment.

Scored tests

- There's a scored test for each chapter (except for the introductory chapter 1). Each is marked out of 50, with the marks for each question indicated. A mark scheme and answers are provided.
- The tests can be used at any time you choose. They are not designed to produce levelled results. But they will help to provide a varied and flexible approach to tracking your pupils' progress.
- They are provided as PDFs, so that you can print them off and photocopy them, and as editable Word files, so that you can amend them to suit your needs and those of your pupils.

Self-assessment forms

- There's a self-assessment form for each chapter (except for the introductory chapter 1). Designed to be used at the end of the chapter, it allows individual pupils to review and analyse their own work.
- The form relates to the text 'Your goals for this chapter' at the start of each chapter in the students' book.

Interactive formative assessments

- Interactive questions answered on-screen, with feedback after every question and auto-marked results.
- Students indicate their confidence level for each answer by using the AfL traffic-light system; they can also opt to receive a hint before answering.
- Students can have a second go at each question before moving on – this is reflected in the feedback they receive.
- These formative assessments help make students aware of what they've learnt, know, and understand – and areas they need to work on.
- All chapters have two formative assessments – except the short chapter 1, which has just one, and the long chapter 9, which has three.
- You can create new questions.

Interactive summative assessments

- Interactive questions answered on-screen, with auto-marking and levelled feedback at the end of the assessment.
- Results for the class are automatically aggregated so you can easily identify areas of concern within the topic.
- There's a summative assessment for each chapter. They provide an effective way of charting pupils' progress.
- You can create new questions.

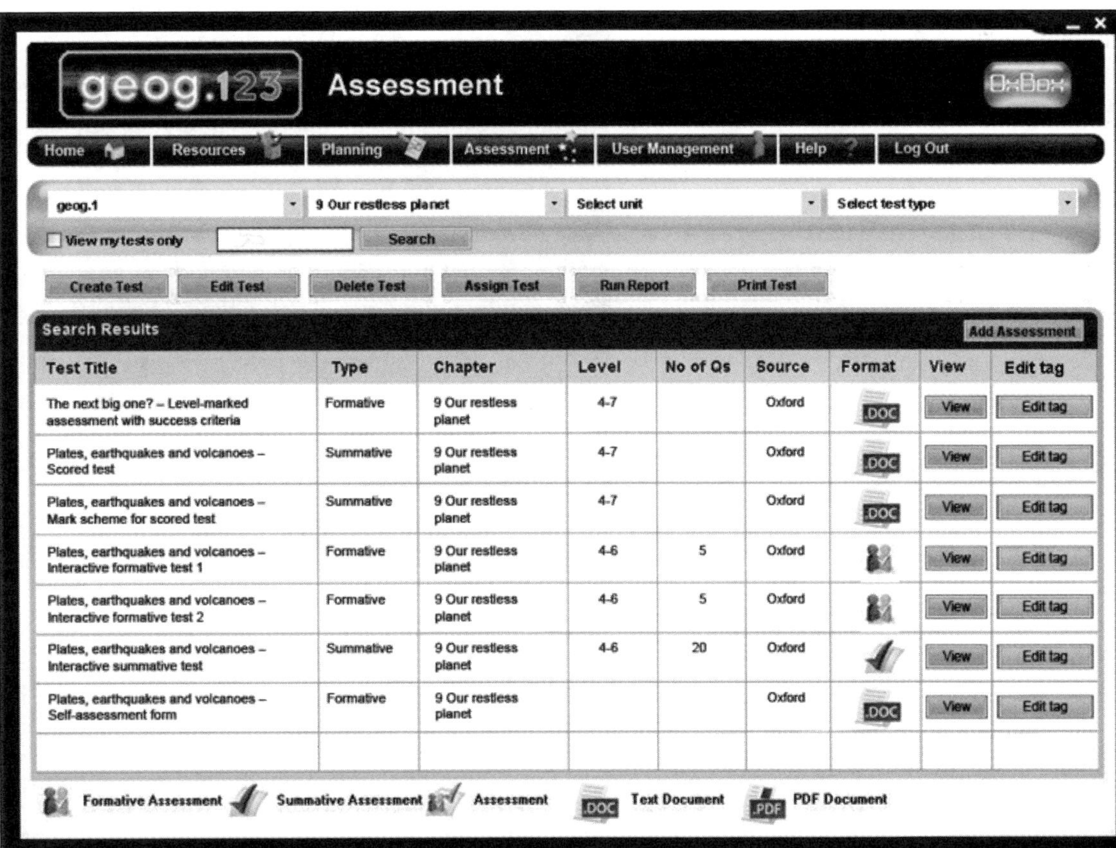

About the *geog.1 workbook*

The *geog.1 workbook* provides support for every double-page spread in the *geog.1* students' book.

Its engaging fill-in activities make it ideal for homework and independent study.

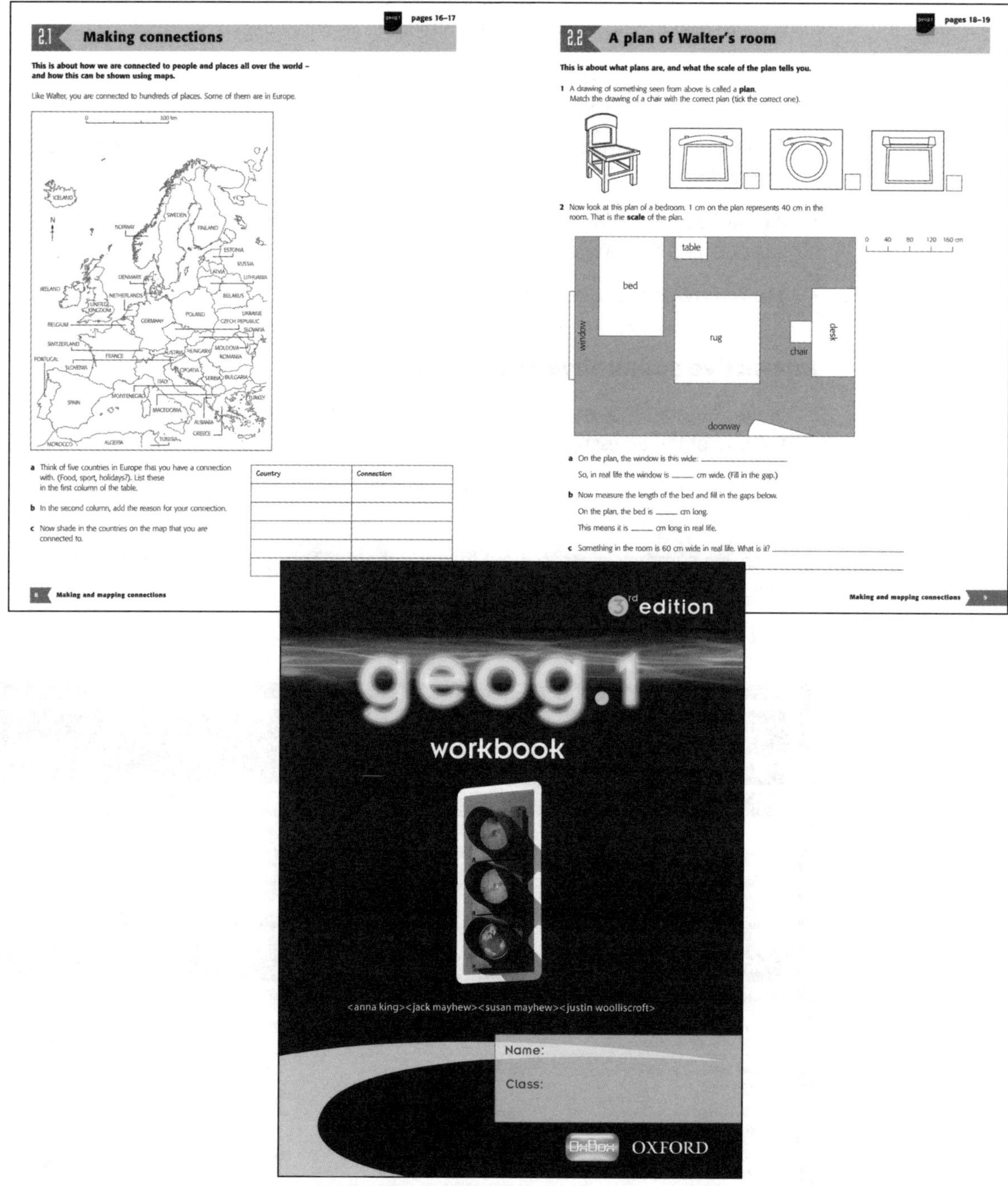
pages 16–17

2.1 Making connections

This is about how we are connected to people and places all over the world – and how this can be shown using maps.

Like Walter, you are connected to hundreds of places. Some of them are in Europe.

a Think of five countries in Europe that you have a connection with. (Food, sport, holidays?). List these in the first column of the table.

b In the second column, add the reason for your connection.

c Now shade in the countries on the map that you are connected to.

Country	Connection

8 Making and mapping connections

pages 18–19

2.2 A plan of Walter's room

This is about what plans are, and what the scale of the plan tells you.

1 A drawing of something seen from above is called a **plan**.
Match the drawing of a chair with the correct plan (tick the correct one).

2 Now look at this plan of a bedroom. 1 cm on the plan represents 40 cm in the room. That is the **scale** of the plan.

a On the plan, the window is this wide: ________
So, in real life the window is ____ cm wide. (Fill in the gap.)

b Now measure the length of the bed and fill in the gaps below.
On the plan, the bed is ____ cm long.
This means it is ____ cm long in real life.

c Something in the room is 60 cm wide in real life. What is it? ________

Making and mapping connections 9

About the *geog.world* CD-ROM

geog.world CD-ROM

- Interactive material for the students' book – most of the material is aimed directly at pupils
- 'geog.aid': interactive skills lessons, interactive glossary
- On-screen activities
- Interactive country data section
- Ideal for individual study and homework
- Networkable
- Teacher's notes throughout – invisible to pupils
- 'Teacher zone' containing extra support material – invisible to pupils
- Ideal for whole-class use via an interactive whiteboard or projector

There's a wide variety of content on *geog.world*. This table gives the different types:

Type of material	What does it do?
Topic work	
Interactive topic lesson	Focuses on a specific theme or Scheme of Work topic; ends with scored questions
Interactive walkthrough	Explains concepts and processes; ideal as a topic starter, and/or for a final review
Webfile	Like a magazine article, with worksheets; the worksheets give practice in a wide range of skills, use of Excel for example; many can be completed onscreen
Scored topic quizzes	Useful for revision, and fun at any time; drawn from a question bank
End-of-topic scored test	This has more focused questions, drawn from a question bank
Hot topic	News story with a link to geography, with graded activities to choose from
Map work	
Mapping (*a country*)	Explores a country through interactive maps; a great way to get to grips with the geography of a country – with a quiz at the end
Countries at a glance	Shows where different countries are, on a world map; a click of a button gives a data card for a country; worksheets let pupils compare countries
Make your own data tables	Pupils can create their own data tables for a range of 30 countries, large and small, rich and poor; worksheets give lots of practice in using Excel
Mapping data	Pupils map development data around the world; worksheets encourage them to look for patterns and correlations (and you can print the maps out for OHTs)
geog aid	A range of resources including interactive skills kit and interactive glossary
Teacher zone	Information and resources for you

1 It's geography

Helping you deliver the KS3 Programme of Study

The purpose of this short chapter is to introduce your new class to geography, capture your pupils' interest from the start, and stimulate a sense of wonder about the world.

With very broad strokes, it sets out the key concepts and topic areas that pupils will cover in their geography course.

It also gives you a chance to use all the different components of the course – the students' book, teacher's handbook, *geog.1 resources and planning OxBox CD-ROM* and *geog.1 assessment file & OxBox CD-ROM* – and see how they work together.

The big picture

This opening chapter sets out the main themes that run through the *geog.123* course, and will be returned to again and again.

- The Earth is being continually shaped by both physical and human processes.
- We humans (*Homo sapiens*) have been here for only a very short time in the Earth's history – about 200 000 years out of 4.6 billion.
- However, we have had a huge impact in that time. We have spread over most of the Earth, farming it, mining it, building on it, and carving it up into over 200 countries.
- We have changed the Earth as we spread, and spoiled many places, and wiped out many other species.
- Now we are learning that we must look after the Earth, and live in a sustainable way.
- We are also learning that we must tackle the great poverty and inequality within our human society.
- The Earth still holds many natural dangers for us, such as floods and earthquakes. We try to protect ourselves from these.

A pupils' version of this big picture is given in the *geog.1* students' book opener for Chapter 1, and in *geog.1 resources and planning OxBox CD-ROM*, for the whiteboard.

It is useful to remind pupils of this big picture from time to time, to help them put their learning in context, and make links. (They are also given a related big picture for each chapter, at the start of each chapter.)

The chapter outline

Use this, and their chapter opener, to give pupils a mental roadmap for the chapter.

1 **It's geography** As the first chapter opener in the book, and the course, this unit is particularly important; see page 11 for notes about using chapter openers.

1.1 **Hey, you over there!** Introduces our wonderful planet Earth, and what's on it, and reminds pupils that we humans have been here only a very short time, compared to the planet – and to some other species.

1.2 **Our planet: always changing** Introduces two key concepts that we'll revisit often: the Earth is being changed by natural forces, and by human actions.

1.3 **Your place on the planet** About a sense of place: encourages pupils to use their imagination about other places, stimulated by photos, then think about their own.

1.4 **It's all geography!** Introduces three strands of geography – physical, human and environmental – and the idea of the geographer as a nosy detective.

Objectives and outcomes for this chapter

Objectives	Unit	Outcomes
Most pupils will understand:		Most pupils will be able to:
• that our planet is an exciting place	1.1	• explain that the Earth is moving around the sun, and spinning as it goes; give its approximate age; give examples of the many species living on it
• that it is always changing	1.2	• give examples of changes brought about by natural processes, and by humans
• that our places on the planet can be very different	1.3	• describe their own place; give some differences between their own place and other places, for example those shown in the chapter photos
• that geography covers a wide range of topics	1.4	• name physical, human and environmental geography as three strands of geography; give examples of at least two topics for each strand
• that asking questions is a key skill in geography	1.4	• come up with at least four questions about a photo

These tie in with the opening lines in each unit, which give the purpose of the unit in a pupil-friendly style.

Opportunities for assessment

geog.1 assessment file & OxBox CD-ROM contains interactive assessments for this chapter. There are other opportunities for assessment too. You could use the worksheets or longer learning activities for the chapter from *geog.1 resources and planning OxBox CD-ROM*, or some of the 'Further suggestions for class and homework' at the end of this chapter.

Getting ready for this chapter

Some of the starters and plenaries suggested for this chapter may need resources prepared in advance. Check out the *Resources* section on the 'Help at a glance' pages that follow.

geog.1 resources & planning OxBox CD-ROM has all the photos and diagrams from the chapter, for whiteboard display, plus movies and interactive materials. You will find these very useful for devising your own starters and plenaries. In addition, *geog.world CD-ROM* is a rich source of further material, including interactive webfiles and skills lessons.

About the chapter starter

The image on page 4 of *geog.1* students' book shows planet Earth from space. The thin blue halo is our atmosphere. The Earth is the third planet from the sun, and held in its orbit around the sun by gravitational attraction (gravity). It is about 150 million km from the sun, and takes 365.25 days to travel all the way round it. And as it travels it spins on its axis, taking 24 hours for a complete spin. We don't know of life on any other planet – so far.

Off to a good start

In your first week with your new class, you might want to set up working practices for the rest of the year. For example:

- provide pupils with a mental roadmap for a new chapter / topic before you start. Flow charts, spider maps and concept maps can be useful here.
- make sure pupils know the objectives for each lesson.
- make starters and plenaries a planned part of every lesson.
- have pupils start their own personal glossary. The glossary at the back of *geog.1* students' book will help with this.
- provide pupils with outline maps of the world and the UK to stick in their exercise books, in which they can mark new places they come across.

1.1

Hey, you over there!

About this unit

This unit begins at the beginning, by introducing planet Earth. The aim is to start instilling a sense of wonder about the planet, and excitement about geography. And, very importantly, to set the scene for later work on human and environmental geography, by helping pupils understand that we humans are very recent arrivals.

Key ideas

- Our planet has been here for 4.6 billion years, held in place by the attractive force (gravity) betweeen it and the sun.
- It is teeming with different species. Many have been here for billons of years.
- Humans like us (*Homo sapiens*) appeared only about 200 000 years ago – and our numbers are growing fast.
- The surface of our planet is continually changing, thanks to physical processes – and the action of us humans.

Key vocabulary

gravity, atmosphere, species (see the glossary at the end of this book)

Skills practised in 'Your turn'

- Numeracy skills: some simple maths
- Literacy skills: writing an e-mail to a friend on another planet
- Thinking skills: reviewing and assessing facts; trying to explain the Earth's spin is slower in some places than others (difficult!)

Unit outcomes

By the end of this unit, most pupils should be able to:

- explain the terms given in 'Key vocabulary' above
- give at least three basic facts about our planet
- say that humans have been here only a very short time compared with the planet, and even compared with other species

Resources

For all starters, and plenaries **2**, **3**, **5** and **6**: all images and maps from the book are also on *geog.1 resources and planning OxBox CD-ROM*, for display on a whiteboard

Ideas for a starter

1. Look at the image of the Earth, on page 6 of the students' book (or display it). Ask pupils to write down three facts about planet Earth. Compile a list of facts on the whiteboard.
2. Look at the image of the Earth, on page 6 of the students' book (or display it). How do you think it was taken? Who might have taken it? Where from?
3. Look back at the image of the Earth on page 4 of the students' book (or display it). What's all the dark blue stuff? Can you name the large area of dark blue, on the left? What's the blue stuff around the rim of the Earth? What's the white wispy stuff?
4. Look at that image of the Earth (from **3**). Where on the Earth are you, right now?

Ideas for plenaries

Plan plenaries for strategic points throughout the lesson, as well as at the end.

1. Everything is attracted to everything else by a gravitational force. We usually call it just gravity. You don't notice it for little things. But when one of the things has enormous mass (like the Earth) you notice it a lot. Who can demonstrate that we are attracted to the Earth by gravity? (Pupils could jump up, or throw something up. All fall back to the Earth again.) This could lead to discussion of the attraction between the Earth and the sun, and the Earth and the moon.
2. What's the moon? (You could display the photo from page 6.) Where is it? How long does it take for the moon to travel around the Earth once?
3. At this moment, do you think it's morning or night, in Australia? Why? (Pupils can look at Australia on the map on page 141 of the students' book, and the diagram for question 3. Or you could display these.)
4. We go round the sun once a year. Do you think it has any effect on the weather? Tell us!
5. There are fewer elephants than there used to be. Why do you think that is? (You could display the photo from page 5.)
6. How many times longer have jellyfish been on the planet, compared to us? (You could display the photo from page 5.)
7. Which do you think are the three most important facts you have learned about planet Earth today? Why?

Further class and homework activities

Interactive activity for Unit 1.1 on *geog.1 resources and planning OxBox CD-ROM*

Worksheets 1A or 1B on *geog.1 resources and planning OxBox CD-ROM*

Fill in a records certificate on *geog.1 resources and planning OxBox CD-ROM*

Suggestions 1 – 5 on page 30 of this book

Answers to 'Your turn'

1 b They complete a full journey around the sun once every year of their lives. So, eleven times by their eleventh birthday.
c 2160 times faster

2 c shows the correct answer. (1 billion = 1000 million.)

3 a A is turned away from the sun, at this point in the Earth's spin.
b At A. Imagine the globe does one spin. That takes 24 hours, no matter where you are on it. Point C has to travel furthest in this time, to get back to where it started. So it must be going fastest. A has to travel least far in the same time, so the spin is slowest there.
c We can't feel it because everything is spinning with us, even the atmosphere.

4, 5 Answers will vary. In **5**, encourage pupils to think up as many great things about the planet as they can.

1.2 Our planet: always changing

About this unit

This unit introduces a key concept from the KS3 Programme of Study: the Earth's surface is being shaped and changed by both natural and human processes.

Key ideas

- The Earth's surface is being changed by natural processes. These result from:
  - currents of hot rock flowing inside the Earth
  - rivers, waves, glaciers and the wind, flowing on the Earth's surface
  - the action of the weather, atmosphere and plants (heat and cold, oxygen and rain, plant roots) on rocks; their combined effect is called **weathering**.
- These natural changes are usually very slow. But some can be fast, and dangerous. (For example when there's an earthquake, or landslide, or a big flood.)
- The Earth's surface is also being changed by human activity (farming, building, mining, cutting down forests, and so on).
- These changes are happening quickly, compared with most natural changes. And some are causing big problems, for us and for other species.

Key vocabulary

natural, weathering, fossil fuel, global warming (see the glossary at the end of this book)

Skills practised in 'Your turn'

- Literacy skills: writing lists, including a list of short bullet points
- Thinking skills: analyse information; arrange in order of importance; use imagination about the Earth before humans; come up with responses to some fundamental questions about looking after the Earth

Unit outcomes

By the end of this unit, most pupils should be able to:

- give at least three examples of ways the Earth's surface is being changed naturally
- give at least three examples of how humans are changing the Earth's surface
- give at least two examples to show that natural changes can be dangerous to us
- give at least three examples to show that human changes can cause problems

Resources

For starters **1** and **2**: all images from the book are on *geog.1 resources and planning OxBox CD-ROM*
For starter **4**: a lump of rock and a jar of soil

Ideas for a starter

1. Keep text books closed. Display the two sets of images from page 8 of the students' book. Ask pupils to identify the key difference between the two sets.
2. Keep text books closed. Display the first set of images from page 8 and invite pupils to say how the Earth's surface is being changed, in each image. Do the same for the second set.
3. Keep text books closed. Ask: Can you think of any ways the Earth's surface is changing? Write a list on the board. Then see if pupils can group the changes under headings: *Natural* and *Due to humans*
4. Hold up a jar of soil. Ask: What is it? A thousand years ago, it looked quite different. Can anyone tell me why? Then produce the rock. It looked like this! Discuss the change from rock to soil as one example of a natural change.

Ideas for plenaries

Plan plenaries for strategic points throughout the lesson, as well as at the end.

1 Overall, do you think we humans are in control of our planet? Give reasons.
2 Which do you think is the most dangerous change, of all the changes given in the unit?
3 Which do you think has changed the Earth's surface most, nature or humans?
4 Do you think we humans are pests? What would mountain gorillas think?
5 All these words appear in the unit:

   TCLOFNIC RTUAANL MHNUA CREIALSG WNOST
   RRVISE RFEOSTS TRSECNUIO OSDOLF RPSBOMLE

   Who can be the first to unscramble them? And then say what each one means!
6 You could use question **6** of 'Your turn' as a plenary.

Further class and homework activities

Worksheet 1C on *geog.1 resources and planning OxBox CD-ROM*

Suggestions 6 – 12 on page 30 of this book

Answers to 'Your turn'

1 a None. All we can do is protect ourselves from the dangers they hold.

b Yes. They have been going on for billions of years.

c There are many examples for this, but pupils will not be aware of most of them. Here are some that you might want to discuss:

Hot currents inside the Earth

- They have led to the world's spectacular mountain ranges, like the Himalayas and Alps. Giving us stunning scenery, and great places to go climbing, skiing, hiking.
- They have caused parts of the Earth's surface to get pushed up and lowered over millions of years, and oceans to fill and empty
- so they're why we get many oil wells on land, rather than under the ocean (where they start).
- Lava from volcanoes produces very fertile soil.
  (But there is not much to be said in favour of earthquakes.)

Currents at the Earth's surface

- Again they have led to spectacular scenery, including valleys, sand dunes in the desert, dramatic coastlines.
- Waves created beaches.
- Rivers have created fertile soil in their flood plains, by depositing silt.
- By carrying eroded material to the oceans, rivers have helped build up thick layers of sediment on the ocean floor, burying organisms that eventually turned into oil and gas – which we depend on for fuel.

Weathering

- We could not survive without the weathering of rock.
  It produces soil, and we need soil to grow most of our food.

d Dangers: volcanic eruptions, earthquakes, tsunami, river and sea floods, sandstorms, cliff collapse due to weathering. (We also fight a continual battle against weathering of other things: buildings, pavements, paintwork, iron structures and so on. Sometimes weathering of these things can lead to danger. For example old neglected buildings can collapse, or steel cables rust through.)

2 Pupils might not notice any changes. But assure them they are going on. For weathering, you could point out local weathering of buildings, window frames and so on. The same is happening to rock.

3 Pupils should list at least the things on page 8 of the pupils book.

4 There are likely to be some changes going on in the area, even if just roadworks, or someone building an extension.

5 Our activities in causing (or at least greatly accelerating) global warming could lead to the most harm. It will affect all species, and all humans, with the poorest countries the most vulnerable.

6 These questions will hopefully lead to lively class discussion.

1.3

Your place on the planet

help at a glance

About this unit

This unit presents some very different images of people's places. It should stimulate pupils' interest in geography, and help develop their geographical imaginations, and their sense of their own place. They may begin to appreciate the differences, and similarities, between people and places around the world.

Key ideas

- We all have a place on the planet – and our places can be very different.
- In geography, it helps to be able to imagine what a place is *really* like to live in – and it's fun too.
- Our own places are special – even if we don't like them that much. We carry memories and images of them in our heads.

Key vocabulary

image

Skills practised in 'Your turn'

- Geography skills: gathering information from photos; finding places on a world map
- Communication skills: describing what a place is like, verbally or in writing
- Thinking skills: imagining what a place is like to live in, from a photo; calling up mental images of a place; deducing that we each have a unique sense of our place

Unit outcomes

By the end of this unit, most pupils should be able to:

- recognise that people's places can be very different
- recognise that you can gather a lot of information about a place, from a photo
- find places on a world map
- describe some features and characteristics of their own place

Resources

For starters **1** and **2**, and plenaries **1** – **4**: all images from the book are on *geog.1 resources and planning OxBox CD-ROM*

Ideas for a starter

1. With books closed, show one image from the unit. Ask pupils to describe what they see. (You may be able to reveal the photo little by little.) Ask: 'How do you think it came to be like this? Where do you think it is? What would it be like to live here?'
2. With books closed, show one image from the unit. Ask pupils what words spring to mind when they look at this image. Make a list on the whiteboard.
3. With books closed, ask pupils to tell you about their place, or the local area. Invite them to make a graffiti wall of words, on the whiteboard.

Ideas for plenaries

Plan plenaries for strategic points throughout the lesson, as well as at the end.

1 Look at each photo from the unit, in turn. (You could display them.) Imagine this is your place. Write a speech bubble with your feelings about it. Give just one sentence for each photo. Then swap bubbles with a partner, and match each other's to the photos. Do you match correctly?
2 Look at the photos. (You could display them.) Choose the two places you think are the most different from each other. Explain your choice.
3 Look at the photos. (You could display them.) Choose the two places you think are the most alike. Explain your choice.
4 Choose two photos. (You could display them.) Say what a person from each place would think about the other place.
5 You have to choose a photo to show *your* place, to go with this set. What will your photo show? Why? What would people in the other places think about it?
6 Do you think it's good to look at photos of other places, in geography? Explain.
7 Could photos give you the wrong idea about a place? How could you avoid that?

Further class and homework activities

Worksheet 1A on *geog.1 resources and planning OxBox CD-ROM,* if not used already.

Profiling the school environment on *geog.1 resources and planning OxBox CD-ROM*

Suggestions 13 – 15 on page 30 of this book

Answers to 'Your turn'

1 c Pupils will probably choose **F**, since the trees have been not been chopped down and the buildings look like simple huts. But it is not possible to tell from **C** how much humans are changing the tundra, since the herders will carry their tents with them when they and their reindeer move.

2 Encourage pupils to use their imaginations for this one. It's a good way to help them develop a sense of place.

3 A is in Iraq, in Asia.
B is in Mali, in (West) Africa.
C is in Siberia, in Russia, in Asia. (Some sharp-eyed pupils may point out that part of Russia is in Europe, which is correct. But Siberia is in the Asian part.)
D is in Recife in Brazil, in South America.
E is in Tokyo, in Japan, in Asia.
F is in Tonga, in Oceania. (You might need to point out for this one that the world is round – since Tonga appears in the Pacific Ocean on the left on the world map in the students' book.)

4, **5** and **6** Answers will vary. Encourage discussion here.

7 The correct answer is no, overall, since we each have our own experiences of, images of, and feelings about, a place.

1.4 It's all geography!

About this unit

This unit should again stimulate enthusiasm about geography. It sets out the kinds of topics pupils can look forward to, under three headings: physical, human, and environmental geography. It also sets out a key message for the course: geographers ask questions! 'Your turn' gives pupils the chance to practice asking questions.

Key ideas

- Geography covers a wide and exciting range of topics. It can be divided into three areas: physical, human, and environmental geography.
- Physical geography is about the Earth's natural features, processes and events.
- Human geography is about how and where we live on the Earth – how we feed, clothe and shelter ourselves, and earn our living.
- Environmental geography is about how we interact with our environment. For example about how we damage or protect places, or create pollution.
- The way to be a good geographer is to get nosy – ask questions and look for clues.

Key vocabulary

physical geography, human geography, environmental geography

Skills practised in 'Your turn'

- Geography skills: studying photos for clues; asking questions about what photos show
- Literacy skills: completing definitions in own words
- Thinking skills: classifying topics and reasons; coming up with reasons and answers; looking for similarities and connections

Unit outcomes

By the end of this unit, most pupils should be able to:

- explain the terms given in 'Key vocabulary' above
- give examples of at least two topics for each of the three areas of geography
- give at least four examples of questions they can ask about a photo
- state that asking questions is a key part of geography

Resources

For starter **1**: *geog.1 resources and planning OxBox CD-ROM*
For starter **3**: a set of questions on strips of paper, one per student, with room for the student's name, covering physical, human and environmental geography (for example: Do they get snow in winter?); three boxes to collect the strips in

Ideas for a starter

1 Use the interactive activity for Unit 1.4, on *geog.1 resources and planning OxBox CD-ROM,* as a starter.

2 Pupils shout out topics they think are part of geography. Write them on the board. (They may need prompting for environmental topics.) Underline any that are physical geography and ask pupils what these have in common. Elicit a definition of physical geography. Repeat for human and environmental geography (use different colours). Students will probably call out some skills and resources (map reading, atlases, globes). Put these in separate groups. You could label them *Skills* and *Resources*.

3 Write definitions of physical, human and environmental geography on the board in big letters. Have a box for each on the table. Give each student a question on a strip of paper. Students write their names on their strips and put them in what they think are the correct boxes. Discuss the contents of the boxes.

Ideas for plenaries

Plan plenaries for strategic points throughout the lesson, as well as at the end.

1. Choose a person from a photo on page 13 of the students' book. (You could display the photos.) Think of three questions you'd ask the person about being in that place. What do you think he or she would say?
2. Display an interesting photo. (It could be from Unit 1.3 or anywhere in the book.) Ask pupils to ask questions about what it shows. You want at least 10 questions! You could do this against the clock. Then give any answers you can. How would they find answers to the other questions?
3. Why do you think it's so important to ask questions, in geography?
4. Say: 'Ask me a question about geography.'
5. Is it hard to ask questions? Could it be fun? Do you think it will get easier with practice?
6. Which are the two most important things you learned today?

Further class and homework activities

Our world movie on *geog.1 resources and planning OxBox CD-ROM*

Interactive quiz for Chapter 1 on *geog.1 resources and planning OxBox CD-ROM*

Suggestion 16 on page 30 of this book

Worksheets 1D, 1E and 1F, on *geog.1 resources and planning OxBox CD-ROM*

The Picture Quiz on *geog.1 resources and planning OxBox CD-ROM*

Asking the right questions in *geog aid* on *geog.world CD-ROM*

Interactive assessments for this chapter on *geog.1 assessment file & OxBox CD-ROM*

Answers to 'Your turn'

2 a physical **b** human **c** environmental **d** human
e physical **f** environmental

3 *Physical*: sandy beach, warm sunny weather, the sea (out of sight).
Human: they can afford it; they can relax here; the deckchairs show the people are being looked after; it is not too crowded.
Environmental: it seems to be a clean place that's well looked after.

4 a People are going around in cycle taxis in a flood. A few are walking. It is a busy place – a town or city.

b It may have rained a lot for a long period. A river may have burst its banks. A dam may have burst.

c It's natural for rivers to flood, when there is heavy rain. But people are likely to have made this flood worse. For example, the town may be built too close to a river that floods often.
Too many trees may have been cut down in the river's drainage basin. (Trees help to prevent floods.) People in the UK and other countries may also be responsible: we are affecting weather everywhere by burning so much oil, gas and petrol. Burning these fossil fuels helps to warm the Earth up, leading to worse storms and floods in many countries.

6 a Both photos show people. The weather is important in both. The 'chairs' are similar shapes. But there are more differences than similarities.

b Perhaps some of the things in the first photo (clothing, shoes, beach chairs, beach bags) were made in the Asian country – perhaps even by the cyclists' relatives or passengers.
Global warming may be affecting the weather in both photos.
Your pupils may be able to suggest other connections.

1 Further suggestions for class and homework

Most of these suggestions are addressed to your pupils. Where research or further resources are needed, the internet will almost certainly provide the answer. (Eg *google* and choose *Web* or *Images*.)

Hey, you over there!

1 **Day and night** Ask pupils to design a demonstration showing why we get day and night. Offer a globe, and let them decide what else they need. (Someone will think of a torch.) Then ask them to show why people are getting up in Australia while we're just going to bed in the UK. ***/**/*****

2 **The seasons** A search for *seasons animations* on google will provide you with several to choose from. You should be able to find one at the right level for your class. ***/**/*****

3 **Man in the moon** What's the moon? Where is it? How far away? How big, compared to the Earth? Find out from a library book, or the internet, and tell us all about it.
Pupils could answer by finding a photo of the moon, sticking it on a page and writing notes around it. You can display these on the wall. Some pupils will be able to create a PowerPoint presentation. ***/**/*****

4 **ET writes home** You have arrived on planet Earth from another planet. Write a letter home, telling them what the Earth is like, and why you find it very strange! ***/**/*****

5 **Adopt a planet** The Earth is just one of the sun's planets. Find out about the others. Then choose one of them, and tell us all about it. Where is it compared to the Earth? In what ways is it like the Earth? In what ways is it different? And the big big question: does anyone live there? ***/**/*****

Our planet: always changing

6 **On the move** Here's one way our planet is changing: the land you are sitting on is moving slowly around. It is being dragged by those warm currents inside the Earth. In fact hundreds of millions of years ago, the land that forms the British Isles was at the equator! Your task is to tell the story of Britain's travels over the last 250 million years, as a long strip cartoon for the classroom wall.
This would be a challenging group project. The aim is to get pupils excited about the story. You'll need to give pupils guidance about where to do their research, and perhaps provide some simplified material.
The result would in effect be a timeline showing where Britain was at different times relative to the Equator (guesswork!). It could also show when the dinosaurs appeared, when humans first appeared, when the British Isles split from the rest of Europe, and so on. The strip cartoon could have maps showing the breakup of the supercontinent Pangaea interspersed with other drawings. Each cell could have say 40 words of text below it. ****/*****

7 **We've only just arrived!** If we use 24 hours to represent the age of planet Earth, we humans arrived just 4 seconds ago! That's a sobering thought – and inspiration for another challenging group project: to construct a large 24- hour clock for the classroom wall, and mark in events in the life of the planet – or a long timeline marked in hours, as a simpler option. Give pupils some or all of the information in the table on the next page. Help them decide how to draw the clock or timeline, and how to link the information to it. They could illustrate the events with drawings. ***/**/*****

8 **Whatever happened to the dinosaurs?** You are a dinosaur. (Which kind? You can choose.) You have travelled to the present in an amazing time machine. Tell us what happened to you all, that long long time ago. And now that you're here, you'll stay for a snack. What would you like? ***/****

9 **And what about the dodo?** Once, thousands of dodo lived on the island of Mauritius. Now there are no dodo anywhere. What happened to them? Write their story – and don't forget to add a drawing of the dodo, and a map showing where Mauritius is. ***/**/*****

10 **Find out about mountain gorillas** Page 9 of the student's book shows a mountain gorilla. Where do they live? What do they do? What problems are they facing?
You could present your answer as a page for a website, or as a PowerPoint presentation. ***/**/*****

11 **Gorilla chat** Make up a conversation between a mountain gorilla and her young one, about those humans. ***/**/*****

12 **Alphabet run** One way humans changed the planet was to divide it into countries. Now there are just over 200 countries. Do an alphabet run, with one country for each letter of the alphabet. (Ignore X.) And then shade in your countries and label them, on a blank map of the world. ***/****

Your place on the planet

13 **Write a letter** Write a letter to one of the people named under the photos in Unit 1.3. Tell the person a little about your life and your place, and ask about his / hers. ***/****

14 **Lots of places** Extend the presentation in Unit 1.3 around the classrooom wall. Pupils can bring in photos of people they know, in real places, or photos from magazines, or collected from elsewhere. Each photo should have a few lines of text underneath, as in Unit 1.3. ***/****

15 **Tell me more** Find out more about one of the places or countries in the photos in Unit 1.3. Prepare a short presentation about it. ***/****

It's all geography

16 **Swop pics** First, for homework, pupils find an interesting photo they think is connected with physical, human or environmental geography. They make up questions about what's going on in the photo (to which they know the answers) and write them down.
Then pupils work in pairs. They swop their photos and questions – and try to answer the questions with as little help from the other person as possible. They can award each other marks for anwers they get right. ***/****

Further suggestions for class and homework

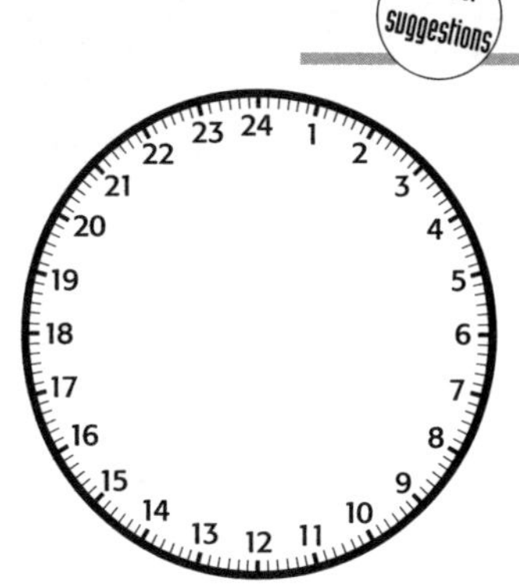

Information for suggestion 7: We've only just arrived!

The Earth is 4.6 billion years ago.
Let's pretend 4.6 billion years is 24 hours.
So the Earth was formed at 00:00 on the 24-hour clock.
And today is 24:00 on the clock.
Each hour on the clock represents nearly 200 million years.

About this many years ago	Time on our clock (in hours, minutes, seconds and fractions of a second	Event
4.6 billion	00:00	the Earth forms from a spinning cloud of dust, rocks and gas
	00:45	the surface of the Earth hardens into a solid crust
4.2 billion	01:50	the first oceans begin to form, as a result of torrential rain
4 billion	03:15	life starts, when a chemical structure of some kind begins to reproduce itself
3.5 billion	05:30	a cell that is the ancestor of all our cells forms
		over a long period, different types of cells develop; in time they will lead to bacteria, insects, plants and all the other kinds of living things
1 billion	19:00	the first many-celled plants appear in the oceans
900 million	19:15	the first many-celled animal develops (it probably looks like a sponge)
700 million	20:20	ocean plants start growing at the edges of the water; soon they will move onto land
530 million	21:10	the first fish develop in the oceans
450 million	21:40	the first animals leave the oceans to live on land; they have protective shells
375 million	22:00	the first four-legged animals evolve from fish; fins have evolved into limbs
310 million	22:22	different kinds of organisms continue to evolve: mammals, birds, reptiles, fish, insects, bacteria ...
250 million	22:40	95% of living things get killed off – perhaps by massive volcanic eruptions; but some survive
230 million	22:47	dinosaurs have begun to evolve from reptiles, and will soon became the dominant animal
65 million	23:39	dinosaurs die out when a huge meteorite hits the Earth; the dust and gas from the impact block out the sun
6 million	23:58	a small African ape living at this time will become our ancestor
2 million	23:59:22	the first human-like apes appear
200 000	23:59:56	the first humans like us appear, probably in East Africa, and start spreading all over the Earth
10 000	23:59:59.80	somewhere in the Middle East, humans begin to settle down and farm
8000	23:59:59.84	sea levels rise, due to melting glaciers, and cut off the British Isles from the rest of Europe
5000	23:59:59.90	writing is invented (probably first in the area that is now Iraq)
250	23:59:59.995	the Industrial Revolution begins in the UK, and spreads to some other countries
115	23:59:59.998	the first petrol-driven car is produced.
	23:59:59.9983 - 23:59:59.9988	humans fight two World Wars (1914 – 1918, and 1939 – 1945)
	23:59:59.9993	Neil Armstrong becomes the first human to set foot on the moon (1969)
	23:59:59.9998	You are born!

2 Making and mapping connections

Helping you deliver the KS3 Programme of Study

This chapter addresses these areas of the Programme of Study:

Key concepts

Space Understand the interactions between places and the networks created by flows of information, people and goods; know where places and landscapes are located.
Scale Appreciate different scales - from personal and local to national, international and global.
Interdependence Explore connections between places.

Key processes

Geographical enquiry Ask geographical questions; collect, record and display information; analyse and evaluate evidence, presenting findings to draw and justify conclusions. **Graphicacy and visual literacy** Use maps at a range of scales, photographs, satellite images and other geographical data (including OS maps and aerial photographs); construct maps and plans at a variety of scales.
Geographical communication Communicate knowledge and understanding using geographical vocabulary and conventions in both talk and writing.

The big picture

This chapter introduces, or touches on, some key themes of the KS3 Programme of Study.

- We are connected to people and places all over the world, in many different ways. And we can show these connections on maps.
- Maps are diagrams to show where places are, and what they're like in terms of size, shape, and so on.
- There are many different kinds of maps, giving different types of information.
- A plan is an accurate map of a small area. Plans help you introduce ideas of aerial view, accurate measurement, and scale, to the student.
- Being able to read maps, use map scales, make sketch maps, and use compass bearings, are basic geographical skills.

A pupils' version of this big picture is given in the *geog.1* students' book opener for Chapter 2, and in *geog.1 resources and planning OxBox CD-ROM*, for the whiteboard.

The chapter outline

Use this, and their chapter opener, to give pupils a mental roadmap for the chapter.

2 **Making and mapping connections** As the pupils' chapter opener, this unit is an important part of the chapter; see page 11 for notes about using chapter openers

2.1 **Making connections** How we are connected to people and places all over the world, and how this can be shown on maps

2.2 **A plan of Walter's room** Interpreting and drawing simple plans; drawing lines to scale

2.3 **Your mental maps** From the maps in our heads to sketch maps based on them

2.4 **Real maps** We move from an aerial photo to a sketch map based on it, then to a map of the same area, drawn to scale, and finally to the same map with grid lines

2.5 **Using grid references** How to use four- and six-figure grid references

2.6 **How far?** How to measure linear and non-linear distances on a map

2.7 **Which direction?** Using simple compass bearings to follow and give directions

2.8 **Ordnance Survey maps** What they are and how to use them

2.9 **How high?** How height is shown on an OS map (contour lines and spot heights)

Objectives and outcomes for this chapter

Objectives	Unit	Outcomes
Most pupils will understand:		Most pupils will be able to:
• that we are connected to people and places everywhere	2.1	• give examples of their own connections at local, national and international level
• the concept of scale	2.2, 2.4, 2.5, 2.6, 2.8, 2.9	• work out real (actual) distance given a line and scale; draw lines to different scales; convert distances on a map to actual distances using the map scale
• what a plan is	2.2	• recognise, interpret, and draw a simple plan
• what grid references are, and their purpose	2.4, 2.5, 2.7, 2.8, 2.9	• give, and use, simple letter / number, and four - and six - figure grid references, to locate places
• how to measure distance on a map	2.6, 2.7, 2.8, 2.9	• measure linear and non-linear distances on a map, and use the scale to work out the actual distance
• how the compass points are used to give directions	2.7	• follow and give directions, using compass bearings
• what a sketch map is and how it differs from other maps	2.3, 2.4, 2.8. 2.9	• draw a sketch map from a mental map, a photo, and OS maps
• what an OS map is and how it represents features	28, 2.9	• identify and locate places and features on an OS map, using four and six-figure grid references
• how height is shown on an OS map	2.9	• interpret contour lines and their patterns, and spot heights, on an OS map

These tie in with the opening lines in each unit, which give the purpose of the unit in a pupil-friendly style.

Opportunities for assessment

See the formal assessment materials for this chapter on *geog.1 assessment file & OxBox CD-ROM*. They include a level-marked assessment with success criteria and a feedback form, interactive assessments, a scored test, and a self-assessment form.

There are other opportunities for assessment too. For example, you could use some of the more extended 'Your turn' questions in the students' book, worksheets or longer learning activities from *geog.1 resources and planning OxBox CD-ROM*, or some of the 'Further suggestions for class and homework' at the end of this chapter.

Getting ready for this chapter

Some of the starters and plenaries suggested for this chapter may need resources prepared in advance. Check out the *Resources* section on the 'Help at a glance' pages that follow.

geog.1 resources & planning OxBox CD-ROM has all the photos and diagrams from the chapter, for whiteboard display, plus movies and interactive materials. You will find these very useful for devising your own starters and plenaries. In addition, *geog.world CD-ROM* is a rich source of further material, including interactive webfiles and skills lessons.

About the chapter starter

The images on page 14 of *geog.1* students' book are all satellite images or photographs. Maps would be more help. And they are fundamental to geography. See suggestions 1–4, on page 52 of this book, for further activities related to this chapter starter.

2.1

Making connections

About this unit

The unit starts by showing how Walter is connected to people and places all over the world. His connections are then shown on maps, and pupils have to identify the places. Students classify his connections as local, national, and international, before going on to think about their own.

Key ideas

- We are connected to hundreds of people and places – in our local area, across the country, and around the world. For example through relatives and friends, the items we buy in shops, and where we go on holiday.
- You can show these connections on maps.

Key vocabulary

local, national, international (see the glossary at the end of this book)

Skills practised in 'Your turn'

- Geography skills: identifying places marked on a map
- Literacy skills: using the glossary; an extended piece of writing about what life would be like, without our connections to other countries
- Thinking skills: classifying connections as local, national, international; coming up with their own connections

Unit outcomes

By the end of this unit, most pupils should be able to:

- define the terms given in 'Key vocabulary' above
- list ways in which they are connected to other places
- classify their own connections as local, national, international

Resources

For starter **1**: a varied selection of items from shops (food, clothing and other items), all with labels giving their country of origin; for example a Spanish orange, a T-shirt made in China, rice from India, a British newspaper

Ideas for a starter

1. Hold up the items you have brought in, one by one and ask: Where do you think this came from? Lead pupils to the correct answers, and list these on the board, with the items, under the heading *Where items came from*. Also ask: Who do you think made it / grew it? to remind them that real people were involved.
2. Ask: Who has relatives or friends in the UK? Where in the UK? What about other countries? Start a list of connections with the heading *Where our relatives and friends are*.
3. Ask: Where have you visited, or had a holiday, in this country? In other countries? List the places on the board, under a suitable heading.
4. Ask: In what (other) ways are we linked to other places?

It won't take long to build up an impressive list of connections. Explain that we are linked to hundreds of real places and real people all over the world – even if we never go there or meet them.

Ideas for plenaries

Plan plenaries for strategic points throughout the lesson, as well as at the end.

1 Are maps a good way to record connections? Give reasons.

2 Do you think being aware of all your connections will make life more interesting?

3 Do you think everyone around the world has as many connections as you? Why/Why not?

4 Do you think you affect people in other places, when you buy something? Give reasons.

5 Imagine you could travel to the country of origin of one of the items you saw at the start of the class. Where would you choose? Why? What would you like to find out about this place, while you are there?

Further class and homework activities

Interactive activities for Unit 2.1 on *geog.1 resources and planning OxBox CD-ROM*

Mapping migration on *geog.1 resources and planning OxBox CD-ROM*

Suggestions 1–9 on page 52 of this book

Captain Cook's second voyage in *geog.1, Making and mapping connections* on *geog.world CD-ROM*

Answers to 'Your turn'

1 A = Isle of Man; B = Northumberland; C = Cornwall; D = Surrey; E = Shrewsbury; F = Nigeria; G = Japan; H = China; I = Los Angeles; J = Kenya; K = Hong Kong; L = Jamaica.

2 a International – Nigeria, Hong Kong, Kenya, China, Japan, Los Angeles (as well as Jamaica)

b Local – Anfield, Kirkdale

c National – Warkworth (Northumberland), Cornwall, Isle of Man, Shrewsbury, Surrey

3 This exercise could be developed in class or for homework, taking in foods, TV programmes and so on. See 'Further class and homework activities' above.

4 This will make pupils think – about their food, clothes, other manufactured goods, and about social and cultural links. Encourage discussion on trade and communications, both across the world and within the UK.

2.2

A plan of Walter's room

About this unit

This unit is based on a plan of Walter's room, and aims to help pupils understand the concepts of 'aerial view', and scale, which are important in developing mapwork skills. 'Your turn' provides plenty of practice in using a scale to find 'real' or actual lengths, and in drawing lines to represent lengths, using different scales.

Key ideas

- A plan is an aerial (bird's-eye) view of a place. It usually shows a small area such as a room, or a floor of a building – but it could show a whole section of a town or city.
- Plans are drawn accurately, to scale.
- The scale tells you how size on the plan relates to the size in real life. It is shown as a number ratio, or using a scale line.

Key vocabulary

plan, scale

Skills practised in 'Your turn'

- Numeracy skills: measuring line lengths; converting scaled lengths to actual lengths; drawing lines to represent lengths, using different scales; drawing a very simple plan
- Thinking skills: using plans to decide whether, and where, a piece of furniture will fit in a room; thinking about what should or should not be shown on a plan

Unit outcomes

By the end of this unit, most pupils should be able to:

- explain what a plan is
- interpret, and draw, a simple plan
- explain what scale means, and show a scale in three different ways
- draw lines to represent lengths, using different scales
- use scales to convert scaled lengths to actual lengths

Resources

For starter **1**: one or more metal measuring tapes
For starter **2**: a piece of A4 paper cut up in advance – see notes and drawing below
For starter **3**: architects' plans; room plans from stores such as IKEA and MFI
For starter **4**: all images from the book are on *geog.1 resources and planning OxBox CD-ROM*

Ideas for a starter

1. Suppose you want to carpet this classroom. You want to make a drawing of the floor, to bring to the carpet shop. What will you do first?
   Then ask one or more pairs of pupils to measure the length and width of the classroom floor. Ignore doors, windows and other features, to keep the starter short.
   Show the measurements on the board and discuss how to draw the floor by scaling down the measurements. You could start with a scale of 1:10.
2. Confirm the idea of scale using A4 paper, as on the right.
   Ask the class to compare the quarter sheet (cut out in advance) with the whole one. How do the shapes compare? How do the lengths of the corresponding sides compare? What is the ratio (scale)?
   Repeat using a quarter of a quarter sheet. What is the ratio (scale) this time?

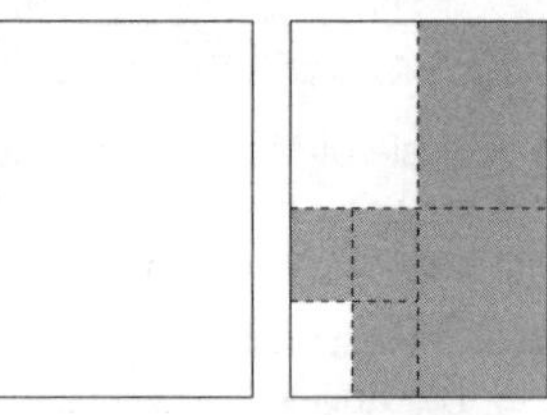

3. Show pupils a variety of plans, if you can.
4. With books shut, display the plan for Walter's room. Ask: What does this show? What do you notice about it? Can you tell what size the room is in real life? How?

Ideas for plenaries

Plan plenaries for strategic points throughout the lesson, as well as at the end.

1 You could use also starters 1, 2 or 3 as plenaries.
2 A student is chosen to explain to the class why scale is used.
3 Turn to your neighbour and explain what problems there might be if the scale was not shown on a plan.
4 What scale is your desk at?
5 What height would you be if you were shrunk using a scale of 10:1?
6 Which groups of people might use plans in their work?
7 Did you find it difficult working with scale? What was the difficult part?

Further class and homework activities

Worksheet 2A on *geog.1 resources and planning OxBox CD-ROM*

Suggestions 10–15 on page 52 of this book

Answers to 'Your turn'

Note: many pupils will find questions **5** and **6** difficult.
5b and **5c** involve half-centimetres. For **4**, **5** and **6** they must be able to use the relationships 100 cm = 1 m and 1000 m = 1 km.

1 X = tall white bookcase; Y = smaller black bookcase

2 300 centimetres (or 3 metres)

3 a 300 centimetres
b 150 centimetres

4 Their lines should be:
a 2 cm **b** 4 cm **c** 10 cm

5 a 6 m **b** 19.5 m **c** 10.5 m

6 Their lines should be these lengths:
1 cm 20 cm 10 cm

7

Walter's room	On the plan	In real life
How wide is it?	12 cm	360 cm
How long?	12 cm	360 cm
How long is the bed?	6.5 cm	195 cm
How wide is the big window?	5 cm	150 cm
How wide is the doorway?	2.5 cm	75 cm

8 a the top
b They should draw a rectangle 1.5 cm by 2 cm.
c It will easily fit through the doorway.
d It will fit nicely by the bed.

9 This will lead to a discussion about whether things like books and games should be shown on the plan. Plans don't usually show temporary features.

10 Below are detailed instructions. You could give these to pupils to follow, for drawing a plan around the school.

Drawing a plan of a room

- Collect everything you will need: a measuring tape that shows centimetres, a sheet of rough paper, a pencil, a ruler, and paper to draw your final plan on.
  (Steel tapes are best for measuring, if you can get one. Graph paper is good for drawing a plan.)
- Draw a rough plan of the room on your rough paper, with lines and labels for all the things you will show: door, windows and so on.
- Ask someone to help you for the next three steps.
- Clear a space around the walls, windows, and door to make measuring easier.
- Measure each wall, window etc in turn. Make sure to keep the measuring tape straight.
- Write the measurements on your rough plan, as you go.
- Choose a suitable scale. (Your plan can fill the whole page.)
- Using the scale, and the measurements, work out the length of each line to draw on your final plan.
  Write these on your rough plan, and circle them.
- Draw your final plan, using the pencil and ruler.
- Write the scale beside your plan.
- Give your plan a title.

Your mental maps

About this unit

This is a fun introduction to maps, related to the work on images of a place in Unit 1.3. It will help pupils develop their geographical imaginations. And they will be pleased to realize that they are already mapmakers, and are using their mental maps successfully!

Key ideas

- We all have images of places in our minds. We can 'see' them with our eyes shut.
- We also have a sequence of mental images, like a movie, of how to get from one place to another.
- Together, these images form our mental maps, that help us to get around. If they're good enough, we don't get lost.
- You can develop and improve your mental maps by observing what's around you. It's fun to do – and good mental maps help us cope with the world.

Key vocabulary

mental map, sketch map (see the glossary at the end of this book)

Skills practised in 'Your turn'

- Geography skills: giving directions for a route, based on a sketch map; drawing a sketch map from a mental map; assessing the accuracy of a sketch map of Britain
- Thinking skills: calling up a mental map of a place; making judgements

Unit outcomes

By the end of this unit, most pupils should be able to:

- explain what a mental map is, and give an example
- draw a sketch map from memory, of a place they know well
- say what they need to do, to improve their mental maps

Resources

For starter **4**, the image is on *geog.1 resources and planning OxBox CD-ROM*

Ideas for a starter

1 With books shut, pupils draw their route to school, adding road and street names where they can. They have 5 minutes. Then they compare maps with their partners. What did they find easy or difficult about drawing their maps, and why? Lead to the idea of mental maps, made up from a sequence of images.

2 Ask: Tell me how to get to ... (somewhere nearby, that the class knows well). Ask pupils *how* they were able to tell you. What exactly did they picture in their minds? Explain that these sequences of images are their mental maps. Repeat for a place they know less well. Why can't they give such good directions this time? Explain that we have many mental maps, and some are less complete than others.

3 A pupil goes to the whiteboard. The pupil's task is to draw a map of somewhere the class knows well, prompted by the class. Is the result accurate? Discuss with the class *why* they were able to give instructions. Lead on to mental maps, the sequences of images that they carry in their heads.

4 Look at the map on page 20 of the students' book (or with books shut, display it on the board). Where's it of? What does it show? Could you draw a map like this easily? Where would you draw it of?

Ideas for plenaries

Plan plenaries for strategic points throughout the lesson, as well as at the end.

1 So, who'll tell the class what a mental map is, and what you'd expect it to have?
2 In what ways is a mental map like one you'd buy in a shop? In what ways is it different? Which do you think is more fun?
3 Do you need to be good at drawing, to have good mental maps in your head?
4 Name a place for which you have only a poor mental map, with lots of gaps. Why is it like this?
5 So, how do you build mental maps in your head? What do you think the process is?
6 Do you think it would be helpful to have good mental maps? Give reasons for your answer – and examples.
7 What kind of features would you try to add to your mental map of a place, to make it better? Write these on the board. There must be no repetition.
8 So how would you set about making your mental maps better? Would it be fun?
9 Do you think you should try to add as much as possible to your mental maps? The class could vote on this. (There is no point making them cluttered.)

Further class and homework activities

Worksheet 2B on *geog.1 resources and planning OxBox CD-ROM*

Suggestions 16 – 20 on pages 52 – 53 of this book

Answers to 'Your turn'

1 A map you carry around in your head.

2 You could convince pupils that they have mental maps by asking them for directions to somewhere. For example from the classroom to the school entrance or similar.

3 b They are things that are important to him: where friends live, football, school, bus stop and so on.

4 a
- Go out front door and turn right.
- Walk along Anfield Road until you see Arkles Lane on the left.
- Then turn into Arkles Lane. Tim's is the fourth house on the right.

b
- Go out front door and turn left.
- Walk to the end of Arkles Lane, and cross over to Oakfield Road.
- The bus stop is on the left, round the corner.

c There are two ways you could go:
- Go along Walton Lane (with Priory Road on your left).
- Take the first road on your left (Anfield Road).
- Go along Anfield Road. You will see the stadium on your right.

Or:
- Go along Priory Road.
- Take the first road on your right. This is Arkles Lane.
- Then take the next road on your right. It is Anfield Road. The stadium is on your left.

For **4c** you could ask pupils:
– Which way looks shorter, on Walter's map?
– Can you be sure it is shorter in real life? Why not? The answer is, of course, that his map is not to scale.

For all of question **4**, point out that the sucess of the directions depends on how good Walter's map is.

5 c ii Our mental maps show what is important to ourselves. So they are likely to be different for different people (and not least, ideas of distance will be different). This could be a problem if you are trying to give people clear directions.

7 To see if it's working, you could ask them to repeat question **5a** at a later date, and compare their new maps with their earlier efforts.

2.4

Real maps

About this unit

This unit should help pupils understand that maps show an aerial view, and that grid lines on a map are useful. We move from an aerial photo of Warkworth to a sketch map of it, then to an accurate map of it, and finally to the same map with grid lines.

Key ideas

- ◆ An aerial photo is a view from the air. And so is a map.
- ◆ Sketch maps are rough maps to show what a place is like. They are not meant to be accurate, and are not drawn to scale.
- ◆ Accurate maps are drawn to scale, and the scale is marked on them.
- ◆ A grid drawn on a map makes it a lot easier to say where places are on the map.

Key vocabulary

aerial photo, sketch map, annotations, scale, gridlines

Skills practised in 'Your turn'

- ◆ Geography skills: interpreting an aerial photo; drawing a sketch map from a photo; comparing a sketch map and a map drawn to scale; saying where a place is, on a map; giving simple grid references
- ◆ Thinking skills: devising a scoring system; looking for similarities and differences; assessing the value of grid lines

Unit outcomes

By the end of this unit, most pupils should be able to:

- ◆ explain what an aerial photo is
- ◆ draw a labelled and annotated sketch map from a photo
- ◆ say what the difference is between a sketch map and a map drawn to scale
- ◆ say why grid lines on a map are useful
- ◆ give and use simple letter/number grid references

Resources

For starters **1** and **2**, and plenary **3**: all images from the book are on *geog.1 resources and planning OxBox CD-ROM*

Ideas for a starter

1. Ask pupils to call out the features they can see, on the aerial photo of Warkworth. (Look at the photo in the book, or display in on the whiteboard.)
2. Look at the photo of Warkworth. Why do you think they built the castle right there? Which do you think came first, a castle or a bridge?
3. Who'll remind the class what a sketch map is?

Ideas for plenaries

Plan plenaries for strategic points throughout the lesson, as well as at the end.

1 Is it easy to draw a sketch map from a photo? Can you think of anything that would make it easier? (No, not tracing paper.)

2 Write the letters KLAFT down the board. Ask pupils what the letters stand for, in relation to sketch maps. When a pupil guesses correctly, write in the word.
K – Key
L – Labels
A – Annotations
F – Frame
T – Title

3 One pupil calls out the name of something on map C. (You could display it on the whiteboard.) Another has to say where it is on the map, as accurately as possible. Repeat for two more pairs of pupils.
Then repeat for map D. It should quickly be obvious that grid lines make life easier.

4 Write a list of characteristics of maps and aerial photos on the board, that pupils have met already. For example:
it's to scale
it has a key
it's a view from above
it has a north arrow

Pupils come up and write these words alongside, in the appropriate places: aerial photo, plan, sketch map, accurate map.

5 Write this list on the board.
aerial photo
sketch map
plan
accurate map
Beside each item, pupils have to write what, and whom, it is useful for.

6 Why do geographers think maps are so great?

Further class and homework activities

Worksheets 2C and 2D on *geog.1 resources and planning OxBox CD-ROM*

Maps movie on *geog.1 resources and planning OxBox CD-ROM*

Suggestions 21 and 22 on page 53 of this book

Answers to 'Your turn'

3 a Similarities: same place; river, castle, bridges, woods and roads marked.

b The main differences are in scale, level of detail, and accuracy:
C is to scale, so it is more accurate.
It gives more detail in terms of buildings.
It distinguishes between different types of roads
It uses some icons and abbreviations.
It does not show trees.
It does not have annotations.

4 Students might notice that it's quite difficult to say where the castle is, in words. 'In the bottom half of the map' and 'in the neck of the loop' are some descriptions. But let them work through **5** and **6** before commenting on this.

5 a B2 **b** C4

c i In C3: small part of main street, other street, church, post office, other buildings, lane, footpath, river

ii In B4: street (road), church, other buildings, footpath, wood, river

6 Students should notice that the grid lines make it a lot easier to say where something is on the map, and to find things.

Using grid references

About this unit

The unit starts with an aerial photo, and a simple map of the same area, which pupils can compare. This helps to confirm the idea of a map as an aerial drawing. The map has a grid – but now the grid lines have numbers only, unlike the map in Unit 2.4. 'Your turn' gives practice in using four- and six-figure grid references, ready for OS work later.

Key ideas

Most of these ideas have been met already.

- Aerial photos and maps are closely related. Both give a bird's eye view of a place.
- Like plans, accurate maps are drawn to scale.
- Accurate maps should have a title, frame, north arrow, scale and key.
- Grid lines are also useful, to help you find things on the map quickly.
- A four-figure grid reference shows the square in which a place or feature lies.
- A six-figure grid reference show its position more accurately.

Key vocabulary

aerial photo, map, grid lines, four-figure grid reference, six-figure grid reference

Skills practised in 'Your turn'

- Geography skills: comparing an aerial photo and a map; using four- and six-figure grid references to locate places; interpreting maps and relating them to 'real life'
- Thinking skills: coming up with a way to measure distance on a map

Unit outcomes

By the end of this unit, most pupils should be able to:

- explain the terms given in 'Key vocabulary' above
- state what features an accurate map should have (scale, key and so on)
- give, and use, four- and six-figure grid references to locate places

Resources

For starters **1** – **4**, and plenary **5**: all images from the book are on *geog.1 resources and planning OxBox CD-ROM*

For plenary **1**: a selection of maps showing grid lines (atlas maps, street maps, OS maps)
For plenary **2**: a globe
For plenary **3** and **4**: a metre rule

Ideas for a starter

1 Look at the photo of the River Mole valley, on page 24 (or display it on the whiteboard). Where was it taken from? List all the features you can spot. Share your list with a neighbour. Now look at the map. Can you find all those features on it?

2 Compare the map and photo, on page 24. (You can display them on the whiteboard.) Which is better at telling you what the area is like? Why? Which would be more help, if you were looking for the school? Why?

3 Compare the map and photo, on page 24. (You can display them on the whiteboard.) In what ways are they similar? In what ways are they different?

4 Compare the map on page 24 with map D on page 23. (You can display them on the whiteboard.) What do you notice about the way the grids are labelled?

Ideas for plenaries

Plan plenaries for strategic points throughout the lesson, as well as at the end.

1 Show the class a variety of maps, with grid lines.

2 Show the class a globe, and ask what the special grid lines on it are called.

3 Carefully draw a large grid on the board like the one on the top right of page 25 of the students' book. (You could do this in advance. A metre rule may help.)
Label the grid lines with 2-digit numbers. Then mark a scattering of letters (A, B, C...) in the grids (ten or twelve will do). Call out a letter. When a pupil calls out its correct 4-figure grid reference, cross it out or delete it. (A pupil can call out only once.)
You can do this against the clock. If any are left when time's up, you win!

4 Repeat **3** but this time for six-figure grid references. You will need to write small neat letters. When a pupil calls out a grid reference, ask the class to judge whether it's correct.

5 Now compare the grids again, for map D on page 23, and the map on page 24. (You can display them on the whiteboard.) Ask:
– Which grid reference system is easier to use? Why?
– Which lets you say where something is, more exactly? Why?

Further class and homework activities

Suggestion 23 on page 53 of this book

Where on Earth? (an extended worksheet) on *geog.1 resources and planning OxBox CD-ROM*

Where on Earth? (an interactive lesson) in *geog.1*, *Making and mapping connections* on *geog.world CD-ROM*

Answers to 'Your turn'

1 a 3245
b 3145
c 3044

2 a a tunnel
b a right-angle bend in a track
c a bridge over the river

3 a 324456
b 322459
c 323463

4 a well

5 There are trees and bushes growing along the river banks - and these show up on the photo.

6 You will see the trees and bushes along the river banks. You might be able to see the river through the trees, and get a glimpse of Cowslip Farm.

7 It's just over half a kilometre (0.55 km), measured from the lower end of both sets of farm buildings.

8 Around 315459. The sign is for motorists going north on the A24. It tells them that they can turn right onto the B2209 to get to Mickleham, soon after the bend on the A24. So the sign must be on the A24, before the bend.

How far?

About this unit

In this unit pupils learn how to work out the distance, as the crow flies and by road, between two places on a map. In 'Your turn' they get practice in using these skills.

Key ideas

- You can find out the distance between two places, using a map.
- You can measure the linear distance ('as the crow flies') or the distance along a route such as a road or railway.
- You use the scale on the map to convert this to the actual distance.

Key vocabulary

straight line distance, as the crow flies, pivot

Skills practised in 'Your turn'

- Geography skills: measuring distance on a map; following directions on a map; using grid references
- Literacy skills: writing instructions, based on a map, for getting from one place to another

Unit outcomes

By the end of this unit, most pupils should be able to:

- explain the terms given in 'Key vocabulary' above
- measure the distance between places on a map, using a strip of paper and a linear scale
- give, and follow, directions based on a simple map

Resources

For starter **1**: a piece of string (around 2 m long); a metre rule or tape measure
For plenary **2**: all images from the book are on *geog.1 resources and planning OxBox CD-ROM*

Ideas for a starter

1. Mark two heavy dots on the board, at least 60 cm apart, to represent places, and write made-up place names beside them. Then write a scale on the board. (For example *1 cm represents 1 km*.) Ask: How far apart are these places? How can you find out?

   Now ask a student to measure the straight line distance between them using a metre rule or tape measure. The class uses the scale to convert this to the 'real' distance.

   Next draw a wavy line between the dots to represent a road. Ask: How far is it by road from one place to the other? How could you work this out? If pupils need prompting, hold up the piece of string and ask: Would this help?

   Ask a student to measure the distance using the string. Again the class uses the scale to convert this to the 'real' distance.
2. How would you measure the distance between X and Y (name two local places)? Students may suggest using the mileage meter on a car. How would you measure it without travelling to the two places? Any suggestions? Vote for the best one.

Ideas for plenaries

Plan plenaries for strategic points throughout the lesson, as well as at the end.

1. Put these places in order of distance from London, by plane: New York, Birmingham, Cairo, Paris, Melbourne. (The map on pages 140–141 of *geog.1* students' book may help.)
2. Two people set out from Chapel Farm Park (2611) on the map on page 27, to go to Crabtree cottages (2512). One is riding a horse and the other is driving a car. Discuss with your neighbour who you think will arrive first, and who will have travelled the shortest distance, and why. (You could display the map.)
3. Students compare their answers for question 3 in 'Your turn'. Were they all the same? If not, why not? What can go wrong when measuring like this? Do you think it gives an accurate result?
4. How do you think they measure distance between places, for road signs? (This could become a homework project. See suggestion 25 on page 53.)

Further class and homework activities

Worksheet 2E on *geog.1 resources and planning OxBox CD-ROM*

Suggestions 24 – 26 on page 53 of this book

Journey to school on *geog.1 resources and planning OxBox CD-ROM*

Answers to 'Your turn'

1 1.6 km

2 1.45 km

3 About 1.3 km

4 Chapel Farm Park

5 Crabtree Cottages

6 a Juniper Hall, 275124; Boxlands 274109

b The directions should go something like this:

From Juniper Hall travel left to the T-junction. Then turn left onto the B2209 and continue south for about 0.8 km until you join the A24 at the roundabout. Go south on the A24 for about 0.8 km, and turn left onto a minor road. Boxlands is 0.15 km along this road.

2.7

Which direction?

About this unit

This unit introduces the compass points N, S, E and W, and the 'in-betweens' (NW, SW, NE, SE). 'Your turn' gives pupils plenty of practice in using these bearings to follow and give directions.

Key ideas

- North, south, east and west are the four key directions.
- More directions can be added between these points.
- North west means north *of* west, south east means south *of* east, and so on.

Key vocabulary

north, north east, north west, and so on

Skills practised in 'Your turn'

- Geography skills: using compass bearings to describe direction, and follow a route on a map; using simple grid references (letter/number); using a linear scale to measure distance
- Literacy skills: writing instructions for a 'treasure hunt' on a map, to collect letters to build a word

Unit outcomes

By the end of this unit, most pupils should be able to:

- point out the other directions (S, E, W, NE, NW, SE, SW) when told where north is
- follow simple instructions using these compass bearings
- write simple instructions using these bearings, for someone else to follow

Resources

For starter **1**: a globe
For starters **2–4**: a compass
For plenary **5**: *geog.1 resources and planning OxBox CD-ROM*

Ideas for a starter

1. Ask a student to point out where the North Pole and South Pole are, on a globe.
2. Show the class a compass. Ask what it does. How does it work? Ask: Where is north from here? What is the opposite to north? What other directions do you know?
3. Draw a simple compass (N, S, E and W) on the board. Ask pupils what it is. Then ask/establish which way North is from the classroom.
4. Students become living compasses. They rotate on the spot, holding out their right arms straight in front, to point to a direction that you (or other pupils) call out, relative to a 'north' marker. If you want the whole class to be compasses, try this activity outside!

Ideas for plenaries

Plan plenaries for strategic points throughout the lesson, as well as at the end.

1 What kinds of problems might there be, if we did not have compasses, or the key directions N, S, E and W?

2 Some people have jobs, or hobbies, where compass bearings are really important. Think up some examples. (Pilots? sailors? any others?)

3 An easy way to remember where west and east are, on the compass: they spell out WE.

4 A small team of pupils is asked in advance to make up 20 quiz questions about the map on page 139, using bearings. (Or you may wish to do this yourself.) For example: Which is the most northerly city shown on the map? Name a city starting with B, directly west of London. What sea lies off the east coast of England? The team then asks the rest of the class these questions. The class gets 1 mark for each correct answer. The quiz team gets 1 mark for each wrong one. (Or the quiz could be against the clock.)

5 The interactive activity for Unit 2.7 on *geog.1 resources and planning OxBox CD-ROM* could be used as a plenary.

Further class and homework activities

Interactive activity for Unit 2.7 on *geog.1 resources and planning OxBox CD-ROM* if not used already as a plenary

Worksheet 2F on *geog.1 resources and planning OxBox CD-ROM*

Suggestions 27 – 30 on page 53 of this book

Answers to 'Your turn'

1 a south **b** east **c** south west
d north west

2 a riding school **b** hostel **c** ice cream parlour
d bike hire

3 a south **b** north west

4 a south **b** north west **c** south east

5 About 110 metres

6 He stayed in cottage 1.

7 The word they should have made is 'tomato'.

Ordnance Survey maps

About this unit

This unit presents the first OS map of the course. It's a fairly simple map that includes Warkworth, which also appeared in the photo on page 22. 'Your turn' gives pupils practice in identifying OS symbols and using grid references.

Key ideas

- Ordnance Survey (OS) maps are always to scale and show a lot of detail.
- The OS maps that pupils meet in *geog.1* are at scales of 1:25 000 and 1:50 000 (or 1 cm to 250 m and 1 cm to 500 m).
- OS maps use numbered grid lines, and standard symbols to represent different features. (See the key for the symbols on page 138 of the student's book.)

Key vocabulary

Ordnance Survey, symbols

Skills practised in 'Your turn'

- Geography skills: reading an OS map and identifying OS map symbols; using four- and six-figure grid references for an OS map; comparing an OS map with a photo; measuring distance on an OS map using the 1:25 000 scale; drawing a sketch map from an OS map
- Thinking skills: drawing conclusions about population, tourism, and coastal dangers, from information shown on the OS map

Unit outcomes

By the end of this unit, most pupils should be able to:

- explain what Ordnance Survey maps are, and what kinds of features they show
- interpret OS symbols using a key
- use four- and six-figure grid references, for an OS map
- use an OS map to look for clues and gather information about a place
- draw a sketch map from an OS map, to show a route

Resources

For starter **2**: a set of flash cards with OS symbols on
For starters **3** and **4** and plenaries **1**, **2**, and **4**: all images from the book are on *geog.1 resources and planning OxBox CD-ROM*
Note: your pupils will find rulers helpful for working out grid references

Ideas for a starter

1. You are a map designer. How would you show a forest on a map? a river? a school? a church? a bridge? a phone box? a picnic area? (A short list of items could be written on the board.) Work with a partner to design symbols to use. Swap these (no labels!) with another pair of pupils and see if they can guess which is which.
2. With the books closed, hold up some flash cards with OS symbols on (or draw them on the board). Ask pupils to guess what the symbols mean.
3. Look at the OS map from page 31. (You can display it on the whiteboard, with the books closed.) What does the large blue area represent? What about the yellow area? What is the wide blue squiggle? What are the little beige rectangles? (and so on). Pupils try to guess without looking at the key.
4. The place in the photo on page 22 is shown on the OS map on page 31. Where? (You can display the photo.) What features from the photo are shown on the map?

Ideas for plenaries

Plan plenaries for strategic points throughout the lesson, as well as at the end.

1. Look at the scale on the OS map. (You can display the map and scale on the whiteboard.) How far apart are the grid lines, in cm? What distance does that represent on the ground? What distance does 1 cm represent?
2. What clues can you find on the OS map, about how people in the area earn a living?
3. When might you find an OS map useful, outside school? For example would it be useful on holiday? If you were a walker or camper?
4. I spy with my little eye … a public phone box (or Birling golf links, or Hermitage Farm, or similar). A pupil calls out something he or she sees on the OS map on page 31. Other pupils must quickly give a four-figure grid reference. Have a timekeeper, and see how many things can be found in five minutes. Or allow only so many seconds for each one. (You could display the map on the whiteboard for this.)
5. OS bingo: pupils choose any nine symbols from the key on page 30 and draw them into a 3 X 3 grid. The teacher calls out a list of features and pupils cross them off. The first to cross odd all nine symbols wins.
6. How do you think OS maps get made? (This could become a homework project. See suggestion 34 on page 53.)

Further class and homework activities

Worksheet 2G on *geog.1 resources and planning OxBox CD-ROM*

Police chase! and *OS Lotto* on *geog.1 resources and planning OxBox CD-ROM*

Suggestions 31 – 34 on page 53 of this book

Answers to 'Your turn'

1 The river is the River Coquet. It flows into the North Sea at Amble.

2 a 2407 **b** 2504 **c** 2705

3 a New Barns **b** a caravan park **c** Warkworth Castle **d** Hermitage Farm **e** a cemetery **f** a lighthouse

4 4 cm on the OS map represents 1 km in real life. (So 1 cm on the map represents a quarter of a kilometre, or 0.25 km, or 250 metres.)

5 The top of the photo is north.

6 Violet lives in the house on the corner at 248056.

7 The population of Amble is 5600 (or 3.5 times the population of Warkworth). The map shows that Amble has a larger built-up area; it has 3 or 4 times as many buildings as Warkworth (but not 5 or 6 times as many). You can also tell that Amble is larger because it has five schools, while Warkworth has just one.

8 a five (one in 2503, one on 2603, one in 2604, two in 2704)
b four (all in 2604)
c two (one in 2504, the other in 2704)

9 a post office: 247060 (or 267046) **b** club house: 254066
c phone box: 275042 (or 234067) **d** mast: 266039 (or 265041)

For **c**, leader lines point to the exact location. Students may have difficulty with a grid reference for the second phone box in **c**, since only part of the square is shown.

10 campsite in 2506 and caravan sites in 2704 and 2506; caravan park in 2505; two parking areas in 2704; information centre in 2604; picnic sites in 2506 and 2604

11 These are some of the things visitors can do:
visit some historic spots – the ruins of the castle and hermitage, the old bridge in Warkworth, and the marked rock in 2303; explore Warkworth and Amble; explore the National Trust area in 2508; lie on the beach, or swim; play golf; take boat trips out to sea; go sailing in the sea in their own boats; go fishing in the river or sea; take long walks by the river; clamber about on the rocks by the sea, looking in rock pools; have picnics; enjoy camping or caravanning.

12 the lighthouse in 2705; the beacons in 2704 and 2705; the lifeboat station at 266047

13 a It's just about 3 km from Violet's home to the school in 2503.
b Pupils' sketch maps could look like this one (but larger):

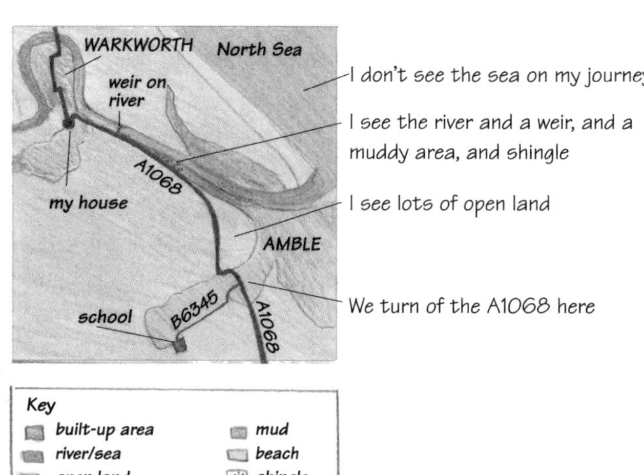

How high?

About this unit

This unit is about how land height is shown on an OS map. 'Your turn' gives practice in finding heights at different places, identifying steep and flat land, and deciding whether a route goes uphill, downhill, or along flat land.

Key ideas

- OS maps use contour lines and spot heights to show how high land is, in metres above sea level.
- Contour lines join places at the same height above sea level.
- Contour lines are at regular height intervals: every 5 m on a 1:25 000 map, and every 10 m on a 1:50 000 map.
- The further apart the contour lines, the flatter the ground is. The closer they are, the steeper it is.
- A spot height is a number on the map, showing the exact height at that spot, in metres above sea level.

Key vocabulary

contour lines, spot heights

Skills practised in 'Your turn'

- Geography skills: interpreting contour lines; reading spot heights; using six-figure grid references; drawing a sketch map to show a route
- Thinking skills: planning a route that fits a set of criteria

Unit outcomes

By the end of this unit, most pupils should be able to:

- explain what contour lines and spot heights are
- tell the height at a place on an OS map, by using contour lines and spot heights
- interpret the pattern of contour lines, to decide how flat or steep land is, and which way it slopes

Resources

For starter **2**: half of a large potato (the cut surface should be the widest part)
For plenaries **2**, **3**, and **5**: all images from the book are on *geog.1 resources and planning OxBox CD-ROM*
Note: your pupils will find rulers helpful for working out grid references

Ideas for a starter

1 You are a map designer. How would you show hills on a map? Students may suggest using shading. Point out that it is not very accurate. Any other suggestions?

2 After introducing contour lines, demonstrate them in 3D using half of a large potato.
Place the half potato as shown.
Say that its base is at sea level.
Ask a student to hold a ruler upright beside the potato, so that the 0 mark on the rule is aligned with the base.

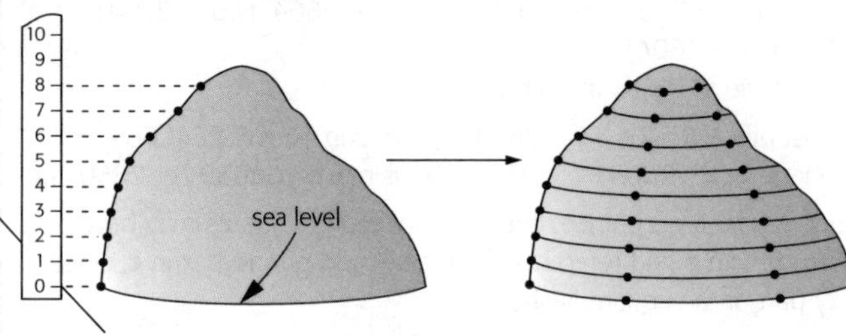

Now mark points up the side of the potato, corresponding to 1 cm intervals on the ruler. Repeat at intervals around the potato. Then draw rings joining the points at equal heights. The rings represent contour lines. Invite pupils to look at the contour lines from the side, then from directly above.

Ideas for plenaries

Plan plenaries for strategic points throughout the lesson, as well as at the end.

1 The contour lines on the map on page 32 of *geog.1* students' book are at height intervals of ten metres. How high is ten metres? Higher than the classroom? Higher than an electricity pole?

2 Look at the contour lines on the map on page 31. (You could display this.) At what height interval are these? Can you explain the difference? (Hint: compare the scales.)

3 Overall, which of the two areas is flatter: the one in the map on page 32, or the one in the map on page 31? (You could display these.)

4 What do you think the pattern of contour lines around the school would be like?

5 It's been snowing hard. You want to go sledging in the map area on page 32. Give a six-figure grid reference for where you'd like to start sledging. (It would be good to display the map for this.)

6 Here are five answers. What do you think the five questions are?
a) The height above sea level
b) The contour lines are far apart
c) The contour lines are very close together
d) Every ten metres above sea level
e) Every five metres above sea level

7 How do you think OS mapmakers find out the heights of places? (This could become a homework project. See suggestion 35 on page 53.)

Further class and homework activities

Interactive quiz for Chapter 2 on *geog.1 resources and planning OxBox CD-ROM*

Worksheets 2H and 2I on *geog.1 resources and planning OxBox CD-ROM*

Suggestions 35 and 36 on page 53 of this book

Assessment materials for Chapter 2 on *geog.1 assessment file & OxBox CD-ROM*

Review 'Your goals for this chapter' on page 15 of *geog.1* students' book

Answers to 'Your turn'

1 A = 3, B = 1, C = 2

2 a 4703 **b** It's beside the village of Alton

3 a all the land along that line is 200 metres above sea level
b a height of 190 metres above sea level (the contour lines are at intervals of 10 metres)

4 a 100 metres
b 150 metres
c 95 metres (see the spot height)

5 a square 0642 – more contour lines seem to be closest here. Students might suggest 0742 too. The contour lines in 0539 are close, but not as close as in those two.
b square 1240 – it appears to have the largest area without any contour lines. Students might suggest 1241 or 1242 – it's a close call. 1242 does have a large flat area – but also a steepish slope.

6 It appears to be quite hilly, in particular with a steep slope down to the River Churnet, and Toot Hill across the river. (Plenty of contour lines, close together.)

7 a downhill (to the little river); note that the leader lines point to the exact locations of the phones;
b the road going northwards from the bridge goes along flat land first, then turns eastwards and goes uphill
c along flat land

8 a Along almost flat land – no contour lines appear to cross it. It also meanders a lot, which is a sign that it's flowing on flat land.
b A river flows from high land to low. Judging by the spot heights, this river is flowing southwards. There is a spot height of 103 m in square 0742, 91 m in square 1041, and 87 m in square 1039.

9 Students should have fun with this.
They can pass by Alton Towers. There's woodland, and a castle at Alton, and weirs on the Chernet, and lots of bridges.
There's a lake or reservoir near Waste Farm, and old earthworks west of Alton.

2 Further suggestions for class and homework

Most of these suggestions are addressed to your pupils. Where research or further resources are needed, the internet will almost certainly provide the answer. (Eg *google* and choose *Web* or *Images*.)

Where is ...?

1 My address – illustrated! Instead of 'Where is Walter?' do 'Where am I?' Use the ideas in the chapter opening unit to show your own address. You can use drawings, photos, and aerial photos if you can find them. (Try the internet?) Otherwise you could trace maps. **

2 Whose address is it anyway? Repeat **1** for a famous person in the UK or abroad. (For example the President of the United States.) The class has to guess who it is! **

Aerial photos and satellite images

3 Find out about aerial photos Page 14 in *geog.1* students' book has an aerial photo of Liverpool. Find out how aerial photos are taken, and write 100 words about them. You could mention what kind of weather they are taken in, and who might use them, and for what. ***

4 Find out about satellite images Page 14 in the students' book shows satellite images of the Earth from space. How are these images produced? Where are the satellites? (Try an internet search for *satellite image Earth*.) ***

Mapping connections

5 Mapping your own connections Make a list of different places you are connected to, through family and friends. (At least 12.) Mark these places on outline maps of the UK and /or the world. Beside each place write what the connection is. You could add drawings, photos or postcards. (For this, stick your map on a larger piece of paper.) *

6 The world in my kitchen Check food and soft drinks labels at home, or in a shop. Write a list of at least 15 items and where they come from. Mark the places on a map, stuck on a large sheet of paper. Add a drawing of each item, or cut out images from shop catalogues. *

7 The world in my life Keep a diary of all the places *outside* the UK that touch your life over the next week. For example places where your food, clothes, or people you meet come from, or places you see on TV. Mark them on an outline map of the world. Beside each, write what the connection is. **

8 TV trail! List all the places in the UK mentioned on the TV news over the next week. Find them in an atlas and mark them on a large outline map of the UK. Beside each place, say why it was mentioned. Then see if you can classify them into groups, according to this. For example groups like *Politics* and *Sport*. Underline each place with a different colour depending on its group, and add a colour key. **

9 Newspaper trail! Repeat activity **8** for 25 places *outside* the UK, mentioned in today's newspaper. **

Plans and scales

10 Scale plan Measure a room at home, for example the living room. Draw a plan to scale. Mark in any fixed items (such as doors, windows, radiators, a fireplace). *

11 Your bedroom plan Draw an accurate plan of your bed-room, or a room you'd like have as a bedroom, on squared paper. Mark in any fitted items such as windows, doors, radiators, fitted wardrobes. Then draw in the furniture you have, or would like to have, to scale. You can colour it in. **

12 My ideal house You have won a prize – a plot of land measuring 150 metres x 100 metres, and money to build a house and garden on it.
Draw a rough plan of the house and garden. Graph paper will help. (Rough means 'not to scale'. It does not mean 'untidy'!) Design any symbols you need, and include a key to explain what they are. */**/***

13 You've shrunk! You find a strange blue bottle with a label that says 'Drink me'. So, being curious, you do. And suddenly you find you have shrunk, in a ratio of 10:1. What height are you now? What problems will this cause you? Describe a day in your life and all the problems you encounter. */**/**

14 You've grown very large indeed! You find a strange red bottle with a label that says 'Drink me'. So, being curious, you do. And suddenly you find you have shot up in height, in a ratio of 1:10. What height are you now? What problems will this cause you? Describe a day in your life and all the problems you encounter. */**/**

15 Measure up Britain Look at Great Britain on page 139. (It's the largest island on that map. Ignore the smaller British islands, like those around Scotland, for now.) About how long is this island at its longest point? Use the map scale to find out. About how wide is it at its widest point? About how wide is it at its narrowest point? Draw a rough map of the island and mark these distances on. **

Mental maps and sketch maps

16 Britain as you know it! We all have mental maps of places. Draw your own mental map of Great Britain (or the British Isles), and mark in where you think you live. No peeking at wall maps, or any other maps, while you do this! Next, swap maps with a partner, and compare them with an atlas map. Give each other a score. **

17 The way to improve your mental maps is: look around you and observe, as you go places. But how will you know if your mental map of a place is improving? Work with a partner to design a mental map test for the area around the school. (And test yourselves in a few weeks.) ***

18 Bird's eye view Take the class to a high (safe) place to draw a sketch map of the surrounding area. Then let them walk around below to check the names of streets, buildings and so on. **

19 Sketch map: journey home On your next journey between school and home, look out for street names and landmarks. Then make a sketch map of the route. Mark in anything that would allow a stranger to follow the route easily. Find out how long it is, and mark this on your sketch map too. **

20 Sketch map: treasure island You are a pirate. You have hidden a trunk full of treasure on a desert island. Draw a sketch map to show where. Add lots of detail: shipwrecks, old anchors, palm trees, lagoons, hills, caves. Don't forget the scale (in paces) and a North arrow. Now write instructions to tell a partner how to get to the treasure. Give compass bearings, and distances in paces.
Try it out on your partner. Did it work? ***

Maps and grid references

21 A class map collection Cut out maps from magazines, newspapers, travel brochures. Try for as many different types of map as you can. See if you can include maps with grid lines on. Bring them into school and make a class collage of maps. Can you sort them into different groups? *

22 A map of your local area Find a map of the area around the school. The bigger the better! Then off you go with a digital camera and take photos within this area. Make a display for the classroom wall, with the map in the centre and photos around it. Link them with arrows (or thread) to their locations on the map. Add interesting annotations. (This could become an ongoing class project.) */**/***

23 Lines of latitude and longitude The lines drawn on a globe or a map of the world are a type of grid line. They are called lines of latitude and longitude, and they help you say exactly where on the Earth a place is. But because the Earth is a sphere they are curved, not flat.
Find out more about these lines, and how they are used to locate places. Then prepare a leaflet about them, or a presentation for the class. Don't forget drawings or other visual aids. And don't forget to mention those two very important lines, the Equator and the Prime Meridian.
Give latitudes and longitudes of some places, including your nearest town or city, as examples. Explain how these are a bit like 6-figure grid references. ***

How far?

24 My distances Get two blank maps – a world map and a British Isles map. Mark your home spot on each map.
Next, find out how far you are, as the crow flies, from different places. For example London, your nearest seaside resort, Edinburgh, Disneyland, New York, Mexico City, Hong Kong. Mark these places on your maps. Mark arrows from your home spot to them, and write the distances on. **

25 How do they measure? How do they measure distances between places, for road signs? You could try ringing or e-mailing the local council to find out. Nominate one person in the class to do this. **

26 Further and further Find out the distance around the Earth from pole to pole, and around the Equator. Are both the same? If not, why not? Then find how far the Earth is from the moon, and from the sun. Show all these measurements on one diagram. **/***

Which direction?

27 Lost in the desert! You and your camel are lost in the desert. If you keep going north you will reach the coast, and safety. But you have no compass, and no-one to ask directions from. What will you do? Close your eyes and imagine what it is like there, how you feel, and how you will solve your problem. Now write a short story describing how you find your way to the coast. **

28 Teaching directions Design a simple compass wheel to teach children the directions N, S, E and W. It could be something like a clock face made of cardboard, with two hands. (Or you might have a much better idea.) Explain how your invention will be used. */**/***

29 Compass history Do some research on the history of the compass, and find an interesting way to present this. ***

30 Sunrise, sunset The sun rises in the east, and sets in the west. Why is this? Work out a way to explain it to the class, using a globe and torch. ***

Ordnance Survey maps

31 Our grid references Study a local OS map (1:25 000 is preferable) and locate your home, your school, other places that are important to you, and some local landmarks. Write down six-figure grid references for them. **

32 Sketching from your local OS map Choose an area from your local OS map (at least 9 squares from a 1: 50 000 map). Make a sketch map of the area to show a stranger what it is like. Add shading for high ground. Add symbols for the main features, and a key. **

33 Design an OS game Design a game to teach children OS symbols. */**/***

34 Making OS maps How do the OS map-makers make their maps? Do they travel all around the country, looking at everything? Find out, and write an introduction to OS map-making, for nine-year-olds. ***

How high?

35 How do the OS map makers measure height? Find out and then explain to the class. This is a challenge! ***

36 Mountain high The OS maps you've seen so far had some gentle hills– but no mountains! Find out the heights of the world's top 10 tallest mountains, and show this data on a bar chart. Add the height of your local area, and Ben Nevis, Britain's tallest mountain, for comparison. **

3 Settlement

Helping you deliver the KS3 Programme of Study

This chapter addresses these areas of the Programme of Study:

Key concepts

Place Understand the physical and human characteristics of real places (what a place is like, how it became like this, and how it is subject to forces for change). **Space** Know where places and landscapes are located, why they are there, the patterns and distributions they create, how and why these are changing and the implications for people. **Environmental interaction** Understand that the physical and human dimensions of the environment are interrelated; explore sustainable development and its impact on environmental interaction. **Physical and human processes** Explain how human processes shape places, landscapes and societies.

Key processes

Geographical enquiry Ask geographical questions; think critically, constructively and creatively; display information; analyse and evaluate evidence, presenting findings to draw and justify conclusions. **Graphicacy and visual literacy** Use maps at a range of scales, photographs, satellite images and other geographical data (including OS maps and aerial photographs). **Geographical communication** Communicate knowledge and understanding using geographical vocabulary and conventions in both talk and writing.

The big picture

These are the key ideas behind this chapter.

- Humans first began to farm around 10 000 years ago – which meant settling in one place.
- A variety of factors influenced their choice of where to settle. (Good flat farmland was one.)
- Many of their early settlements grew over the centuries into villages, towns and cities.
- The historical development of settlements has led to a pattern of land use, which you'll find in many British towns and cities.
- Settlements have always changed, and are still changing. And change means conflict.

A pupils' version of this big picture is given in the *geog.1* students' book opener for Chapter 3, and in *geog.1 resources and planning OxBox CD-ROM*, for the whiteboard.

The chapter outline

Use this, and their chapter opener, to give pupils a mental roadmap for the chapter.

3 **Settlement** As the pupils' chapter opener, this unit is an important part of the chapter; see page 11 for notes about using chapter openers

3.1 **Settling down** How humans began to settle, and factors that influenced their choice of site

3.2 **Example: settling in Aylesbury** How and why the Saxons settled in Aylesbury

3.3 **How Aylesbury grew** How and why settlements grow, with Aylesbury as example; we step through its history, and explore its growth in terms of both area and population

3.4 **The pattern of growth** There's a pattern in the way settlements grow, and we can use a simple model to show it; we explore the pattern using a simplified map of Aylesbury

3.5 **Be a land-use detective!** How to identify land-use patterns on OS maps, again with Aylesbury as example

3.7 **How's Aylesbury doing today?** Every settlement has its good and bad points – and here we explore Aylesbury's

3.7 **A new challenge for Aylesbury** Aylesbury is targeted as a growth point for new homes, in response to the UK's housing shortage; here we explore why new homes are needed, and some implications for Aylesbury

3.8 **Sustainable development for Aylesbury** Introduces the concept of sustainable development, and uses it to explore the new developments planned for Aylesbury

Objectives and outcomes for this chapter

Objectives	Unit	Outcomes
Most pupils will understand:		Most pupils will be able to:
• that settlements began to develop when humans began to settle down as farmers	3.1	• describe how and why humans began to settle
• that a combination of geographical and human factors influenced the choice of site	3.1, 3.2	• give at least five factors that would have influenced the choice of site
• that a combination of geographical and human factors caused many settlements to grow into the towns and cities we know today	3.3	• describe how Aylesbury grew from an early Saxon settlement, and give at least four factors that help a settlement to grow
• that there is a pattern in how settlements grew and developed, and we can trace this in the pattern of land use in British towns and cities today	3.4	• describe how the pattern of land use developed, and draw a simple model for it
• that we can find out a great deal about the pattern of land use, and the functions in a place, from OS maps	3.5	• be able to identify different types of land use, and different functions, on an OS map
• that settlements have good and bad points, for the people who live in them	3.6	• give examples of good and bad points about a settlement
• that settlements are always changing	3.3, 3.4, 3.6, 3.7, 3.8	• explain why settlements change, and give examples of changes
• that a combination of human factors has led to a big demand for more homes in the UK	3.7	• explain the growing demand for houses; explain what greenfield and brownfield sites are, and suggest some pros and cons for each type of site
• that we can choose to develop places so that they support a more sustainable way of living	3.8	• explain what sustainable development means, and how a development such as a housing estate could be made sustainable

These tie in with the opening lines in each unit, which give the purpose of the unit in a pupil-friendly style.

Opportunities for assessment

See the formal assessment materials for this chapter on *geog.1 assessment file & OxBox CD-ROM*. They include a level-marked assessment with success criteria and a feedback form, interactive assessments, a scored test, and a self-assessment form.

There are other opportunities for assessment too. For example, you could use some of the more extended 'Your turn' questions in the students' book, worksheets or longer learning activities from *geog.1 resources and planning OxBox CD-ROM*, or some of the 'Further suggestions for class and homework' at the end of this chapter.

Getting ready for this chapter

Some of the starters and plenaries suggested for this chapter may need resources prepared in advance. Check out the *Resources* section on the 'Help at a glance' pages that follow.

geog.1 resources & planning OxBox CD-ROM has all the photos and diagrams from the chapter, for whiteboard display, plus movies and interactive materials. You will find these very useful for devising your own starters and plenaries. In addition, *geog.world CD-ROM* is a rich source of further material, including interactive webfiles and skills lessons.

About the chapter starter

The photo on page 34 of *geog.1* shows the centre of Aylesbury, Bucks. Aylesbury was first settled by the Saxons around 571 AD. The large church is St Mary's, which dates from the 13th century. It stands on the site of a Saxon church. Note Market Square, with its market stalls: Aylesbury grew as a market town, and its market is still alive and well.

3.1 Settling down

About this unit

Using the strip cartoon format, this unit tells how humans first began to settle down, and gives the factors that influenced their choice of site. The ideas are confirmed, and explored a little further, in 'Your turn'.

Key ideas

- As humans evolved, they moved from hunting to farming, and began to settle down. (They began to farm only about 10 000 years ago.)
- They cleared land and put up dwellings. The result: **settlements**.
- A **site** is the land a settlement is built on.
- Various factors influenced the choice of site. For example: suitability for farming; access to water, fuel and other materials; shelter offered; access for trade; ease of defence.

Key vocabulary

dwelling, site, settlement

Skills practised in 'Your turn'

- Geography skills: analysing photos and drawing conclusions from them
- Literacy skills: using the glossary; completing definitions
- Thinking skills: summarising (using a spider map); coming up with reasons; identifying important factors and deciding whether they would have applied in the past; suggesting reasons why their own settlement was first chosen as a place to settle in

Unit outcomes

By the end of this unit, most pupils should be able to:

- define the terms given in 'Key vocabulary' above
- explain how and why settlements started
- give at least five factors that influenced the choice of site, for early settlers

Resources

For starter **1**: information to help you complete the timeline eg pictures of early humans
For plenaries **1** and **2**: all images from the book are on *geog.1 resources and planning OxBox CD-ROM*

Ideas for a starter

1. Ask: How old are you? How old is your oldest relative? How old is this town/city? How old is the human race? How long ago were the dinosaurs here? How old is the Earth? When did people first settle in Britain? (Don't worry about wrong answers.)

   Now draw up a timeline like this:

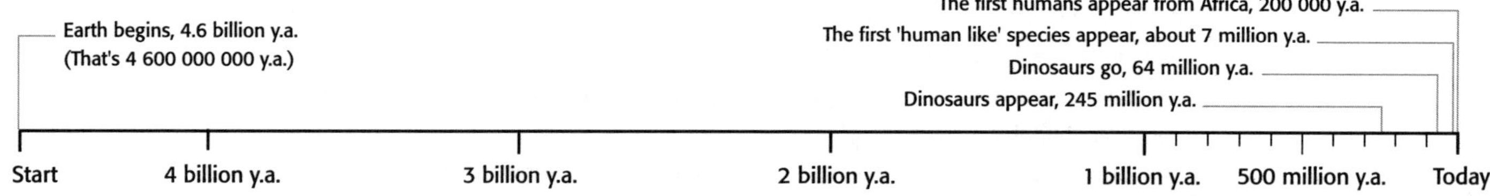

   Point out how short our human history is – and how we only really started spreading across the Earth in a big way about 10 000 years ago. Since then we've changed the face of the Earth with farms, towns and cities.

2. It is 10 000 years ago. You are leading a small group across a heavily-forested landscape, looking for a place to start farming. What kinds of things do you think you will look for? What kinds of things will you worry about? Do a mind-movie!

Ideas for plenaries

Plan plenaries for strategic points throughout the lesson, as well as at the end.

1 Look at the photo on page 22 of *geog.1* students' book. (You could display it.) What do you think this place looked like 5000 years ago, before anyone lived here? What factors do you think attracted settlers to this site?

2 Look at photo B on page 37 of *geog.1* students' book. (You could display it.) If people had found this place 1000 years ago, would they have thought it a good place to settle in? Describe the resources you can see in the photo. Put them in what you think is their order of importance, the most useful one first. What else would early settlers have wanted to find out about the place?

3 Think about the factors that affect the choice of a site. Which are about physical geography? Which are about human geography? Are some about both? (You could try drawing a Venn diagram.)

4 Question time! Think back over the lesson and write down three questions related to what you have learned. The teacher will ask a member of the class to try to answer them. (Pupils could be warned in advance to prepare for this.)

Further class and homework activities

Worksheet 3A on *geog.1 resources and planning OxBox CD-ROM*

Suggestions 1and 2 on page 72 of this book

How settlements grow in *geog.1*, *Settlement*, on *geog.world CD-ROM*

Answers to 'Your turn'

1 Students should include all the factors mentioned on page 36: good flat land, water, wood for fuel, materials for making things, shelter, ease of access, protection from enemies.

2 a A settlement is a place where people live (like a town or city).

b A site is the land a settlement is built on.

c The early settlements were usually situated near rivers, and a place to get wood for fuel and building shelters.

3 A, C, D and E show settlements: you can see signs that people have built dwellings and are living in these places. But in B, the tent is just a temporary shelter.

4 For **A**: access to water, for washing, travelling by boat, and fishing; (this place is on the coast so the water would be salty, and not drinkable;) near wood for fuel and for building wooden houses; the bay seems sheltered; the forest and surrounding hills provide shelter too.
For **C**: this is an oasis in the desert, and was chosen because it has water (for drinking, watering crops, washing) which is probably the only water for some distance.
For **D**: on a hill top, so easy to spot enemies approaching; surrounded by flat land which may be fertile, and was probably once heavily wooded – it still appears fairly wooded.
For **E**: in a pass between mountains so there is access; the site is flat compared to the surroundings; it is sheltered by the mountains; it would be easy to see enemies approach through the pass; judging by the grass, the land looks good for grazing animals; there would have been plenty of trees for timber to build wooden houses; with all those mountains, and given that it is not an arid climate, there are bound to be plenty of springs, waterfalls and streams; the first settlers may also have chosen the site because they liked the view!

5 Below are some of the important factors. Those that did not apply in 5000 BC are underlined. Many factors that applied in 5000 BC still apply today, but the reasons may have changed. Here goes:
- flat land (to make the building of houses and access roads easier)
- with easy access to other places (so that people will be able to get to work in other places, and therefore be willing to live there)
- near an adequate water supply (from rivers, aquifers, or reservoirs, otherwise water shortages could become a problem)
- where fuel (electricity, gas) can be provided easily (otherwise laying on services like electricity and gas could cost too much)
- <u>land that is not of special scenic, environmental or scientific interest</u> (otherwise building on it may be forbidden, or cause a public outcry)
- <u>land that is affordable</u> (the government or developers will have to buy it from its owners)
- land that does not have other more important uses (otherwise building on it would not make sense)
- land that is not at risk of flooding by a river or the sea (otherwise flooding could be a continual problem, and with global warming it is likely to get worse)
- <u>near towns or cities that are overcrowded</u> (so that it can take the overspill, and relieve congestion)

Most new settlements today are built to relieve congestion in other places. That's not likely to have been a problem 5000 years ago! But flat land was generally preferred in 5000 BC, as it is today.

Example: settling in Aylesbury

help at a glance

About this unit

This unit takes Aylesbury as a case study. We look at the site as it may have been when the Saxons arrived in 571 AD, and compare a map of how it may have looked 1300 years ago with an aerial photo of the town today. In 'Your turn' pupils explore the choice of site, and compare aerial photos (vertical and oblique) with an OS map of Aylesbury.

Key ideas

- 7000 years ago, Britain was covered in thick forest. Only small groups of hunters lived here.
- Around 6000 years ago, the first significant influx of people arrived – farmers from mainland Europe.
- Over the centuries, they were joined by many other groups of people: for example Celts, Romans, Saxons, Vikings, and Normans. (This brings us up to 900 years ago. There have been many more recent arrivals, as you will see in Chapter 5.)
- The Saxons were the first to settle properly in Aylesbury. They chose the site because it offered many advantages.
- A site with advantages grows.

Key vocabulary

Romans, Saxons

Skills practised in 'Your turn'

- Geography skills: analysing a landscape in a drawing; interpreting an aerial photo; comparing a sketch map and OS map with aerial photos; giving four- and six-figure grid references
- Literacy skills: writing a letter to a cousin back home describing the new settlement
- Thinking skills: evaluating different sites for a settlement, and selecting the one that seems the most suitable

Unit outcomes

By the end of this unit, most pupils should be able to:

- define the terms given in 'Key vocabulary' above
- say who were the first people to settle in Aylesbury, and give reasons why they settled there
- evaluate and compare different sites, from the point of view of an early settler

Resources

For starter **2**: books with sketches and photos relating to early settlers and settlements would be useful; for example showing Celts and Celtic forts, Roman soldiers, Roman villas and forts, Saxon villages, Norman soldiers and Norman castles

For plenaries **1**, **2** and **3**: all images from the book are on *geog.1 resources and planning OxBox CD-ROM*

Ideas for a starter

1. How many people do you think lived in Britain 7000 years ago? (Hardly anyone.)
2. 7000 years ago there was hardly anyone in Britain. Where do you think people came from? How would they have reached here? Can you name any of the tribes who came, a long time ago? Why do you think they wanted to come here?
3. It's mind-movie time! Imagine it is 7000 years ago – and you have come by boat to Britain from Europe. (But of course it is not called Britain yet.) You are standing right here where the school is. What do you see around you? What do you hear? What are you wearing? You want to settle down and farm. What will you have to do first?

Ideas for plenaries

Plan plenaries for strategic points throughout the lesson, as well as at the end.

1. Compare the map from 700 AD and the aerial photo, on page 39. (You could display them.) What do you think made Aylesbury grow so much? Pupils shout out, you write a list. (This topic is taken up again in the next unit.)
2. Compare the photos of Aylesbury on pages 34 and 39. (You could display them.) What is similar about them? What's different? How was this difference achieved? (You could mention the terms *vertical* and *oblique* in your discussion.)
3. Look at the photo of Warkworth on page 22. (You could display it.) The early settlers settled in the loop of the river. Why do you think they chose that site? What do you think they were concerned about?
4. What do you know about the history of your own settlement? (A prize for anyone who can tell you about it?)
5. On your way home from school, you come across a time traveller who has stumbled into the present from way back in history. He was one of the people who started your settlement. Think up at least five questions to ask him.
6. You have to carry out an enquiry about the history of *your* settlement. Make up an enquiry question to answer. Where will you do your research?

Further class and homework activities

Worksheets 3B and 3C on pages 61 and 62 of *geog.1 resources and planning OxBox CD-ROM*

Suggestions 3 – 8 on page 72 of this book

Answers to 'Your turn'

1 Students are likely to give site Z the top score overall.

2 He may have been worried about being attacked, or flooded out. Site X is the easiest to defend, and safest from flooding. The other two sites have easier access to water, timber and farmland.

4 Encourage pupils to tell Oeric all about daily life, and the new huts, and where they get their water and fuel. The photo of the reconstructed Saxon village, on page 38 of the students' book, should help.

5 These days people in Aylesbury are no longer concerned about access to local timber or farmland. They can buy timber, and food, from all over the country or all over the world. They are not too concerned about defence either. (Individuals may be concerned about crime in the town, though, which is a bit different.)

However they will still be concerned about ease of access to other places (especially since many residents commute to London and Milton Keynes for work).

Flooding is a problem from time to time on the outskirts of Aylesbury, so will be of concern to some people.

Water supply is still a concern in all our towns and cities, although we don't think too much about it. If the demand for water outstrips the supply we quickly run into problems. (Water is often rationed during dry summers.)

5 a 7914, 8014, 8114, 8213, 8313, 8413

b 8214 (the Manor Park area extends into 8114)

c 8214

6 Students should find the roundabouts, and the railway station, easy to find on the OS map. There is a cluster of buildings in the lower left of the photo that is easy to match to the college in square 8113 of the OS map.

7 a 817139

b the open market. Look for the white stall tops in the lower left of the photo. That area is Market Square, which is in Aylesbury's central business district (or CBD). As pupils will discover in Unit 3.3, Aylesbury grew as a market town. It is still considered a market town today.

3.3

How Aylesbury grew

About this unit

This unit looks at the kinds of things that help settlements grow, again taking Aylesbury as example. In 'Your turn' pupils draw a line graph showing population growth for Aylesbury, and annotate it with notes about events that encouraged growth.

Key ideas

- Settlements with advantages grow. (For example if they are close to good farmland, or other desirable natural resources.)
- Settlements surrounded by good farmland, on routes that offered easy access from other places, often grew as market towns (and many are still market towns today).
- A settlement grows because the population increases by birth, and because people move in from other places, usually to find work.
- The Industrial Revolution caused an explosion in the size of many settlements, because new factories were set up and people flocked from rural areas to work in them. These settlements turned into industrial towns and cities.

Key vocabulary

market town, Industrial Revolution

Skills practised in 'Your turn'

- Numeracy skills: estimating the area of settlements, by counting squares on maps; simple calculations (division); drawing, extrapolating, and annotating, a line graph
- Thinking skills: coming up with explanations

Unit outcomes

By the end of this unit, most pupils should be able to:

- explain the terms given in 'Key vocabulary' above
- estimate the area of a place on a map, by counting squares
- draw and annotate a line graph showing rise in population
- explain that the growth of a place is the result of a variety of factors, natural and human
- give at least four factors that would help a settlement to grow

Resources

For starter **1**: maps of your local settlement over the years, showing how it has grown, and old photos, would be good for stimulating discussion

For plenaries **1**, **2** and **4**: all images from the book are on *geog.1 resources and planning OxBox CD-ROM*

Ideas for a starter

1. Choose any sizeable local settlement whose population you know. Say: 1500 years ago (or whatever), hardly anyone lived in _____. Now the population is ____. How do you think it got so big? This will lead into a discussion of why settlements grow.

   (The history department can probably provide past population data for a local settlement.)
2. Who can name the largest settlement in this country? (London is by far the largest.) Who can point it out on the map? How many people? (Over 7 million.) Why do you think it started there? Was it always that big? What made it grow? Why has it grown so much more than your settlement?
3. Name two local settlements that pupils are familiar with, one large and one a hamlet. Ask: Why is Y so much larger than X? Who can think up some reasons?

Ideas for plenaries

Plan plenaries for strategic points throughout the lesson, as well as at the end.

1. Look at the first map at the top of page 41 of *geog.1* students' book. (You could display it.)
   a) Can you match it to the second map? Where does it fit?
   b) A set of three almost-straight lines slopes from the middle of its right edge, down to below the jail. What do you think they represent? The OS map on page 45, and the dates in Table 2, will give you clues.
2. Look at the photo on page 22. (You could display it.) Warkworth hasn't grown much. Suggest some reasons.
3. As a settlement grows, it needs more of many different things. Like houses and … Go round the class, adding to the list. Without repetition or hesitation!
4. Look at the OS map of Aylesbury on page 45. (You could display it.) What will happen if it keeps growing?
5. Is your settlement growing? What is your evidence? What's making it grow?
6. Start a spider map on the board (like the one on page 37 of the students' book). In the loop write *Factors that help towns grow*. Then ask pupils to come up and write in factors (or call them out and you write). Factors could include: good road and rail links; good sea and air links; successful businesses (eg factories); special features such as a port or a beach; good farmland around it; good shops; tourist attractions (such as historic buildings); good leisure facilities (cinemas, clubs, restaurants).

Further class and homework activities

Worksheets 3D and 3E on *geog.1 resources and planning OxBox CD-ROM*

The story of Totnes movie on *geog.1 resources and planning OxBox CD-ROM*

Suggestions 9 and 10 on page 72 of this book

How settlements grow in *geog.1*, *Settlement*, on *geog.world CD-ROM*

Answers to 'Your turn'

1 a It grew because of its market – which was the result of the good farmland around it, and easy access – and it still has an open market today. Although the town does have some industry, it did not become a big manufacturing centre, unlike some other towns (that quickly grew into cities as a result).

2 About 4 sq km

3 a Around 14.5 sq km

b About 3.6 times larger

4 a 5000

b By 2005, the population had grown over 13 times larger than it was in 1830.

5 By extrapolating their graph, pupils should estimate the population in 2010 to be around 75 000. (In fact it's likely to be more than this. Aylesbury has been targeted as a growth centre for new housing, and many new homes are being built there, as pupils will find out in Unit 3.7.)

6 a It made it easier to transport goods, which helped businesses to grow. So people would have moved there to get work.

b Local cattle produced plenty of milk for this industry. The factory would have brought more work to the town – in fact it became one of Aylesbury's largest employers. It later became a Nestle factory. But it closed in 2002, and the historic building was demolished in 2004 (to the distress of many people) to make way for 136 modern flats.

c At first the railway would have been largely used to transport goods (and ducks) from Aylesbury to London and vice versa, helping businesses in Aylesbury to flourish, and attracting more workers to the town. Today it means people can live in Aylesbury, where housing is cheaper than in London, and commute to London (or elsewhere) to work.

d It attracts shoppers from the surrounding areas. This helps to make a town richer. So more shops and services will open. So more people will move there to live and find work.

3.4 The pattern of growth

About this unit

This unit describes how settlements grew over the centuries, and how this growth led to a pattern of land use. The pattern can be summarised using a simple urban model. In 'Your turn', pupils explore how well Aylesbury fits the model.

Key ideas

- There is an overall pattern to land use in a town or city. For example we don't get shops, factories and houses all jumbled up together.
- This is how the pattern developed:
  - settlements grow outwards, so the oldest buildings are usually in the centre
  - as settlements grew, homes in the centre were taken over by businesses (since the centre was easiest to reach from all directions), and the people moved to the edges of the settlement; the result is a central business district (CBD)
  - the new homes were built at the edges of the settlement since there was room and land was cheaper; so the settlement spread outwards – and housing generally gets more modern as you travel out from the centre
  - early factories were built close to rivers, railways and canals (for water, steam, transport), and to the centre of town (where the rivers, railways and canals were)
  - terraced housing for the factory workers was often built close to the factories
  - modern industry tends to be on the outskirts of a town or city, where land is cheaper, but close to main roads (for transport)
- We can use a model (a simple generalised picture) to demonstrate these patterns. But note that no settlement will fit the model exactly.
- Note too that redevelopment around the centre (for example old factories knocked down to make way for flats) means the pattern is still developing and changing.

Key vocabulary

central business district, model, industrial area, outer and inner suburbs, terraced houses

Skills practised in 'Your turn'

- Geography skills: analysing a map to look for patterns; matching photos to the map
- Thinking skills: evaluating how well a real place fits the model; coming up with reasons and consequences

Unit outcomes

By the end of this unit, most pupils should be able to:

- define the terms given in 'Key vocabulary' above
- explain how a pattern of land use developed in settlements
- explain how the pattern can be shown by a simple model, and sketch the model
- look for ways in which a real place fits the model
- use the pattern of roads in a place as a clue to the location of the CBD

Resources

For starter **1** and plenary **2**: sketch map and photos of your local settlement, to display,
For plenaries **2** and **3**: all images are on *geog.1 resources and planning OxBox CD-ROM*

Ideas for a starter

1. Where is the centre of your settlement? Why do you think so? What's there? Why are these things there, rather than somewhere else in the settlement?
2. Suppose you are planning a brand new town. Where will you put the shops? Why? Where will you put the houses? Schools? Parks? Factories? Railway station? Would it be best to mix everything up together? Why?/Why not?

Ideas for plenaries

Plan plenaries for strategic points throughout the lesson, as well as at the end.

1 Warn the class in advance that you will ask pupils to demonstrate later what they have learned. Later, ask one student to draw the urban model on the board (with instructions from the rest of the class if necessary). Another answers questions about it, posed by the rest of the class, by pointing to the correct area on the model. (For example: Where are the houses likely to have the largest gardens?)

2 Do you think this model fits your own settlement? Discuss. (You could display it.)

3 Do you think this model would work for a village? (You could display it.) How would you change it to suit a village? Show us!

Further class and homework activities

Interactive activities for Unit 3.4 on *geog.1 resources and planning OxBox CD-ROM*

Suggestions 11 – 15 on pages 72 – 73 of this book

Out and about in Darlington on *geog.1 resources and planning OxBox CD-ROM*

Land use in towns and cities in *geog.1*, *Settlement*, on *geog.world CD-ROM*

Land use in Oxford in *geog.1*, *Settlement*, on *geog.world CD-ROM*

Answers to 'Your turn'

1 a true **b** true **c** true **d** true **e** true **f** true

2 House **1** is at **A**. It is one of the old houses in the very oldest part of Aylesbury. House **2** is at **B**, in an area of modern housing.

3 a The second photo down (the building by the canal).

b Advantages: near the CBD for work, shopping, cinemas etc; close to the main road to London; and living beside a canal can be very pleasant, if the canal has been cleaned up. For one thing, you can take walks along the canal bank.

4 a To transport materials (such as paper and ink) and finished printed goods, by canal. The printing company (Hazel, Viney, Watson) came from London and presumably London continued to be its main market. A printworks would also need water, and perhaps it pumped water from the canal.

b D gives easier access than **E**, to lots of customers. **D** is not that far from the CBD, and surrounded by residential areas, which is a good place for a big supermarket to be. It's also close to a road network for bringing in supplies. **E** has good road access, but is isolated, by comparison.

5 a It doesn't fit with the model. From the model you'd expect older housing here, this close to the CBD.

b It was built on the site of older buildings, that were demolished.

6 a i Allows shoppers, and goods, to get to the town centre easily.

ii Likely to be congested at peak travel times.

b 'Ring roads' are usually built to let traffic move across a town or city without having to pass through the busy CBD; they relieve congestion in the CBD. They may also be needed when parts of a CBD are pedestrianised (traffic prohibited in some streets).

3.5

Be a land-use detective!

About this unit

This unit shows how much you can learn about land use in a place, from an OS map. Again Aylesbury is our example. In 'Your turn', pupils identify different kinds of land use, and housing, on an OS map of Aylesbury.

Key idea

- An OS map provides many clues about the pattern of land use in a town or city.

Key vocabulary

industrial, terraced housing, housing estate, land use, function (see the glossary at the end of this book)

Skills practised in 'Your turn'

- Geography skills: analysing an OS map for clues about land use; using four- and six-figure grid references; comparing an OS map with a low oblique aerial photo
- Thinking skills: recognising clues; evaluating different areas of housing to find the best match for a set of criteria; finding examples of land used for different functions

Unit outcomes

By the end of this unit, most pupils should be able to:

- define the terms given in 'Key vocabulary' above
- explain in general terms how an OS map helps you identify patterns of land use
- identify the CBD of a town or city, on an OS map, and give evidence to back up their choice
- identify other types of land use on the OS map, including different types of housing, and give evidence to back up their choice

Resources

For starter **1** and plenary **1**: all images from the book are on *geog.1 resources and planning OxBox CD-ROM*
For starter **3**: a set of flash cards, with the abbreviations used on OS maps
Note that your pupils will find rulers helpful for working out grid references
For plenary **5**: a 1:25 000 OS map for the local area, and photos of different types of local land use

Ideas for a starter

1 Look at the OS map on page 45 of *geog.1* students' book. (You could display it.) In which squares do you think the CBD is? Why do you think so? (This is question **1** of 'Your turn'.)

2 What are the houses like in your street? Are they in long rows, or in pairs, or detached? In straight lines, or curves, or small clusters? Do they have gardens? Write a list of all the different characteristics on the board. Now ask how these characteristics might be shown on an OS map. What might gardens look like? Will you be able to tell how tall the houses are?

3 With the books closed, hold up flash cards with OS abbreviations on (eg PH, Ind Est). You could hold each up for say 5 seconds, and pupils write down what they stand for. Then pupils swap their answers with other pupils. Ask around the class for answers. Students get 1 mark for each correct one.

4 Write these words on the whiteboard:

Industrial estate   Science park   Business park   Works

Ask pupils to say what the difference between them is, if they can.

Ideas for plenaries

Plan plenaries for strategic points throughout the lesson, as well as at the end.

1 From the OS map on page 39 of *geog.1* students' book, see if you can pick out:
– a street with semi-detached houses
– an area with detached houses
Give four-figure grid references. (You could display the map.)

2 Mr and Mrs Jenkins live at 825140 on the map on page 45 of the students' book, in a house like the third one from the left, at the bottom of page 42. They have two young children and a dog. Mr Jenkins drives to work, to the industrial estate in 7914. Mrs Jenkins also drives to her work, in the hospital in 8211. Now they want to move house. Discuss this with your neighbour, and suggest some reasons why.

3 The Jenkins family move to a house at 815119 on the map. Make a drawing to show what this house might be like. Do you think they will be happier here? What are the advantages and disadvantages for them, compared with where they lived before? Discuss with your neighbour.

4 Pupils choose any full square they wish, on the OS map on page 45. They draw a spider map to summarise the land use in it. In the loop of the spider map they write *Land use in my OS square* but they keep the location of the square a secret. Then pupils swop spider maps, and try to identify each other's squares on the map and give four-figure grid references for them.

5 Students study a 1:25 000 local OS map and identify houses and other buildings they know. Show them photos to match to places on the map.

6 What do you think about OS maps? Are they fun? Are they useful?

Further class and homework activities

Worksheets 3F and 3G on *geog.1 resources and planning OxBox CD-ROM*

Suggestions 16 and 17 on page 73 of this book

A tale of two cities in *geog.1, Settlement*, on *geog.world* CD-ROM

Answers to 'Your turn'

1 b The main part is in square 8113. It extends into 8114 and 8213.

2 It's in 8113. It's south of the big church, and near large buildings. (In fact it's around 819137 on the OS map.)

3 7914, 8114

4 Encourage pupils to look at the area around the house, the distance to the CBD and so on. They may be surprised at how much they can deduce from the map. For example:

It's a terraced house with a back garden. The back garden backs onto an alleyway that runs between back gardens. The house appears to be in a 19th century terrace. It's close to the canal, and the sites where the condensed milk factory and printworks were. (See the map on page 43 of the students' book.) So it could once have been lived in by a worker from one of those factories. Victoria Park is nearby. Queen Victoria reigned from 1837 to 1901 so that gives another clue about the age of the housing.

If you lived in this house you could probably walk into the centre of Aylesbury in less than 10 minutes. (It's about 1km away). You could also walk or cycle to one of the many schools nearby. And go karting in the karting centre, and go for walks along the Grand Union canal. The big square building near the karting centre is the Tesco superstore, so you don't have far to go for shopping.

5 a D seems best. Modern, plenty of open space around it, on the right side of town for London, and near the A41 to London.

b A is modern but on the wrong side of town for London;
B is a 19th century terraced house in a crowded area;
C is not modern enough –1930s to 1950s housing.

6 a Here are some examples:

Function	Example	Grid ref
housing	Southcourt	8212
shopping	superstores	8014
education	schools	8213
health care	hospital	8211
tourism	information centre	8113
leisure / fun	karting	8213
law and order	Young Offender Institution	8214
rail transport	railway station	8113

b There are several other functions pupils could add, some of greater importance than others. For example:

industry
road transport
cemetery
Territorial Army centre
vegetable growing (allotments)
bus transport (bus station)
places of worship
waste disposal (sewage works)

3.6 How's Aylesbury doing today?

help at a glance

About this unit

Every settlement has good and bad points. This unit takes a look at Aylesbury's, based on real comments made by residents and other 'stakeholder' groups, during workshops run in 2006 by Aylesbury Vale District Council.

Key ideas

- Every settlement has good points, and bad points that people grumble about.
- The grumbles are usually about things like poor services, and traffic congestion.
- Settlements are always changing.
- Ideally the changes will be for the better, in response to people's grumbles, rather than making things worse.

Key vocabulary

commute, dormitory town, low-level jobs, high-value businesses, business park, redevelop (see the glossary at the end of this book)

Skills practised in 'Your turn'

- Geography skills: comparing a photo and development plan; finding the location of the development on an OS map
- Literacy skills: using the glossary; giving definitions
- Thinking skills: looking for evidence; identifying and matching; evaluating; reaching conclusions; assessing their own local area, to come up with good and bad points

Unit outcomes

By the end of this unit, most pupils should be able to:

- define the terms given in 'Key vocabulary' above
- give examples of good and bad points about Aylesbury
- explain what redevelopment means, and that it can improve a place
- give some good and bad points about their own settlement or local/school area

Resources

For starter **3**: all images from the book are on *geog.1 resources and planning OxBox CD-ROM*

Ideas for a starter

1. Ask pupils to create a graffiti wall on the whiteboard with good and bad points about a settlement they all know well (or the local or school area) – with good points in one colour, and bad points in another. There should be no duplication.
   Then discuss whether the good points and the bad points could be grouped under headings. For example, transport? Leisure? Ask them to come up with suggestions. (Note: this corresponds in effect to question **6a** and **b** in 'Your turn'. See also plenary **1**.)
2. Ask pupils to write down three good and three bad points about their own settlement. Compare lists with others in the class. Are the lists similar or different? Discuss. (See question **6a** and **b** in 'Your turn, and see also plenary **1**.)
3. Look carefully at the photo of Aylesbury on page 34. (You could display it). Can you suggest anything that might be good about living there – and anything that might not be so good? What is your evidence?

Ideas for plenaries

Plan plenaries for strategic points throughout the lesson, as well as at the end.

1 Look at the good points and grumbles about your local area (from starter **1** or **2**). Do you think other people would give the same ones? For example if you were all mums with small children, or retired people?

2 Is it anyone's fault that settlements have some bad points? Is anyone responsible? Could you be responsible in any way?

3 Pick out the main grumble about your local area. (The class could vote on the choice.) You want something done about it. Who will you approach?

4 (Instead of **3**) You live in Aylesbury. Pick out one of the grumbles about Aylesbury. You want something done about this. Who do you think you should approach?

5 Should local people have a say about changes in land use (redevelopment), even if they do not own the land?

6 Can you think of any spots in your local area that would benefit from redevelopment? What would you put there? (This also appears as a homework suggestion.)

7 Draw a scale like the one below, and put an arrow on it to reflect the overall opinion of the class about your settlement, local area, or school area. Ask for shows of hands to decide where the mark should go.

Further class and homework activities

Interactive activity for Unit 3.6 on *geog.1 resources and planning OxBox CD-ROM*

Suggestions 18 – 21 on page 73 of this book

Answers to 'Your turn'

1 For definitions see the glossary in the back of this book, or on pages 142 – 143 of the students' book.

2 a trains too infrequent, bus service not great, not easy to get to motorway, ring road hard for pedestrians to get across, traffic jams, buses expensive

b a lot of the town ruined, some building horrors, not many good places to eat, not many places to go except pubs, shops not that great – and tourists are likely to grumble about transport too

c shops not great – you'd go elsewhere for special things, and then transport grumbles would apply too!

3 a 17 000 more people commute out every day than commute in.

b Aylesbury has been losing jobs, and the jobs on offer there are mostly low-level and low-paid.

c Bad. The people who commute out eat elsewhere, and make friends elsewhere, so may not really feel part of a community in Aylesbury. They may do their shopping in the places they commute to (like London and Milton Keynes), so Aylesbury shops are losing out. The out-commuters help companies in these other places to be successful. Aylesbury would benefit from their skills and talents. Besides, this many people commuting out every day adds to traffic jams and train congestion at peak travel times.

4 a In fact everything in the list could help to prevent Aylesbury becoming a dormitory town, including making the town centre more attractive. (That would help to attract new employers.) Improving the road links will make it more attractive to new industries, as will improving people's work skills.

b Improving the road and rail links, and bus service, will make it easier for people to commute out. Raising work skills, without having enough local jobs, means the newly-skilled people will travel elsewhere to get work.

5 grumbles about not enough to do, not enough good places to eat, shops not great, some parts of town looking a mess

6 This should get some lively discussion going.

3.7

A new challenge for Aylesbury

About this unit

This unit describes the urgent need for new homes in the UK, and shows the areas targeted for growth. Aylesbury is in the main growth area, and is to have around 15 000 new homes between 2007 and 2020. In 'Your turn', pupils explore reasons for the high demand, the greenfield/brownfield issue, and what this growth will mean for Aylesbury.

Key ideas

- The UK needs at least 3 million more new homes, between 2007 and 2020.
- They will be built on a mix of greenfield and brownfield sites – and the choice of sites is, and will continue to be, a source of conflict.
- Greenfield sites are sites that have not been built on before (which usually means in the green belt around towns and cities, and in rural areas).
- Brownfield sites are sites that have already been built on, but have become neglected or derelict, and can be redeveloped. These are usually within towns and cities.
- The main area targeted for new homes is in south east England, in an area largely north and west of London – and which includes Aylesbury.

Key vocabulary

greenfield sites, brownfield sites

Skills practised in 'Your turn'

- Geography skills: gaining information from a range of maps; comparing maps; comparing photos
- Literacy skills: delivering the opinion of a Roman commander
- Thinking skills: finding the 'message' in drawings; giving reasons; identifying conflicting, and compatible, points of view; evaluating sites; predicting impact

Unit outcomes

By the end of this unit, most pupils should be able to:

- give at least three reasons why more new homes are needed
- say where in the UK most of them will go, and why
- explain what greenfield and brownfield sites are
- explain why there is conflict over where to build the new homes
- give examples of things a settlement needs to think about, in getting ready for many thousands more people

Resources

For starters **1** and **2**: photos of new houses and flats, complete and at various stages of construction; they could be from developers' brochures, or online from their websites. For plenaries **1** – **3**: all images from the book are on *geog.1 resources and planning OxBox CD-ROM*

Ideas for a starter

1. Show some photos of homes from brochures or websites. Then ask: What is a home? What different kinds of homes are there? Show them on a spider map. How many homes do you think there are, in the UK? (There are around 25 million households – independent units where people live alone or with others.)
2. With books closed, show some photos of new houses and flats. How many homes do you think there are in your settlement? The government says the UK needs lots more new homes each year. Guess how many? The person who guesses nearest 240 000 wins. How does this compare with the number of homes in your settlement?

Ideas for plenaries

Plan plenaries for strategic points throughout the lesson, as well as at the end.

1. Look at map A on page 48. (You could display it.) Which region do you live in? Is it targeted for more housing? (Look at the key.) If yes, why? If no, why not?
2. Look at the photo of the brownfield site on page 48. (You could display it.)
   This is an old flour mill. It's at 827138 on the OS map on page 48. (It's across the canal from the big building – a Tesco superstore – beside the karting centre.)
   – List as many good points as you can about building homes on that site.
   – List any bad points you can think of.
   – Underline the main point in each list.
   Pupils could work in small groups for this, or the whole class could work together.
3. Look at the photo of the greenfield site on page 48. (You could display it.)
   It was taken in square 8314 on the OS map on page 48. Repeat **2** for this photo.
4. Have any new homes been built in your local area? What was there before?
   Have people moved in yet? Where do you think they came from? Why might they have needed new homes?

Further class and homework activities

Where should all the new houses go? on *geog.1 resources and planning OxBox CD-ROM*

Suggestions 22 – 24 on page 73 of this book

Answers to 'Your turn'

1 a A The population is increasing.
B More couples are getting divorced, and more families are breaking up.
C People move to other parts of the country, where there may not be enough homes. (In particular, in the UK, many move to the already-crowded south east, for work.)
D Many properties are run-down and/or derelict, and need to be replaced.

b More and more people are choosing to live alone.
The average age at which people marry is rising.
New industries may start up in places where there are not enough homes.
Cities continue to attract people, especially young people (for work, fun, nightlife).
Many people from other countries come to the UK to find work. For example from other EU countries such as Poland.

2 a The main area targeted for new housing is in south east England.

b Much of this area has a high population density, or is near to London, the capital city and by far the largest city in the UK. Much of the area, including London, has higher average earnings than most parts of the UK. So it continues to attract people looking for work, not only from the rest of the UK but from the rest of the EU, and other countries. Add to that a high divorce rate, and the rise in numbers of people choosing to live alone. The result is a serious housing shortage in the south east.

3 Near London, so can take some pressure off London housing – people could move there and continue to work in London; surrounded by farmland that could be taken over for housing, its location and road pattern make it easy to access (although people do grumble about poor access to motorways).

5 a The country dweller is likely to be in conflict with the builder.

b The town planner, because she thinks brownfield sites should be used, in order to regenerate the town.

c The farmer with land to sell might get on well with the builder who wants greenfield sites.

6 Students will probably think the brownfield site a wiser choice.

7 a Both Berryfields and Weedon Hill are greenfield sites.

b Most will be on greenfield sites.

c There are remains of several historic sites in the area. These are protected and can't be built on. (In any case, one very large estate might not be as successful as two smaller ones.)

8 They could add: dentists, nurses, refuse collectors, nursery teachers, postal workers, shop staff, estate agents, and so on. (The new arrivals will of course take up some of these and other jobs.)

9 a gas and electricity, from the companies that provide these; you'll lay down pipes and cables to connect to their networks.

b by laying pipes from the new homes to the (Thames Water company's) water mains, then put taps on the end! (Thames Water in turn pumps the water for Aylesbuty from aquifers near the River Thames.)

c build roads through the estate, to the main roads; provide parking spaces or garages for the cars that will be the main mode of travel for at least some people

b the estates are being built along main roads (and there's a new road joining them).

10 The commander will probably be very pleased to see 'his' road, the A41, being so well used. He will probably think it very wise to have a business park on the London side of Aylesbury, as this will encourage companies who want easy access to the capital. Providing easy access to places, for soldiers and supplies, was always his main aim.

3.8 Sustainable development for Aylesbury

About this unit

This unit introduces sustainable development, a key concept in the Programme of Study. It uses Aylesbury's plans for managing growth as example. In 'Your turn', pupils explore the concept, with particular reference to a new housing estate.

Key ideas

- Sustainable development means development that will improve our lives, and not lead to problems in the future.
- It has three strands: economic, social and environmental.
- *Economic* is about money and earning a living. We ask questions like: Is this development affordable? Will it provide jobs? Will it increase economic well-being?
- *Social* is about our quality of life, health, education, leisure time, and so on. We ask questions like: Will this development add to the quality of our lives?
- *Environmental* concerns both the natural environment (wildlife, air, water, other natural resources) and our built environment (homes, streets …). We ask questions like: What impact will this development have on wildlife? Does it waste energy?
- If a development has a negative impact in *any* of those strands, it is unsustainable. It will lead to future problems.

Key vocabulary

sustainable development, economic, social, environmental, insulated, global warming, recycling (See the glossary at the end of the book.)

Skills practised in 'Your turn'

- Literacy skills: making up statements about unsustainable development
- Thinking skills: assessing the sustainability of a development; classifying features of a housing development, using a Venn diagram

Unit outcomes

By the end of this unit, most pupils should be able to:

- explain the terms given in 'Key vocabulary' above
- explain the three strands of sustainable development, in simple terms
- give examples of ways in which a new development, such as a housing estate, could be made sustainable.

Resources

For starter **2**: a strip of green card and a strip of red card for each pupil

Ideas for a starter

1. We use more water and electricity every year. We produce more household rubbish every year. There are thousands more cars on the road each year. What if we keep on like this? What might happen? What can we do about it?
2. Build up a scenario about a new factory. Pupils respond to each statement you make about it by raising their cards (green for positive, red for negative). You start very positively, then change. For example: This town needs more jobs. So I'm going to set up a modern factory here, in the industrial area, with jobs for 400 local people. Positive or negative so far? (Pupils raise a card.) The factory will be well-designed and look great. (Positive or negative?) It will have a very smart canteen, with healthy food. It will sponsor a new youth club. It will spew harmful gases into the air. It will pay people very badly. It will have very harsh work rules, that cause its workers great stress. Its managers will act like dictators. It won't be able to sell the things it makes.
   A material used in building it will start to make local people very ill. So, overall, was this factory a good thing? Would it have been better if I had never thought of it?

Ideas for plenaries

Plan plenaries for strategic points throughout the lesson, as well as at the end.

1 Draw this on the whiteboard. Ask pupils to give you one sentence each about a new development, to show they understand the terms at the ends of the arrows.

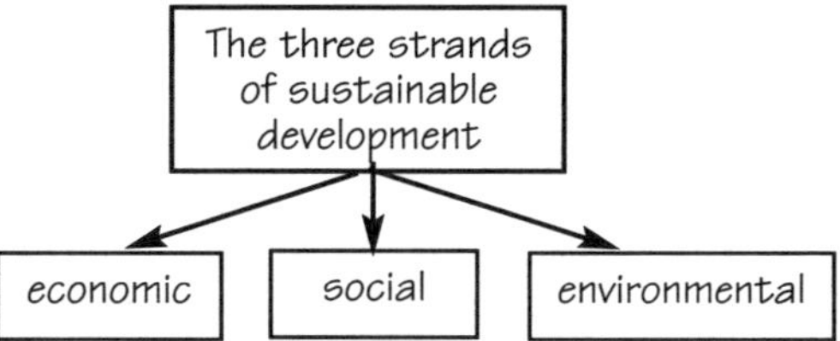

You can give some sample sentences. For example: *It's a new factory, and it will provide good jobs for 500 local people. It uses wind power. It has a really nice gym inside*. They should try to come up with different sentences, not just copy yours.

2 The word 'sustainable' does not apply just to new housing developments. You can use it about many things, even your choice of holiday. See if you can come up with an idea for a sustainable holiday, for yourself.

3 Do you think your school is a sustainable organisation? Discuss!

4 Write the phrase 'sustainable development' in the middle of a page. Create a mind map around the phrase. How many ideas can you come up with, in 120 seconds?

5 Did you find today's work easy or difficult? Why?

6 Do you think what you learned today was valuable?

Further class and homework activities

Interactive quiz for Chapter 3 on *geog.1 resources and planning OxBox CD-ROM*

Worksheet 3H on *geog.1 resources and planning OxBox CD-ROM*

Suggestions 25 – 29 on page 73 of this book

Assessment materials for Chapter 3 on *geog.1 assessment file & OxBox CD-ROM*

Review 'Your goals for this chapter' on page 35 of *geog.1* students' book

Answers to 'Your turn'

1 Lead pupils to consider the three strands of sustainable development one by one. For example:

Economic It will cost a lot to build a new school somewhere else – so knocking it down is a waste of money.
Social This would disrupt life for pupils and teachers. We might have to travel much further to school. And people living around here will not be happy to have a smelly landfill site on their doorstep. It will also bring a continual stream of noisy trucks.
Environmental A landfill site can produce harmful gases, and toxic liquids that soak into the soil; it usually looks horrible too; and the trucks may give out fumes. So it's certainly not an improvement in terms of the environment.

However, pupils might feel a brand new school somewhere else was a great idea!

2 One possible answer is shown on the right. Many pupils will fail to put letters in the overlaps. Point out for example that being able to walk to school (L) brings social benefits (it's pleasant, and gives you exercise), economic benefits (saves on bus fares or petrol) and environmental benefits (it's a non-polluting form of transport). So it really does belongs where all three loops overlap.

3 Pupils should have fun with this one. But suggest that they don't go too far over the top, with their statements.

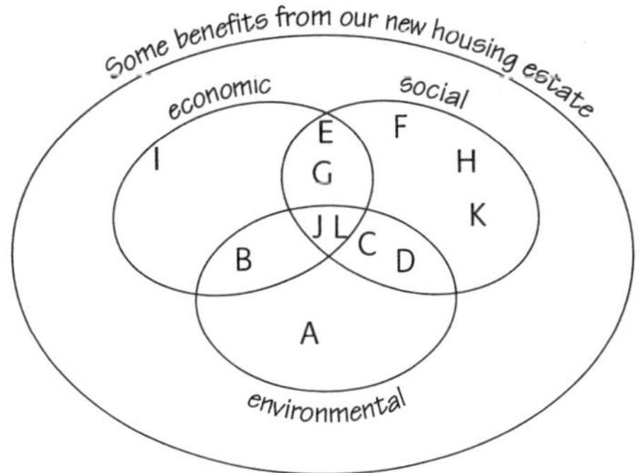

3 Further suggestions for class and homework

Most of these suggestions are addressed to your pupils. Where research or further resources are needed, the internet will almost certainly provide the answer. (Eg *google* and choose *Web* or *Images*.)

Settling down

1 **A timeline for the human race** Draw your own timeline to tell the story of humans from when they first appeared on the Earth. Use a very long sheet of paper (made by sticking several sheets together) which you can then display on the classroom wall.
Shade areas to show the Stone Age, Bronze Age, and so on. Annotate your timeline with interesting and relevant details – for example when humans first started farming, and when the oldest known settlement started, and the population at different times. Add pictures if you wish. The aim is to make your timeline look really interesting, but also clear. ***

2 **The settlement collection** Collect images of different settlements in the UK – postcards, pictures from magazines and so on. Try for images that give clues about why those settlements started. Display the images on the classroom wall, around a map of the UK. Annotate each with notes saying what you think attracted the first settlers to that site. ***

The early settlers in Britain

3 **To Britain, on foot** There were small numbers of people living in Britain about 9000 years ago. They had probably walked all the way here from somewhere else in Europe. How was that possible? Find out, and present your answer as a report for the class. ***

4 **Home sweet home, down the ages** Draw a timeline from about 800 BC to the present. Make it very long, to hang on the classroom wall. Annotate it with drawings or cut-out pictures of different settlements and dwellings over the ages, from the Celts to the present day. ***

5 **The story of my settlement** Why did your settlement start where it did? Who were the first people to settle there? Write a short history of your settlement. Include:
- a sketch map to show how the area may have looked before the settlers arrived. (Use an OS map to help you.)
- an (imaginary) eye-witness account from one of the first settlers, saying why that site was chosen.
- copies of early maps and photos of the settlement, from the history department, or local history books, or the local studies section of the local library. **

Note: this would be an excellent whole-class project.
The class could brainstorm what should go in the settlement story, and where to find the information. Give different groups of pupils different aspects to research.

6 **River towns** Early settlers liked to be near a river. Why? Make a table with two columns. Write in the headings: *River* and *Town or city on this river.* Then see how many rivers, and towns or cities on them, you can fill in for the UK. (One settlement per river.) Or you could fill in the rivers, and the settlements, on a blank map instead of a table. */**

7 **You're a Saxon teenager** You live in a village like the one on page 38 in *geog.1* students' book. So how do you spend your time? (No TV, no computer, no electricity, no books, no bike, no water taps.) Give us an account of your day, in the form of a diary entry. */**

8 **The settler's blues** You have reached Britain in your boat, looking for somewhere to settle down and farm. But all you have found so far are rocks and marshes. You haven't seen another soul. It's cold and wet. Your fur cloak and leggings are soaking. Make up a rap or poem or blues song, to express your feelings. */**/***

Settlement growth

9 **How my settlement has grown in population** Draw a population graph for your settlement, using figures from the history department or the local library. Mark on the graph important events in the history of the settlement, as you did for Aylesbury on page 41 of the students' book. **
Note: this could be an extension of activity **6**.

10 **How my settlement has grown in area** Put together a series of maps, with help from the local library, showing how your settlement has grown in area. Or mark dashed lines on a current map in different colours, showing the settlement boundaries at different times in the past. **
Note: this could also be an extension of activity **6**.

Patterns of growth

11 **Land use field trip** Arrange a field trip in the local settlement. A digital camera would be useful. Students should bring material for drawing field sketches.
Note the different types of land use and different styles of housing. Later create a sketch map showing land use. Shade in different zones and illustrate the map with photos and sketches from the field trip. */**/***

12 **House for sale!** Collect descriptions of local houses for sale, from the local estate agents' offices or websites, and local newspapers. Include photos if possible. Then stick these around a map of your settlement. Can you divide them into different ages of houses? Can you divide them into high -cost., medium-cost, andlow-cost? Can you see any patterns? **

13 **A 'model' transect** Draw a imaginary transect (cross-section) through a city, using the urban model on page 42 of the students' book as a guide. Draw buildings, parks and so on, or cut them out of magazines and stick them in place. Label the different types of land use, on your transect. *
Give pupils some help to start with, like this:

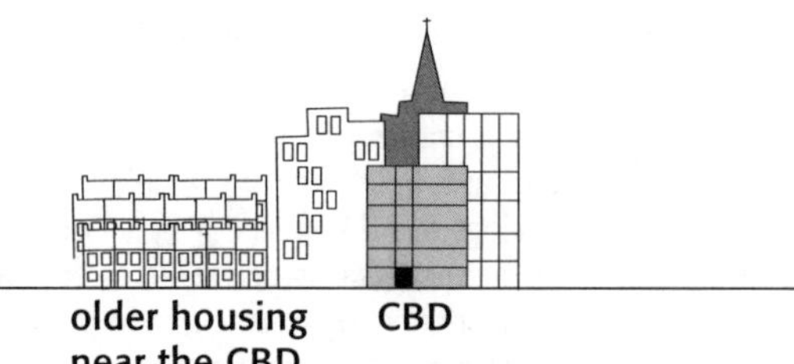

14 An Aylesbury transect Using the OS map of Aylesbury on page 45 of the students' book as a guide, draw an imaginary transect across Aylesbury, through the centre.
Try to keep roughly to scale, in terms of distance along the transect. (Use a fine pencil.) Your transect could run in any direction you wish (north east to south west, for example.) Mark an N arrow on it, and add labels and annotations. *

15 Transect trip Take a trip with pupils across town, in roughly a straight line. Note the different types of land use and housing. Take digital photos, and make field sketches.
Use the photos and field sketches to create an illustrated transect for a wall display. ***

Be a land-use detective!

16 Land use, using clues from an OS map Using a 1: 50 000 OS map, and the ideas in Units 3.4 and 3.5, see if you can draw a sketch map showing land use in your settlement (or in the nearest town, if your settlement is just a hamlet). Mark in the main roads, and the rivers or railways if there are any. Shade the different zones, as for the Aylesbury map on page 43 of the students' book. ***

17 Settlement size, from an OS map Work with a partner and decide on ways to compare the sizes of settlements, on an OS map. For example you could count the number of roads to a settlement, or how many schools or churches it has. You could estimate its area byt counting squares and part squares (as on page 41).And does the size of the letters for its name on the map give you any clues?.
Draw up a table for the things you will note, count and measure, to compare size. Then, using your table and a 1: 50 000 OS map, compare say five settlements in an area. (It could be your area.) Rank them in order of size. */**

Know your services

18 Local services Brainstorm the services provided in your local area. (Define exactly what you mean by local!) Ask pupils to use a local directory to do a service tally. For example how many supermarkets are there? How many doctors' surgeries? Can the services be grouped? (For example shops, transport, health ....) Students can create a bar chart for the different services, arranging them in suitable groups. **

19 Know your services Brainstorm to identify the key local services for any area. For example police, hospital, fire brigade, local council, water company, local newspaper, local radio station. Students draw an annotated map naming their own local services and showing where these are based. **

20 Living in a city: on the one hand ... Turn a sheet of A4 paper sideways. Trace the outlines of your two hands on the paper, leaving a gap in the centre. In the gap, stick a picture of a British city. Now, within the outline of one hand, write down all the advantages you can think of, about living in a city. Within the other, write down all the disadvantages. Which do you think win out, the advantages or the disadvantages? **

21 Living in a hamlet: on the other hand ... Repeat activity **14**, but this time for life in a hamlet in a rural area. Which do you think win out, the advantages of rural life, or the disadvantages? Which wins out overall, city life or life in a rural area? **

We need more homes!

22 New homes! Identify a new local housing estate which is completed or still being built. Visit the site. Find out what it was used for before, how many new homes there are, what kind of homes they are, and what local services there are. Write a report. (The local planning office may help.) **

23 You're in charge You're the minister in charge of housing. The country needs 240 000 new homes a year. So you must make sure there are enough plumbers, carpenters, electricians and so on. How will you do this? Write an action plan. **

24 You're still in charge You have to produce guidelines for developers about how big all the new homes should be, and how much space they should have around them. You don't want them too cramped, but you don't want to use up too much space either. **

Development and sustainability

25 Redevelop! Identify a derelict site in your local area. Mark where it is on a map, and describe what it's like, using text, digital photos, and a field sketch. Say what it was used for before it became derelict. Then say how you plan to redevelop the site, and what it will be used for. Do annotated drawings to show how it will look when development is complete. (This would make a good class project.) **

26 Getting ready for green fields You're a developer. You are planning to build a large new housing estate on a greenfield site. What factors will you need to consider, to make sure it's a good choice of site?
(Some might be factors that the early settlers also had to think about, in Unit 3.1 of the students' book.) What else should you think about, with sustainability in mind? **

27 Design a house for sustainable living There's a competition to design a house for sustainable living. And you intend to show how creative you can be. Off you go! It has to be a house you would like to live in. *

28 A sustainable city Everyone is beginning to think about sustainability. Come up with 10 ideas for what you think a sustainable city of the future might be like. You may want to make annotated sketches. **

29 Summing up sustainability A development is called *sustainable* if it promotes economic, social and environmental well-being. If it promotes only one (or two) of these at the expense of the other(s) then it's not truly sustainable. Design an eye-catching poster to put this idea across. ***

4 Let's go shopping!

Helping you deliver the KS3 Programme of Study

This chapter addresses these areas of the Programme of Study:

Key concepts

Space Understand the interactions between places created by flows of people and goods.
Interdependence Explore social and economic connections between places; understand the significance of interdependence in change, at all scales. **Physical and human processes** Explain how human processes shape places, landscapes and societies.
Cultural understanding and diversity Appreciate how people's values and attitudes differ and may influence social, economic and political issues.

Key processes

Geographical enquiry Ask geographical questions; collect, record and display information; analyse and evaluate evidence, presenting findings to draw and justify conclusions.
Graphicacy and visual literacy Use maps at a range of scales. **Geographical communication** Communicate knowledge and understanding using geographical vocabulary and conventions in both talk and writing.

The big picture

These are the key ideas behind this chapter.

- We can divide the things we buy into two kinds: convenience goods (low-cost, we buy them often, and are happy to buy in any convenient place) and comparison goods (more expensive, we buy less often, and we like to shop around for them).
- Shops sell goods and services, to make a profit. So they must be located where enough customers can reach them easily.
- The more customers the better. So the bigger a settlement, the bigger the range of shops you'll find in it, attracted by the customer base.
- In other words, there is a strong link between shopping and settlement size.
- Shops keep changing: to meet people's needs, and increase profits. The shops themselves change, and what they sell, where they are located, and who owns them. (The development of internet shopping is an example of change.)
- Change usually means that some people benefit – but others may lose out.

A pupils' version of this big picture is given in the *geog.1* students' book opener for Chapter 4, and in *geog.1 resources and planning OxBox CD-ROM*, for the whiteboard.

The chapter outline

Use this, and their chapter opener, to give pupils a mental roadmap for the chapter.

4 **Let's go shopping** As the pupils' chapter opener, this unit is an important part of the chapter; see page 11 for notes about using chapter openers

4.1 **Shopping around** Introduces convenience and comparison goods, and explores the links between shopping and settlement size

4.2 **Out-of-town shopping: Bluewater** A case study of the Bluewater shopping centre in Kent: what it's like, and its impact on the surrounding area

4.3 **Shopping on the internet** How internet shopping works, its impact, and the benefits for different groups of shoppers

Objectives and outcomes for this chapter

Objectives	Unit	Outcomes
Most pupils will understand:		Most pupils will be able to:
• what convenience and comparison goods are	4.1	• give examples of both types of goods
• that there is a link between shopping and the size of settlements	4.1	• explain that some places are too small to support a shop; and that the bigger the settlement, the bigger the range of shops you'll find there
• what out-of-town shopping centres are, and why they were set up	4.2	• describe the Bluewater shopping centre and give at least two reasons to explain its location
• how internet shopping works	4.3	• give the steps in internet shopping
• that shopping has changed over the years, and is still changing	Ch 4 opener, 4.2, 4.3	• give out-of-town shopping and internet shopping as examples of changes
• that the changes may benefit some groups more than others	4.2, 4.3	• give examples of groups who benefit, and suffer, as a result of out-of-town and internet shopping

These tie in with 'Your goals for this chapter' in the pupils' chapter opener, and with the opening lines in each unit, which give the purpose of the unit in a pupil-friendly style.

Opportunities for assessment

See the formal assessment materials for this chapter on *geog.1 assessment file & OxBox CD-ROM*. They include a level-marked assessment with success criteria and a feedback form, interactive assessments, a scored test, and a self-assessment form.

There are other opportunities for assessment too. For example, you could use some of the more extended 'Your turn' questions in the students' book, worksheets or longer learning activities from *geog.1 resources and planning OxBox CD-ROM*, or some of the 'Further suggestions for class and homework' at the end of this chapter.

Getting ready for this chapter

Some of the starters and plenaries suggested for this chapter may need resources prepared in advance. Check out the *Resources* section on the 'Help at a glance' pages that follow.

geog.1 resources & planning OxBox CD-ROM has all the photos and diagrams from the chapter, for whiteboard display, plus movies and interactive materials. You will find these very useful for devising your own starters and plenaries. In addition, *geog.world CD-ROM* is a rich source of further material, including interactive webfiles and skills lessons.

Note that further information about Bluewater can be obtained at www.bluewater.co.uk.

About the chapter starter

The upper photo on page 52 of *geog.1* students' book was taken in Glasgow, in the 1890s. (Exact date unknown.) No self-service then, and few off-the peg clothes. Factory-made clothing did not become widespread until the 1920s, so you were likely to buy cloth, and have a tailor or dressmaker sew it up for you. Shops were family owned, and chain stores were only starting to appear. (In England, Jesse Boots, the Nottingham pharmacist, had over 30 stores by then.) This shopkeeper would probably have given you credit, and sent the bill round later. And there'd be time for a chat!

The lower photo was taken in Oxford. The French Connection chain is part of the French Connection Group plc (which includes French Connection, Nicole Farhi, GreatPlains and Toast). It operates in the UK, Europe, North America, the Middle East, Asia and Australia.

See suggestions 1–3, on page 82 of this book, for further activities related to this chapter starter.

4.1

Shopping around

About this unit

This unit introduces some basic shopping theory. Then in 'Your turn', pupils draw up their own shopping list, and explore the shopping hierarchy on a simple map.

Key ideas

- Convenience goods are low-cost goods that we buy often (eg milk, newspapers). We are prepared to buy them in the nearest convenient place, such as a corner store.
- Comparison goods are more expensive goods that we buy less often, and where choice is more important. We like to compare styles, prices, etc. before we buy. So we're prepared to travel further for them.
- Shops have to make a profit. So they must set up where they'll get enough customers.
- The larger the settlement, the more shops it has, attracted by all those customers.
- As a consequence large settlements have a large sphere of influence. They draw in shoppers from a large area, for comparison goods, because they offer a good choice.

Key vocabulary

convenience goods, comparison goods, profit, sphere of influence

Skills practised in 'Your turn'

- Geography skills: measuring distances on a map; drawing conclusions from information on a map
- Numeracy skills: recording costs; drawing a scattergram (scattergraph)
- Thinking skills: creating a shopping list that meets certain criteria; sorting goods into convenience and comparison goods; making shopping decisions

Unit outcomes

By the end of this unit, most pupils should be able to:

- explain the terms given in 'Key vocabulary' above
- give examples of convenience and comparison goods
- describe and explain the link between the range of shops in a place and the size of its population

Resources

For starter **1**: a packet of crisps; pictures of comparison and convenience goods
For starter **3**: labelled flash cards; Monopoly money (or similar)

Ideas for a starter

1. Say: You want to buy some new clothes. Will you go to (*a local village*) or (*a larger settlement*)? Why? And will you always buy in the first clothes shop you come to? Elicit the ideas that the larger the settlement, the better the choice – and that we like to compare clothes in different shops before we buy. Hence 'comparison goods'.
   Now hold up a packet of crisps. Ask: Would you want to compare these in different shops? Lead on to the idea of convenience goods.
   Finally hold up a series of pictures of goods cut from magazines and ask the class to say whether they are comparison or convenience goods.
2. There's no video rental store in (*a local village*). Why not?
3. Give two pupils flash cards labelled *clothing factory* and *clothing shop* to hold up. Give cards labelled *customer*, and some Monopoly money, to several other pupils. The pupils act out transactions to show what *profit* means, and that more customers means more profit. (For example a customer spends £10, the shop pays the factory £5, and holds up the money that's left.) This could be developed further.

Ideas for plenaries

Plan plenaries for strategic points throughout the lesson, as well as at the end.

1 Work with a partner. Make a list of local settlements and rank them in order of how good they are for shopping, for your age group, with the best first. Now arrange the same settlements in order of size, largest first. What do you notice? Write it down.

2 Here are some answers to questions. But what were the questions? (Sensible ones, related to what you learned today!)
   a) There were not enough customers in the village to make it profitable.
   b) Bread, milk, sweets and newspapers are examples.
   c) It gives shoppers plenty of choice.
   d) What you charge your customers for the goods, minus what you paid for them.
   e) People are willing to travel further to buy that type of goods.
   f) The area around it, that's affected by it.
   g) London.
   h) A jewellery shop.

3 A mystery: you often find shoe shops close together. Why? Does it help customers? Are there any advantages for the shoe shops? Do you think there are any disadvantages? (This could be something for pupils to ponder for homework – see suggestion 11 on page 82 of this book.)

4 Tell me two new things you have learned today.

Further class and homework activities

Shopping survey on *geog.1 resources and planning OxBox CD-ROM*

How to draw a scattergraph in *geog aid* on geog.world CD-ROM

Worksheets 4A and 4B on *geog.1 resources and planning OxBox CD-ROM*

Suggestions 4 – 22 on page 82 – 83 of this book

Answers to 'Your turn'

The answers for **1–4** will vary from student to student.

For question **1**, make sure pupils include a range of items from low-cost to more expensive, in their list. For example, relatively expensive items could include a mobile phone or other electronic product.

In question **3b**, pupils can measure distance using a strip of paper or a piece of thread or fine string to find the length, and then a centimetre ruler as scale. You could point them to page 26 of the student's book.

If pupils have a problem with question **4**, you might like them to work through the lesson *How to draw a scattergraph* in *geog aid* on geog.world CD-ROM.

5 a i Dalton does not enough people to support a supermarket. People will travel to Clinton, Willover or Lipton.

ii For the same reason – a video rental shop needs a larger population than that of a small village, to stay in business.

b It is a large town surrounded by smaller settlements. Between them, Lipton and the surrounding settlements will provide enough shoppers to keep a wide range of shops busy.

c Answers should be along these lines:
The larger a place is, the more shops it will have, and the wider the range of shops, and goods, there will be.

6 a All of them.

b Empton, when people need to go to the post office or are in a hurry for some sweets or basic groceries.

4.2

Out-of-town shopping: Bluewater

About this unit

This unit introduces Bluewater, a large out-of-town shopping centre in Kent.
'Your turn' explores the reasons for building Bluewater in that location, and its impact on the surrounding area.

Key ideas

- Bluewater in Kent is one of the UK's 11 shopping mega-centres. It provides a shopping 'day out', with catering, entertainment and leisure facilities as well as a wide range of shops.
- It is a brownfield development (on an old chalk quarry) built by developers.
- The government is concerned about the effect of such centres on the local economy, and the transport network, and may not allow more to be built.

Key vocabulary

out-of-town shopping centre, developer

Skills practised in 'Your turn'

- Geography skills: analysing maps and photos
- Literacy skills: writing a publicity leaflet; writing a speech
- Thinking skills: giving reasons; drawing conclusions about the likely impact of Bluewater; thinking up ways to help a local town attract its customers back

Unit outcomes

By the end of this unit, most pupils should be able to:

- explain the terms given in 'Key vocabulary' above
- give a reason for the development of out-of-town shopping
- describe at least four features of the Bluewater shopping centre
- give at least two reasons for the choice of location for Bluewater
- describe at least two negative impacts of out-of-town shopping

Resources

For starters **1** and **2**, and plenaries **1**– **3**: these materials are on *geog.1 resources and planning OxBox CD-ROM*
For starter **4**: photos of different types of shop (market stall, corner shop, shopping parade, shopping plaza, chain stores, department store) on paper or in digital form

Ideas for a starter

1 With books shut, display the main photo of Bluewater, from page 56 of the students' book, on the whiteboard. Ask: What do you think it is? Allow pupils to guess, without giving feedback. Then show the boating lake photo from page 57. Any closer? And finally show the inside shot from page 56. Why would people build this kind of place in that spot? Show the main photo again, and discuss the roads and car parks.

2 Show the *Shops* movie as a starter.

3 Students call out all the different kinds of shopping areas they can think of. For example shopping streets in the centre of town, shopping parades, open air markets. Write these on the board and then focus on out-of-town shopping, and launch the lesson.

4 Like **3** but this time you pass round (or display on whiteboard) photos of different types of shop. Ask pupils to name each type. Discuss the idea of different types of shop in different locations. Then move on to Bluewater.

Ideas for plenaries

Plan plenaries for strategic points throughout the lesson, as well as at the end.

1 What are the *main* differences between Bluewater, and the shopping streets in the middle of a town or city? (You could display the main Bluewater photo.)

2 What would it be like, if the government allowed dozens more out-of-town shopping centres to be built? (You could display the main Bluewater photo.) A good thing or a bad thing? Hold a quick debate.

3 One pair of pupils gives all the pros for out-of-town shopping centres like Bluewater, then another pair gives all the cons. (You could display the main Bluewater photo.) The class takes a vote.

4 Choose a pupil to read out his or her speech for question **5b** of 'Your turn'. The rest of the class becomes the Chamber of Commerce and asks questions, and takes a vote on the suggestions.

5 Create a slogan or eye-catching line for a newspaper ad about Bluewater, and the wide range of things you can buy or do there, or the wide range of people it caters for. It must be an acrostic based on *Bluewater*! For example:
Boots **l**amps **u**mbrellas …
Students could work in pairs, or this could be a whole-class activity (or carried on as homework).

Further class and homework activities

Shops movie on *geog.1 resources and planning OxBox CD-ROM*, if not used as a starter

Worksheets 4C and 4D on *geog.1 resources and planning OxBox CD-ROM*

Suggestions 23 – 26 on page 83 of this book

Answers to 'Your turn'

2 a Developers buy and develop (or redevelop) land and then usually rent out the buildings they put up.

b Close to London with its large population; close to the M25 ring road which means it is accessible from all directions; the site was probably fairly cheap and easy to get planning permission for (since it was an old quarry).

c Land is expensive in London; difficult to get a large enough site in the city; difficult to get planning permission.

3 a The dress shop will probably have lost customers.

b Shops in central London may have lost some customers, as Bluewater is easy to get to from London and has lots of space and a good choice of shops.

c It is very likely to have had a negative effect on Lakeside (which is older), since the two shopping centres are so close.

d It may have helped the coffee shop since many shoppers will come by train, and have a coffee while they wait for a train home.

e The newsagent's is not likely to be affected – newspapers are convenience goods. People buy them in the nearest convenient place. So people from Darenth won't go to Bluewater for them.

f Traffic will be worse, since most shoppers will drive to Bluewater, and frequent bus services have been laid on. (The centre has 13 000 car parking spaces!)

4 Students could include these ideas: the old quarry was a waste of land and an eyesore; the lakes and parks have improved the environment; there are lots of jobs for local people; now local people have a great choice of shops, restaurants and cinemas right on their doorstep; there are lots of other activities laid on.

5 a Some suggestions:

Provide different types of shopping from that at Bluewater, eg specialised food shops (delicatessens), farmers' market, organic goods.

Offer specialised services for shoppers, eg personal attention for clothes shopping.

Ensure that access to the town is easy, and that moving around within the town is easy and comfortable (good roads, plenty of parking, free bus from station, pedestrianised areas, areas with outdoor seating, public toilets).

Highlight any special features in the town, eg historic buildings, or any special cultural activities associated with it.

Make the town look more attractive, eg clean and litter-free, well-maintained, create planted areas, plant more trees.

Promote local community activities throughout the year, eg street markets and fairs, craft markets, bands in the bandstand.

4.3

Shopping on the internet

About this unit

This unit explains how internet shopping works. In 'Your turn' pupils explore how well it suits different kinds of purchases, its impact, and its benefits for different groups of people.

Key ideas

- The internet is a network of millions of computers, linked together worldwide.
- You can buy almost anything from anywhere over the internet – so an internet shop can have an enormous sphere of influence. (Amazon.com is a good example.)
- Internet shopping brings benefits – but it also has some negative effects.

Key vocabulary

internet, sphere of influence, website, service provider

Skills practised in 'Your turn'

- Literacy skills: explaining in your own words; using the glossary
- Thinking skills: identifying key differences; assessing the suitability of different items for purchase over the internet; comparing an internet shop and an actual shop from the seller's point of view; assessing the impact and benefits of internet shopping

Unit outcomes

By the end of this unit, most pupils should be able to:

- explain the terms given in 'Key vocabulary' above
- explain in their own words how internet shopping works
- recognise that internet shopping brings benefits, but also has some negative effects
- give at least three examples of groups of people it could benefit, and three examples of negative effects

Resources

For starter **1**: an internet shopping site to explore online, in class (for example Nike's site, or Amazon.co.uk, or a site that sells music – or ask the class to suggest one)

Ideas for a starter

1. Enter the online shop, discussing it as you go. In what ways is it different from a 'real' shop? Where is it located? What's its address? Where are the goods kept? Who serves you? Who works there? How do you pay? Do you have to queue? What about opening hours? What can go wrong? Talk pupils through the buying process.
2. What is the internet? Write up ideas on the board and reach an agreed definition. (This would replace question **1** of 'Your turn'.)
3. Have you or anyone in your house bought anything on the internet? What? From where? How was it delivered?
4. Who can give me examples of:
   - shops where you can both visit the shop *and* buy from it over the internet?
   - shops where you can shop *only* online?
   - shops that don't have a website (yet)?
   - shops that will probably never have a website?

Ideas for plenaries

Plan plenaries for strategic points throughout the lesson, as well as at the end.

1. Build up a list of adjectives on the board to describe normal shopping. Then build up another list to describe internet shopping.
2. Why do so many 'real' shops (like Marks & Spencer) also offer online shopping?
3. Shoplifting and credit card fraud are a problem in 'real' shops. Can customers cheat online shops? Can online shops cheat shoppers? Can shoppers get 'pickpocketed'?
4. Draw four 'talking heads'. Give each a name, and a label with some details about the person (age, what he or she does, where he or she lives). Two of the four love internet shopping. Two dislike it. Write speech bubbles for all four, giving their opinion of internet shopping, and a reason.

Further class and homework activities

Interactive activity for Unit 4.3 on *geog.1 resources and planning OxBox CD-ROM*

Interactive quiz for Chapter 4 on *geog.1 resources and planning OxBox CD-ROM*

Worksheet 4E on *geog.1 resources and planning OxBox CD-ROM*

Suggestions 27 – 30 on page 83 of this book

From mouse to house in *geog.1, Shopping* on geog.world CD-ROM

How shopping has changed in *geog.1, Shopping* on geog.world CD-ROM

Assessment materials for Chapter 4 on *geog.1 assessment file & OxBox CD-ROM*

Review 'Your goals for this chapter' on page 53 of *geog.1* students' book

Answers to 'Your turn'

2 a The shopper does not need to leave home. (Goods are ordered at home, and delivered to the door.)

b The company can have a much wider sphere of influence than if it were relying on a 'real' shop in a street.
(Another key difference for some companies, such as Amazon.com, is that the customer does not physically visit the company, so there is no need for expensive shop premises. However more and more companies now have both 'real' and online shops.)

3 a–c Students will reach different decisions about these items, depending on how well they know the goods. In general they may prefer shops for items they want to try on (like jeans) or try out.

d You might find out about it online, but you are unlikely to buy a house without seeing it.

e Buying a packet of crisps over the internet wouldn't be worth the effort. In general you are unlikely to use the internet to buy a small quantity of convenience goods. (You have to pay for delivery.)

4 a B – city premises are very expensive.

b B – could be worldwide.

c B – the price of the tickets does not need to include a charge to cover the cost of shop premises.

5 a It probably won't be affected. You will still go there for convenience goods, and when you are in a hurry.

b It will suffer as more and more people book holidays and flights over the internet.

c It probably won't suffer too much. People go there largely because they enjoy a day out shopping.

d If fewer people drive to shops there will be less air pollution (but at the same time there will be more delivery vans).

e If fewer people go shopping there will be fewer jobs in shops (but internet companies will employ a number of people).

f More internet shopping means more work for delivery companies, delivering goods.

6 a It saves a lot of time and effort. Instead of travelling miles to shop, the items are delivered to your door – especially good if you don't have a car.

b Shopping can be very hard work for disabled people, and they may need to wait for help in the shops. With internet shopping the goods are delivered to the door.

c Shopping with young children is difficult, especially if you do not have a car. Internet shopping saves a lot of hassle.

d It means you don't have to rush from work to get to shops before they close – and you can have goods delivered to your workplace, if necessary.

7 a i It would mean people travel to the town in the day only to work in offices, and for some services. So town centres could become rather dull places. However, some might change their focus – and become entertainment centres?

ii Many people derive great pleasure from going shopping, and trying things on. So that pleasure would be lost.

b If shops close, the hundreds of thousands of people working in shops and related services would lose their jobs, and might not be able to find others. Town centres could become increasingly run down, unless they changed their focus. People would lose the social benefits of shopping, and some people could become really isolated. Besides, it would make everyone completely dependent on internet access, which can fail or be deliberately disrupted. So in the long term it would not be sustainable.

4 Further suggestions for class and homework

Most of these suggestions are addressed to your pupils. Where research or further resources are needed, the internet will almost certainly provide the answer. (Eg *google* and choose *Web* or *Images*.)

How shopping has changed

1 A brief history of shopping Draw up a list of questions to ask, about the history of shopping, and then find the answers. (Try the local library.) Present your brief history of shopping in the form of a strip cartoon, or a set of annotated drawings or historical images. The results can be displayed. *

2 How and why shopping has changed: a class enquiry Shopping has changed a lot within the last 50 years, and the changes provide material for a satisfying enquiry.
(Students could first work through *How to carry out an enquiry* in *geog aid* on *geog.world CD-ROM*. This skills lesson is suitable for whole-class delivery.)

- The class brainstorms questions that could be asked, to find out how shopping has changed, and then selects the best ones for a questionnaire.
- Students agree a set of criteria to use later, to assess how effective their questionnaire has been.
- Finally they draw up a list of kinds of people they could ask, and how they will go about questioning them.

The results should be pooled, and graphs drawn using Excel or similar. Maps may also be needed.
Discuss the results with the class. Help pupils to identify patterns and trends, and to find explanations. Students assess the effectiveness of their questionnaire, and suggest what could have been improved. Finally they write individual reports. */**/***

3 How the fridge changed shopping! These days many stores use, and sell, fridges. Find out when fridges were invented, and write an essay on how they have changed shops, and people's shopping patterns. ***

Shopping around

4 Convenience or comparison? Collect pictures of things you can buy, and then arrange them in a continuum from very low-cost convenience goods (eg a cheap biro) to very high-cost comparison goods (eg a car? a house? a work of art?). Stick your pictures down on a long strip of paper, and hang this along the wall. Add prices? *

5 Shopping habits Draw a tally chart for all the shopping trips made by you, or someone in your family, for a week (or longer). Brainstorm suitable headings for the tally chart, and discuss the best way to lay it out. Headings might include:

What kind of things were bought
What kind of shop(s)
How much was spent
The distance travelled

There are many ways to use this data. For example pupils could draw a bar graph showing the amount spent each day, or a scattergram of distance travelled against amount spent, and look for patterns and correlation. *

6 Other people's shopping habits A tally chart like the one in **5** could be used for a shopping survey at a local shopping centre. Talk through carefully with pupils how they should behave and what to do if they encounter problems. *

7 Shopping ranks Students produce a map like the one on page 55 of *geog.1* students' book, for shopping in their own area, and annotate it with notes.
– First, discuss and agree with the class how to collect the data. (Between them, the pupils and their families are likely to know something about each settlement in the area.)
– Also discuss what kinds of shops to count. All? Or just food and clothing? And if a settlement is a large town should pupils count all the shops, or just give a general description?
– Then discuss how to draw the map and what it should show. (Include the main roads, for example). Tracing from a 1:50 000 OS map is a good solution, but this might not work for your area.
Students then annotate their map with notes about each settlement: its population, and a summary of its shops.
Add photos if possible.
And finally pupils look for links and patterns: between the number of shops, and number of main roads, and population size, and position of each place in the settlement hierarchy.
Ask pupils to identify the place with the largest sphere of influence. */**/***

8 Sphere of influence Settlements have spheres of influence. So do shops! People travel long distances to shop in Harrods in London, for example.
How would you determine the sphere of influence of a local shop, or shopping centre?
Work with pupils to decide what approaches you could use. (For example are there ads in newspapers, or on local radio, or on TV? Are special shopping trips laid on from other towns? Can people shop there by mail order, or on the internet? Should you do a survey of shoppers leaving the store?) Then choose the approach and allocate the work.
The result could be a map showing the area over which the influence of the store or shopping centre is felt. ***

9 Mail order catalogue Mail order catalogues are one way to create a large sphere of influence. Choose a mail order catalogue and write a report about it. Mention the goods available, how you can order, how you can pay, postage costs, delivery time. *

10 Junk mail Many shops and services extend their sphere of influence through junk mail. Collect junk mail for two weeks. Sort it by type. Make a tally chart of the goods and services being offered and present your results as a pie chart. *

11 A shopping mystery When you next go to town to shop, look out for the shoe shops, and clothes shops. Do they try to get as far away from each other as possible? Or do they like to stick together? Is the same thing true for supermarkets?
Come up with a theory to explain what you notice.
(Hint: bear in mind the two different types of goods!) ***

12 Where are the convenience stores? Convenience stores pop up everywhere. For example in petrol stations, blocks of flats, railway stations. List all the examples you know of. Say where they are – and why they chose that location. **

13 It's so convenient! Where's your nearest convenience store? Write a description. Say what it looks like, what it sells, what its opening hours are, and what other services it offers. For example photocopying, or ads? Add drawings or a digital photo, and a sketch map to show its location. **

14 A street market Like **13**, but this time describe a street market. Try to capture the atmosphere. **

15 Set up a convenience store You're going to set up a convenience store, in your local area. Where? Why there? Draw a sketch map showing your chosen location and annotate it to explain your choice. Give your store a name. *

16 Shopping on parade Take the class to a shopping parade. Record the types of shops and services it offers, and note any changes taking place. The pupils could:

- produce an annotated sketch map, with the shops and services colour-coded by type (eg food, other household services, personal services such as hairdressing and so on)
- draw a bar chart and pie chart and for the different types
- take photos
- consider why the parade is where, and as, it is
- present a report including all the above. */**/***

17 All change? Find a site in the local area where a change of use is underway (from or to shopping) or a shop is expanding. Work out why it is happening. Take digital photos. Interview a few people. Write a newspaper report, or do a radio report. *

18 The shop of my dreams You've always wanted to open a shop. And now the bank says it will lend you the money to get started. So what kind of shop will it be? What will it look like? Where will you locate it, and why? What will be special about it? How will you get customers in? You can add sketches and even floor plans. Enjoy! */**/***

19 Like it or loathe it? Some people love shopping, some hate it. What about you? Write a piece of prose, or a poem or rap, about shopping and you. */**/***

20 What's it all about? Write a space-mail to your friend Gelop on Mars explaining the activity we call shopping. (They don't do it on Mars, and Gelop hasn't heard of money.) *

21 Keep on shopping The government keeps an eye on how much we spend on shopping. It gets worried when we don't spend enough! Why do you think that is?
As part of your answer you could draw a large extended spider map showing all the jobs that depend on our shopping, including jobs in factories. Don't forget to write opening and closing paragraphs. **/***

22 Sum it all up Create a mind map about shopping. Make it look really colourful and interesting. **

Out-of-town shopping

23 Location requirements When planning where to put an out-of-town shopping centre, you have to think carefully about what the requirements are. For example near a motorway? Near a large settlement? Write a list of location requirements for an out-of-town shopping centre. ***

24 Plan a new out-of-town shopping centre Give it a name. Where will you locate it? Do a sketch map showing roads, shops, car parks, leisure facilities, cafés and any special features (for example dry ski-slope? canoe club?). Add field sketches showing the buildings and the landscape around the site. (Are there gardens? fountains? sculptures?) ***

25 Publicity poster Design a poster to get people to shop at your new out-of-town shopping centre. *

26 A sustainable development? Look at this drawing.

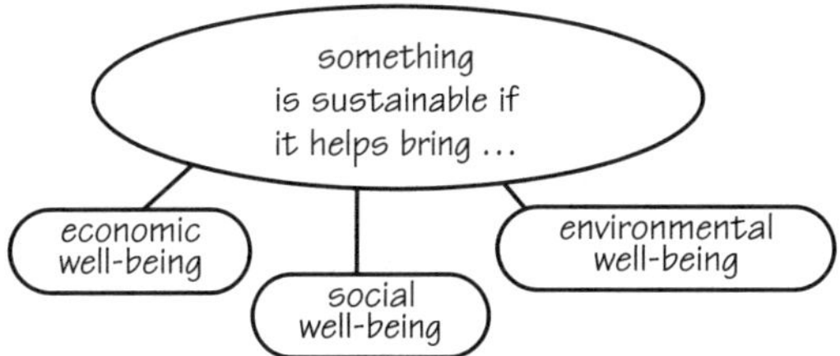

Something is sustainable only if it helps in all three areas.
Is the Bluewater shopping centre a good example of sustainable development? Think about all three aspects, and give it a score. Explain your score.
Would a shop owner in Bexleyheath think your score was fair? How could you make sure it was really fair? ***

Shopping on the Internet

27 Your virtual shop You are setting up an internet shop. What are you going to sell? Make up a name for your company and design a home page for your website. What kind of people will you need to employ? Will you need special buildings, or could you work from home? Write your plans for your new company, divided into suitable sections. ***

28 Compare mail order and internet shopping In what ways are they similar? And different? Students decide on a way to show the comparison. A table with three columns, and headings 'Characteristics', 'Mail order shopping' and 'Internet shopping' would work. Put ticks in the columns. *

Shopping in the future

29 Shopping 30 years from now What will shopping be like thirty years from now? Help pupils to plan an extended piece of writing about this. (Will there be shops as we know them? What about opening hours? Will there still be credit cards? Will there be iris scanning?) ***

30 How strange! Suddenly something very strange happens. An invisible force from another planet closes all our shops, and street markets, and factories, and ports. You can't buy a thing. Describe life after a week has gone by. ***

5 Exploring Britain

Helping you deliver the KS3 Programme of Study

This chapter addresses these areas of the Programme of Study:

Range and content

Undertake study of the UK and learn some key aspects of its changing geography, current issues, place in the world today.

Key concepts

Space Know where places and landscapes are located. **Scale** Appreciate different scales - from personal and local to national, international and global. **Interdependence** Explore the social, economic, environmental and political connections between places. **Physical and human processes** Explain how physical and human processes shape places, landscapes and societies.

Key processes

Geographical enquiry Ask geographical questions; display information; analyse and evaluate evidence, presenting findings to draw and justify conclusions. **Graphicacy and visual literacy** Use maps at a range of scales. **Geographical communication** Communicate knowledge and understanding using geographical vocabulary and conventions in both talk and writing.

The big picture

These are the key ideas behind this chapter.

- The British Isles has been shaped and changed by natural and human processes.
- The British Isles is made up of two countries, the UK and the Republic of Ireland; the UK in turn is made up of four nations.
- Like most countries, the UK is a country of contrasts, both physical and human.
- The UK and other countries are linked in many ways. They are interdependent.

A pupils' version of this big picture is given in the *geog.1* students' book opener for Chapter 5, and in *geog.1 resources and planning OxBox CD-ROM*, for the whiteboard.

The chapter outline

Use this, and their chapter opener, to give pupils a mental roadmap for the chapter.

5 **Exploring Britain** As the pupils' chapter opener, this unit is an important part of the chapter; see page 11 for notes about using chapter openers

5.1 **Your island home** Explores the main physical features of the British Isles

5.2 **It's a jigsaw!** The British Isles is divided into two countries; and the UK is made up of four nations, and divided into regions and sub-regions

5.3 **What's our weather like?** A weather map, some key points about our weather, and our overall temperature and rainfall patterns

5.4 **Who are we?** These once-empty islands have been peopled by immigrants

5.5 **Where do we live?** Population distribution in the UK, and the ten largest cities

5.6 **What kind of work do we do?** Introduces the different sectors of economic activity, and gives an overview of economic activity in the UK

5.7 **High or low earnings?** Average earnings vary from region to region – why?

5.8 **The UK in the world** Explores the links between the UK and other countries, and introduces the European Union, and the Commonwealth of countries

Objectives and outcomes for this chapter

Objectives	Unit	Outcomes
Most pupils will understand:		Most pupils will be able to:
• that the terms *British Isles*, *Great Britain* and *United Kingdom* all mean something different	5.2	• identify the British Isles, Great Britain and the United Kingdom on an outline map
• that the UK is made up of four nations	5.2	• name England, Scotland, Wales and Northern Ireland as the four nations that make up the UK
• that nations are divided into administrative regions and sub-regions	5.2	• name at least four of England's nine regions and identify them on an outline map of the regions
• that the UK has distinct physical features that can be shown on maps	5.1	• name at least four upland areas, and at least four rivers, in the UK and say where they are on the map
• that there are is an overall pattern in the way temperature and rainfall varies around the UK	5.3	• define weather; read a simple weather map; and describe and explain the overall trends in temperature and rainfall around the UK
• that these islands have been peopled by immigrants, who arrived over the centuries	5.4	• name at least five groups of people who came to the UK, including at least one recent group
• that population distribution varies across the UK, largely influenced by relief	5.5	• point out the most crowded and least crowded parts of the UK, and give some reasons to explain the pattern; name the UK's 10 largest cities and mark them in roughly the correct positions on a blank map
• that most workers in the UK earn a living by providing services	5.6	• explain the terms *primary*, *secondary*, *tertiary* and *quaternary*; give examples of jobs in each sector; describe the employment structure in the UK and say how it has changed and is changing
• that some regions of the UK are more prosperous than others	5.7	• point out the main area with highest average earnings, and at least two areas with the lowest, and give reasons to explain the differences
• that the UK and other countries are inderdependent	5.8	• describe some links between the UK and other countries; explain the terms EU and Commonwealth, and give at least five members for each group

These tie in with 'Your goals for this chapter' in the pupils' chapter opener, and with the opening lines in each unit, which give the purpose of the unit in a pupil-friendly style.

Opportunities for assessment

See the assessment materials for this chapter on *geog.1 assessment file & OxBox CD-ROM*. There are other opportunities for assessment too. For example, the more extended 'Your turn' questions in the students' book, or worksheets. (See notes for other chapters.)

Getting ready for this chapter

Some of the starters and plenaries suggested for this chapter may need resources prepared in advance. Check out the *Resources* section on the 'Help at a glance' pages that follow.

geog.1 resources & planning OxBox CD-ROM has all the photos and diagrams from the chapter, for whiteboard display, plus movies and interactive materials. You will find these very useful for devising your own starters and plenaries. In addition, *geog.world CD-ROM* is a rich source of further material, including interactive webfiles and skills lessons.

About the chapter starter

The images on page 60 of *geog.1* students' book are, in numbered order: Westminster Bridge and the Houses of Parliament; the Queen and Prince Philip on a formal occasion; a view of central Birmingham; Gold Hill in the small town of Shaftesbury in Dorset; the White Cliffs of Dover; a match between Manchester City and Aston Villa, and a group of young people at an unspecified British shopping arcade.

5.1

Your island home

About this unit

This unit presents a 3-D relief map of the British Isles, to stimulate pupils' interest.
In 'Your turn', pupils identify some of the physical features of the British Isles, and reflect on the advantages and disadvantages of living on an island.

Key idea

- The British Isles consist of two main islands, and over 6000 smaller ones!
- They have been shaped by many different processes, natural and human. (And apart from glaciation, these processes are still going on.)
- The result is different physical features, and different landscapes.

Key vocabulary

British Isles

Skills practised

- Geography skills: identifying physical features by comparing maps; studying photos and drawing conclusions; describing the location of the British Isles
- Literacy skills: writing a paragraph comparing places in photos
- Thinking skills: giving advantages and disadvantages of living on an island

Unit outcomes

By the end of this unit, most pupils should be able to:

- say what is meant by 'the British Isles'
- name at least four upland areas, and at least four rivers, in the British Isles, and say where they are on the map
- describe where the British Isles is, on the Earth

Resources

For starters **1** and **2**, and plenaries **3** and **6**: all images from the book are on *geog.1 resources and planning OxBox CD-ROM*

For starter **3**: images of very different landscapes from all around the UK and around the world (including some very dramatic ones) on paper or in digital form .

For plenary **3**: A slip of blue card (for mountainous land) and a slip of green card (for flat land) for each pupil.

Ideas for a starter

1 Look at the 3-D relief map on page 62 of the students' book. (You could display it.) What words would you use to describe the British Isles? Pupils call out words. Write them on the whiteboard. Do you think they have always been like tihs? Will they always be like this in the future? Does everyone agree? (Finding out more about their past history would be a challenging homework project. See suggestion 2, page 102.)

2 Do question **1** as a starter. (You could display the map.)

3 Show pictures of very different landscapes from the UK and around the world. Ask the class to say whether each is in the UK or not, and to give reasons for their answers. And if in the UK, ask pupils to guess where. So why does the UK look so different in different places?

Ideas for plenaries

Plan plenaries for strategic points throughout the lesson, as well as at the end.

1 Tell your partner about some natural processes that have shaped the landscape of the British Isles. Now your partner tells you about human processes that have shaped it. Which do you think made the biggest difference, natural or human?
2 Do we have any control over the processes that are shaping the British Isles today?
3 Give each pupil a slip of blue card (for mountainous land) and green card (for flat land). Call out questions about the 3-D relief map. (You could display it.) Pupils hold up a card in response. For example: Which has Scotland got more of, mountainous or flat land? Which has Wales got more of? Which parts do you think get most rain, the mountainous parts or the flat parts? Which do you think get coldest? Which have more people living in them? Which have least farming? You could ask for reasons, or just tell pupils they'll find out whether they were correct later in the chapter. (This prepares them for later work on the influence of relief on population density and weather patterns.)
4 A memory challenge. Write a list of the UK's main physical features on the board (upland areas, a selection of rivers and seas) and present the class with a challenge. Pupils have to find a way to commit these features to memory, so that they will still know where they are, on the map, this time next year. Pupils discuss ways to get images into their long term memories, and agree to try it out for homework. You can put it to the test at the start of the next lesson.
5 What exciting new things did you learn today?
6 Show *Images of Britain* movie as a final plenary, preparing the way for the rest of the chapter.

Further class and homework activities

Interactive activity for Unit 5.1 on *geog.1 resources and planning OxBox CD-ROM*

Mapping the UK in *Exploring Britain* on geog.world CD-ROM

Suggestions 1 – 6 on page 102 of this book (Note that suggestion 1 is for an ongoing piece of work, that can be developed as pupils work through this chapter.)

Answers to 'Your turn'

1 Students may need reminding that the largest island is called Great Britain, or Britain for short.

2 a the yellow shows areas of high land

b a = North West Highlands b = Grampian Mountains
c = Southern Uplands d = Lake District
e = Pennines f = North York Moors
g = Cambrian Mountains h = Wicklow Mountains
i = Dartmoor j = Antrim Mountains
k = Isle of Wight l = Isle of Man
m = Orkney Islands n = France
o = English Channel p = North Sea
q = Irish Sea

2 A = Severn, B = Thames, C = Trent, D = Tyne, E = Tweed, F = Dee, G = River Great Ouse

3 a X = B, Y = A. A is a mountainous area – see page 62 of the students' book.

b i X **ii** It would have been heavily wooded.

c Both places have some water: X is close to the sea (visible in the distance), and Y has a lake. Neither place is flat.
However, that's where similarities end.
X is at a lower altitude (judging by the glimpse of the sea), and further south, which means it is much warmer; there are signs of human occupation (buildings in the distance, and the sheep mean there's farming); the landscape is smooth, rolling, and grassy.
Y is cold, bleak, rugged and rocky; there's some snow on the hills in the distance, but no sign of vegetation, or of human occupation.

4 Students may have very different ideas here, but the question should provoke discussion.

5 Students could mention: north of the equator; between the equator and the Arctic Circle, but closer to the Arctic Circle (so the climate is quite cool); the islands lie on the east of the Atlantic Ocean; they are part of Europe; they lie in the Atlantic Ocean, off the north west of the continent of Europe.

5.2

It's a jigsaw!

About this unit

This unit is about the political structure of the British Isles. It shows how they are divided into two countries, how the UK is made up of four nations, and how nations are further divided into regions and sub-regions, with England as example. In 'Your turn', pupils explore the political structure, and draw a timeline for the creation of the two countries.

Key ideas

- The British Isles is made up of two countries, the UK and the Republic of Ireland.
- The UK is made up of four nations, England, Scotland, Wales and Northern Ireland.
- Each nation is divided into main administrative regions. England has nine of them. These are in turn divided into sub-regions (counties and unitary authorities).
- Dividing a country up into regions and sub-regions makes it easier to manage.

Key vocabulary

countries, nations, regions

Skills practised

- Geography skills: comparing maps in order to build up an address; drawing and shading in sketch maps, to show the British Isles, the UK, Great Britain; identifying the shapes of the different nations
- Numeracy skills: simple calculations (addition); working out the scale for a timeline
- Thinking skills: constructing and annotating a timeline

Unit outcomes

By the end of this unit, most pupils should be able to:

- identify the UK, Republic of Ireland, Great Britain, England, Scotland, Wales and Northern Ireland on an outline map of the British Isles
- say that England is divided into administrative regions, and be able to name, and identify on a map, at least four of them
- give an address for themselves, which includes their administrative region

Resources

For starters **1** – **3**: all images from the book are on *geog.1 resources and planning OxBox CD-ROM*

For plenary **4**: a set of cards with labels on, for a map quiz; a map drawn on board

Ideas for a starter

1. Start with a quick revision quiz about the physical features of the UK (especially if you used plenary **4** on page 87 of this book). For example ask pupils to come up and label or draw in features, on an outline map on the board. Then say we are now going to look at the UK in a different way: political. Look at (or display) map A.
2. Display the 3-D relief map from page 62, then map A from page 64. Ask pupils what the difference is. Explain the terms *physical map* and *political map*.
3. Display maps A, B and C one after the other, from page 64 of the students' book. Ask what they're showing.
4. Draw a table on the board with five columns, but no headings. Write the names of some British towns or cities in the first column, some counties in the next, two administrative regions in the third, two nations in the fourth, and *the UK* in the last. Ask pupils to work out what the headings should be. Discuss, then ask individual pupils for more entries for columns 1–5. (They can use their books.)
5. Warn pupils that you are going to give them a quiz later, about maps A, B and C on page 64 in the students' book. (See plenary **3**.)

Ideas for plenaries

Plan plenaries for strategic points throughout the lesson, as well as at the end.

1. Is Wales a country? Is it a nation? What do you think a nation is? What are the signs that Wales is a different nation from Scotland or England? (Flag, national anthem, national emblems, Welsh language, its own history and culture.)
2. What kinds of problems might there be if the school was just one huge room, not divided into blocks or classrooms? What kinds of problems might there be if the UK was not divided into regions and sub-regions?
3. Map quiz: draw map B from page 64 on the board in advance – but with no labels. (You will need to add some leader lines). Place a set of 15 shuffled cards, each with a label written on, face down on the table. (The 15 labels are for the 2 countries, 4 British nations, and the 9 administrative regions in England, shown on map B.) Books are shut. Divide the class into two teams. Pupils from each team take turns to go to the board, pick the top card, call out what's written on it, then write the label in the correct place on the map. If he or she is correct, that team gains 5 points and the card is discarded. If wrong, the other team has a go with the same card. When only one card is left, the final pupil is not allowed to look at it, but must add the last label without help from a card, for 10 marks.

   You could nominate two pupils, with page 64 open, to be judge and score keeper.
4. Pretend to be Henry II of England and ask a pupil to explain what the name *United Kingdom* is all about.
5. What if Scotland and Wales became independent countries, and Northern Ireland and the Republic of Ireland became one country? Why is the Republic of Ireland called a republic? Some people in the Republic of Ireland don't like the term 'the British Isles'. Why not?

Further class and homework activities

Interactive activity for Unit 5.2 on *geog.1 resources and planning OxBox CD-ROM*

Worksheets 5A and 5B on *geog.1 resources and planning OxBox CD-ROM*

Suggestions 7–12 on page 102 of this book

Answers to 'Your turn'

1 Students may need to find their nearest city, on the map on page 139 of the students' book, and use that as a guide. A political wall map of the UK or British Isles would also be useful.

2 Students' diagrams should be similar to Walter's 'Venn diagram' on page 65 of the students' book.

3 b The shaded areas on the pupils' maps should match those on the maps in the top left box, on page 65 of the students' book.

c Populations, in millions, are:
GB, 58.6 UK, 60.3 British Isles, 64.5
Areas, in sq km, are:
GB, 228 300 UK, 242 500 British Isles, 312 800

d The title could just be: *Facts about the British Isles.*

4 The drawing on the right shows a vertical timeline, for convenience. It's best if pupils draw a horizontal one.
You could point out to pupils that some people in Scotland and Wales want their nations to become separate countries; and some people in Ireland want the two parts of Ireland to be reunited as one country. So 100 years from now, a political map of the British Isles could be different – just as it was in the year 1100.

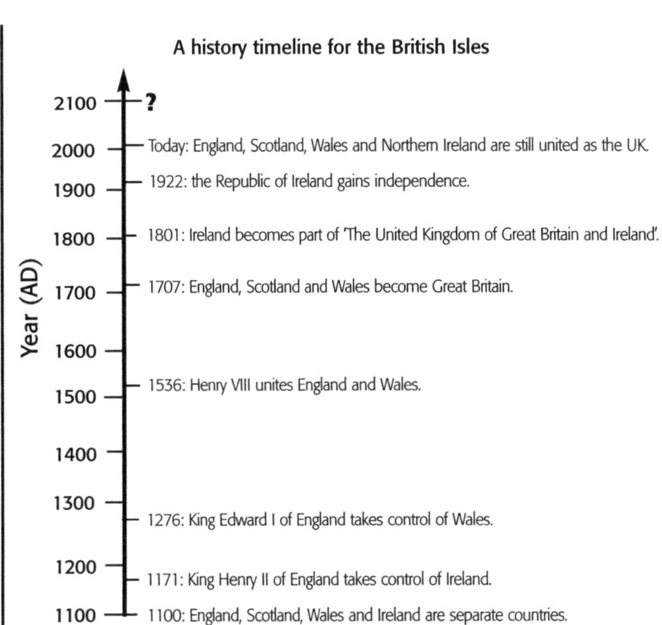

A history timeline for the British Isles
Year (AD)
2100 ?
2000 Today: England, Scotland, Wales and Northern Ireland are still united as the UK.
1900 1922: the Republic of Ireland gains independence.
1800 1801: Ireland becomes part of 'The United Kingdom of Great Britain and Ireland'.
1700 1707: England, Scotland and Wales become Great Britain.
1600
1500 1536: Henry VIII unites England and Wales.
1400
1300 1276: King Edward I of England takes control of Wales.
1200 1171: King Henry II of England takes control of Ireland.
1100 1100: England, Scotland, Wales and Ireland are separate countries.

5.3 What's our weather like?

About this unit

This unit presents a weather map, gives general points about temperature patterns across the British Isles, and shows a map of average annual rainfall. 'Your turn' gives practice in reading weather and rainfall maps. Pupils finally sketch a map of the British Isles, and add labels to show the general temperature and rainfall patterns.

Key ideas

- Weather means the state of the atmosphere. For example how warm, wet, or windy it is.
- The weather in the British Isles can change from day to day, and can be very different in different places.
- But there are some overall patterns:
  - The south is usually warmest, since it is nearest the equator.
  - It gets cooler as you go further north, or onto higher land.
  - The west coast is usually warmer than the east coast in winter, thanks to a warm ocean current called the North Atlantic Drift.
  - The west coast is the wettest part of the UK. This is because the high land in the west forces the moist prevailing south west winds to rise, giving rain.

(Note that 'overall patterns' in fact mean climate. Pupils will study climate in *geog.2*.)

Key vocabulary

weather, North Atlantic Drift, windward, leeward, rainshadow

Skills practised

- Geography skills: reading a weather map; reading a choropleth map showing rainfall; drawing a sketch map
- Thinking skills: explaining rainfall patterns; summarising their learning about temperature and rainfall patterns by labelling a sketch map

Unit outcomes

By the end of this unit, most pupils should be able to:

- define the terms given in 'Key vocabulary' above
- read a simple weather map
- point out the warmest and coolest areas in summer, and the mildest and coldest areas in winter, on a map of the British Isles
- describe the effect of the North Atlantic Drift
- point out the areas with most and least rain every year, on a map of the British Isles

Resources

For starter **1** and plenary **4**: all images from the book are on *geog.1 resources and planning OxBox CD-ROM*

For plenary **6**: a pair of True/False cards (green = true, red = false), for each pupil. and a set of statements for you to call out, prepared in advance

Ideas for a starter

1. Show the weather map on the whiteboard and point out the types of symbols used. So what's the weather like today? Work in pairs and try to describe it using symbols.
2. Rainfall is just one aspect of the weather. What other aspects does weather have? Show them on a spider map. Then agree a definition of weather.
3. What's the weather like today? Do you think it's the same all over the UK? Why not?

Ideas for plenaries

Plan plenaries for strategic points throughout the lesson, as well as at the end.

1. In what ways does the weather affect your life?
2. How would you describe the weather in the UK, overall? (Compared with the Sahara desert, say, or Antarctica?)
3. A pupil draws a diagram on the board, instructed by the class, to show how high land makes rain form. The pupil draws exactly what he or she is told, nothing else.
4. Point out (or display) the rainfall map. It is an example of a choropleth map. Who can tell me what a choropleth map is? Write suggestions on the board, and come up with an agreed definition. Then ask pupils to look through their *geog.1* books for other examples. (Pages 70 and 74 show two.)
5. Draw an outline of the UK on the board. Ask pupils to come up and write 'warmer', 'wetter', 'cooler' and 'drier' in the correct places, without using their books.
6. Call out a set of 15 statements about weather in the British Isles, some true and some false. Bring in knowledge from earlier lessons, with statements like: 'It rains a lot in the Cambrian mountains.' Students check the rainfall map or other information in Unit 5.3, or the map on page 139 of their books, then raise green or red cards, or shout out *True* or *False*.

Further class and homework activities

Interactive activity for Unit 5.3 on *geog.1 resources and planning OxBox CD-ROM*

Making a UK records certificate on *geog.1 resources and planning OxBox CD-ROM*

Worksheets 5D and 5E on *geog.1 resources and planning OxBox CD-ROM*

Suggestions 13 –16 on pages 102 –103 of this book

Answers to 'Your turn'

1 Answers will vary from day to day!

2 heavy cloud, rain, dull, temperature around 7 °C, wind from south west at 30 mph

3 Yes, in general it does match. It was warmest in the south of the British Isles that day, and warmest of all on the west coast of Ireland and in the south west of Britain; it was coldest on the high land in Scotland (Grampian Mountains). But point out to pupils that a weather map will not match the pattern every day. The pattern shows the 'average'.

4 a D **b** A **c** C **d** A

5 The high ground forces warm, moist air to rise. The water vapour cools and condenses. Clouds form and it rains.

6 a The winds that blow most often. In the UK they are south west winds (blowing in from the south west).

b They blow across the Atlantic Ocean, and pick up moisture from the water as they blow.

7 a The west side, where most of the land is high. (Ask pupils to compare the rainfall map with the map on page 62 in their books.) The moist south west winds arrive on the west coast first, and the high land forces them to rise. As the air rises it cools, so the water condenses, leading to rain.

b C is on very high land in the Cambrian Mountains – see pages 62 and 139 of the students' book. And it is close to the coast, where the moist south west winds arrive in. So it gets a lot of rain. B is much lower – again see the maps. It is sheltered by the mountains to the west. (It is on the leeward side of the mountains.) By the time the winds reach B they have lost a great deal of their moisture, so B gets much less rain.

8 This shows where the four labels should go:

What's our weather usually like?

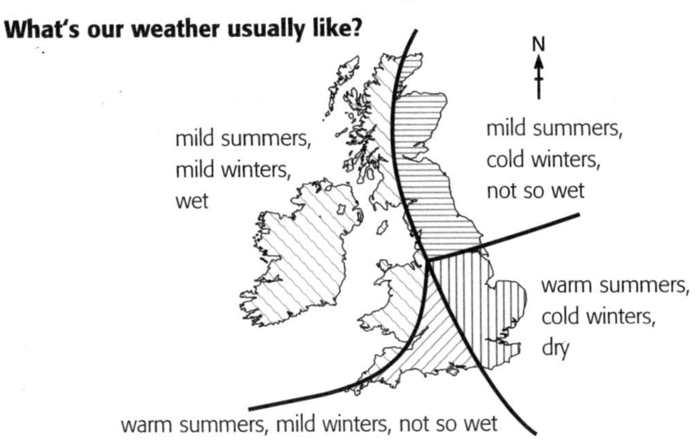

5.4 Who are we?

About this unit

This unit explains how the UK, once empty, has been peopled by immigrants. In 'Your turn' pupils draw a timeline for the waves of immigrants, define some terms and think about what attracted people here at the start, and what attracts them today.

Key ideas

- An immigrant is a person who moves here from another country, to live.
- 7000 years ago, Britain was practically empty – so all British people are descended from immigrants.
- Over the centuries, people have moved to these islands from all over the world, and for a variety of reasons.

Key vocabulary

immigrant, emigrant, economic migrant, settler, invader, refugee, asylum seeker (most introduced in 'Your turn' – see the glossary at the end of this book)

Skills practised

- Numeracy skills: drawing a timeline
- Literacy skills: using the glossary; writing definitions
- Thinking skills: matching examples to definitions; thinking up reasons

Unit outcomes

By the end of this unit, most pupils should be able to:

- define the terms given in 'Key vocabulary' above
- give an example to match each definition
- name at least five groups of arrivals in the UK over the centuries, including at least one recent group
- draw a timeline

Resources

No special resources

Ideas for a starter

1. Once the British Isles was empty. Where did the people come from?
2. Write a list on the board: Celts, Romans, Saxons, Irish, Vikings, Bangladeshis, West Indians. Ask what they all have in common.
3. Ask: How many of you have a parent from another country? a grandparent? a great grandparent? a great great grandparent? any ancestor?
Some are bound to put their hands up.
Say: Actually we should all have our hands up.
4. Write these terms on the board:
migrant in-migrant out-migrant

   Ask: Do you know any migrants? Are there any in your family?
Reach a definition of the term 'migrant'.

   Then ask pupils to guess what the other two terms mean, and to give examples.

   Finally connect these to the more familiar terms 'immigrant' and 'emigrant.'

   Ask whether in-migrant and out-migrant might be better term to use, for any reason.

Ideas for plenaries

Plan plenaries for strategic points throughout the lesson, as well as at the end.

1 New arrivals bring at least some of their culture with them. What does *culture* mean? Draw a spider map showing elements of culture. (Include things like music, language, dress, hair styles, religion, tradition, festivals, food, architecture.)
The spider map could be extended with examples, such as Norman castles, Roman laws, Indian food, reggae music.

2 What other cultures will you come in contact with today? In what ways?

3 Write the slogan *Celebrate our diversity* on the board. What does it mean? Do you think it would make life more exciting if everyone took that attitude?

4 Write on the board 'I am an immigrant' and ask pupils to explain why this is true of everyone in the class.

5 Is today's topic just geography? Does it have anything to do with other subjects?

6 How could you find out about your ancestors? Any ideas?

7 Which group of arrivals would you like to do some research on?
Students work in small groups, agree who to research, and make up an enquiry question. Other pupils can comment on the enquiry question – is it well-framed? (Questions may be modified as a result.) Encourage pupils to choose a range of arrivals to research. They then carry out their enquiries as part of an ongoing class project. (This overlaps with suggestions 18 and 19 on page 103.)

Further class and homework activities

Suggestions 17 –19 on page 103 of this book

Answers to 'Your turn'

1 Immigrant: a person who moves here from another country, to live.

3 a Between the Normans and the Huguenots.

b In the 20th century.

4 a See the glossary at the back of this book or the students' book.

b William the Conqueror, invader; Chiyo, refugee; Philip, asylum seeker; Joy, economic migrant – and an emigrant from Jamaica (but an immigrant to the UK).

5 a To find a good place to farm.

b Most come here for work, from many different countries including other EU countries. (People from other EU countries have the right to work here, with some restrictions.) Many of them are from poorer countries, and want to improve their standard of living, and give their children a better chance in life.
Others come here to escape from war and persecution. They are attracted by the UK's reputation as a fair and tolerant society.
People from former British colonies may feel a stronger connection to the UK than to other countries, so will be drawn here. Many already speak some English.

Where do we live?

About this unit

This unit presents a choropleth map of population density for the British Isles, and gives the 10 largest cities and their populations. In 'Your turn' pupils analyse the map and try to explain the pattern. After further questions on cities, and rural/urban population, pupils summarise the pattern of population density in the UK, in writing.

Key ideas

- Some parts of the British Isles are quite empty – and some are very crowded. This is largely influenced by relief (with mountainous areas the most empty).
- The population density of a place is the average number of people living in a square kilometre.
- Population density is low in rural areas, and high in urban areas.

Key vocabulary

population density, square kilometre, rural, urban (see the glossary at the end of this book)

Skills practised

- Geography skills: identifying an area as urban or rural, from a photo; reading and analysing a choropleth map of population density; comparing maps, to identify cities
- Numeracy skills: interpreting a pie chart (with no percentages marked on); estimating how many times larger one pie slice is than another
- Literacy skills: writing a report summarising the pattern of population density in the UK
- Thinking skills: finding explanations; completing a table using clues from a map

Unit outcomes

By the end of this unit, most pupils should be able to:

- explain the terms given in 'Key vocabulary' above
- answer simple questions about the information shown on a choropleth map
- point out where the most and least crowded areas are, in the UK, and give some reasons to explain the pattern
- name the UK's 10 largest cities and mark them in roughly the correct positions on a blank map (this may need practice for homework)

Resources

For starter **1**: chalk or string to mark out equal areas on the classroom floor

For starter **3** and plenaries **5** and **6**: all images from the book are on *geog.1 resources and planning OxBox CD-ROM*

For plenary **7**: a class set of blank outline maps for the UK

Ideas for a starter

1. Mark out three equal areas (as large as you can) on the classroom floor, or outside. Ask a couple of pupils to stand in one, a larger number in another, and a lot more in the third. Which square has the highest population? Imagine each represents 1 square km. What is the population in each square km? This is called the population density.
2. What is a square kilometre? Discuss with pupils and identify an area of about a square kilometre in the local area. About how many people live in that area? That is called the population density. Would it be different for other squares?
3. With books closed, display the photos from page 71 on the whiteboard. What's the big difference between these places? Which one is more built-up? One is an urban area. Which one? Can you think of the opposite word, for the other?

Ideas for plenaries

Plan plenaries for strategic points throughout the lesson, as well as at the end.

1 From the map, what is the population density in your area? Is it the same in every part of your area? Explain. (It's about *average*.)

2 Write the terms *urban* and *rural* on the board and ask for local examples. Does a hamlet count as urban? (See the answer for question **2** in 'your turn'.)

3 What are the black lines on the map on page 70 of the students' book? (Compare with maps B and C on page 64.)

4 What would a map of population density have looked like, 5000 years ago?

5 Compare the maps on pages 70 and 62 of the students' book. (You could display them.) What do you notice? Can you see any correlation (link) between the two? Can you explain it?

6 Look at (or display) the photos on page 71 of the students' book. Discuss/brainstorm the advantages and disadvantages of living in each kind of place. At the end, take a show of hands to find out which one pupils would rather live in.

7 Give out blank outline maps of Great Britain or the British Isles. Students mark in and label the 10 largest cities. Give them five minutes, working in pairs, to familiarise themselves with the locations of these cities, for example by covering up labels. Then call pupils to the board to either label the city dots on an outline map of the UK, or insert and label city dots on a blank map, or a mixture. (If not used as a plenary this familiarisation could become a homework task. See suggestion 21 on page 103.)

8 Ask pupils to read out the reports they wrote for question **8** in 'Your turn'.

9 Who counts the population anyway? How? Why bother?

Further class and homework activities

Worksheet 5C on *geog.1 resources and planning Oxbox CD-ROM*

Tour guide in *Exploring Britain*, in *geog.1* on *geog.world CD-ROM*

Suggestions 20 – 27 on page 103 of this book

Answers to 'Your turn'

1 the urban area, in B

2 This could lead to a discussion of whether a small village counts as a rural area. In fact hamlets, villages and even small towns are counted as 'rural'. The official definition for the UK is in fact quite complex. The government has classified urban and rural areas with the help of satellite images, looking at the amount of open space in and around a settlement as well as its actual population density. (See www.statistics.gov.uk for more.)

3 a i From 100 to 250 people per sq km, on average.
ii Fewer than 10 people per sq km.
iii Over 1000 people per sq km.

b This is a mountainous area, and it's hard to earn a living here. Mountainous areas are not suitable for farming or many other activities In general people tend to settle on lower flatter land.

c i They are both in England: around London in the lower half of the country, and around Liverpool/Manchester/Leeds/Bradford in the upper half.

ii London is the capital city, the main seat of government, and the UK's financial centre. Many large companies have their head offices here. The area in and around it attracts people because of its wide range of work and entertainment, and well-paid jobs. Liverpool, Manchester, Leeds and Bradford became centres of industry after the Industrial Revolution, and grew very fast as people flocked in, looking for work. Even though their traditional industries have declined, much of the UK's industry is still in this area.

4 The order for the first column is:
England
Northern Ireland
Scotland
Wales

5 A = Glasgow; B = Edinburgh; C = Bradford; D = Leeds; E = Liverpool; F = Manchester; G = Sheffield; H = Birmingham; I = Bristol; J = London

6 a i false **ii** false **iii** true

b Pupils could brainstorm this from two angles:
why people might not want to live in the country (push factors) – too few jobs, poor services; not much to do, isolation etc;
why people might be attracted to city living (pull factors) – work, entertainment, range of services, plenty of people to meet etc.

7 Students' answers for this one may offer you an opportunity for level-marking.

5.6

What kind of work do we do?

About this unit

This unit present the four sectors of economic activity. In 'Your turn' pupils classify jobs into different sectors, complete a paragraph about the UK's employment structure, try to think up further examples of jobs in each sector, including for different locations, and finally answer questions about a graph of changing employment structure.

Key ideas

- Economic activity is any kind of work that people get paid for.
- It can be divided into four different types or sectors:
  primary – gathering materials from the Earth (including the oceans)
  secondary – making or building or processing things (usually in factories)
  tertiary – providing services for others (like teaching, cutting hair, driving taxis)
  quaternary – advanced research
- Most people in the UK earn their living by providing services.
- The employment structure of the UK has changed over time, and is still changing.

Key vocabulary

economic activity, primary, secondary, tertiary, quaternary, service, industry

Skills practised

- Literacy skills: giving a definition
- Numeracy skills: analysing a pie chart, reading a line graph
- Thinking skills: classifying jobs into different sectors; coming up with further examples of jobs for each sector, including in different locations; giving reasons

Unit outcomes

By the end of this unit, most pupils should be able to:

- explain the terms given in 'Key vocabulary' above
- give examples of jobs in the four employment sectors
- describe the structure of employment in the UK today
- describe how the employment structure has changed in the past, and is still changing

Resources

For starter **1** and plenaries **4** – **6**: all images from the book are on *geog.1 resources and planning OxBox CD-ROM*

Ideas for a starter

1. With books closed, display the photos from page 72 of the students' book on the whiteboard. Ask pupils to name the jobs the adults are doing. What do they think are the big differences between the four kinds of job? Without commenting on replies, write each job in a 4-column table, with no headings, one per column. Then slowly add further jobs to the columns, until someone spots what the pattern is. Write in the missing headings (primary, secondary, tertiary, quaternary) and talk them through.
2. Ask pupils to call out jobs. Write each in the correct place in a table with four unheaded columns as above. Then ask pupils to explain the difference between the columns.
3. How many people do you think work for a living in the UK? Guess. Do you think more work in farming than in factories? Do you think more work in factories than in shops and offices?
4. Questions **1** and **2** in 'Your turn'.

Ideas for plenaries

Plan plenaries for strategic points throughout the lesson, as well as at the end.

1. Are there any factories in your local area? What about farms? What about services?
2. Which sector do you think you'll work in, when you grow up?
3. Which sector do you think is the most important, for the country? Pupils can discuss this in pairs or small groups and give feedback to the class.
4. Look at the pie chart for employment structure, on page 72. (You could display it.) This is for the UK overall. Do you think one just for Devon would look different? In what way? What about one just for London? Or for *your* local area?
5. The UK has fewer people in farming, and fewer factories, than it had 50 years ago. Do you think this is a good thing or a bad thing? Pupils discuss this in pairs or small groups and give feedback to the class.
6. Look at the graph showing the changes in employment structure, on page 73. (You could display it.) Suppose the % of workers in the primary and secondary sector drops to zero. Would it matter? Explain.
7. Ask the second 'What if …' question from page 72 of the students' books.

Further class and homework activities

Suggestion 28 on page 103 of this book

Answers to 'Your turn'

1 Work you get paid for

2 a No. You don't get paid.
b Yes. You get paid.
c If you get paid.
d If you are lucky enough to get paid.

3 Primary: oil rig worker, miner, farmer
Secondary: house builder, factory worker
Quaternary: gene researcher, inventor
Tertiary: all the rest

4 The completed paragraph is:
In the UK most people earn a living by providing *services*.
The *tertiary* sector employs about three times as many people as the *secondary* sector, and about *forty* times as many as the *primary sector*.

5 Examples are: tour coach driver, tour guide, working in a tourist information centre, renting out cars, working in hotels, cafés, restaurants and gift shops in tourist areas, working in museums, stately homes and other tourist attractions, writing guide books.

6 a Below are some examples.
P = primary, S = secondary, T = tertiary; D = quaternary.

rural area: P farming; S builder; T vet, D software developer

sea: P fishing; S working on a floating fish-processing factory; T sailing instructor, cook on an oil rig; D researching bacteria at ocean vents, mapping sea floor using sound equipment

mountains: P forestry, quarrying; S a crofting activity such as weaving; T mountain guide, ski instructor; D researching climate change, researching earthquake risk

city: P bee-keeping; S factory worker,. builder; T policeman, actor, taxi driver etc; D medical research

c Students are likely to leave several blank cells, for good reasons. They are unlikely to know about floating fish factories, for example, or be able to think of a quaternary activity in a rural area.
The above lists have examples for each cell – but some are rare!

7 a the Industrial Revolution
b loss of manufacturing jobs to newly-industrialising countries. with lower wages (such as China)
c tertiary sector

5.7

High or low earnings?

About this unit

This unit gives a map showing how average weekly earnings vary across the UK. In 'Your turn' pupils analyse the map, and identify factors that help to make an area wealthy. After comparing photos of areas at different levels of prosperity, pupils draw flow charts to show how a new factory, and a tourist attraction, could help a poor area.

Key ideas

- In the UK average weekly earnings vary from region to region.
- There are many reasons for this. Many are to do with the natural advantages of a region (for example good farmland, oil offshore).
- The government tries to help poorer areas.

Key vocabulary

(none new)

Skills practised

- Geography skills: reading and analysing a choropleth map; drawing conclusions from photos
- Literacy skills: describing a pattern of earnings, using terms as instructed
- Numeracy skills: calculating and interpreting an 'average'
- Thinking skills: coming up with reasons; identifying factors; arranging information in a logical sequence to complete a flow chart; drawing a flow chart to show consequences

Unit outcomes

By the end of this unit, most pupils should be able to:

- answer simple questions about the information shown on a choropleth map
- point out the area of the UK with the highest average weekly earnings, and at least two areas in the lowest band
- give reasons to explain variations in earnings
- give at least four factors that could help make an area wealthy
- explain why a new factory or tourist attraction could help a poor area

Resources

For starter **1** and plenaries **2** and **3**: all images from the book are on *geog.1 resources and planning OxBox CD-ROM*

For starter **4**: images of wealthy and less wealthy areas from around the UK, on paper or in digital form

Ideas for a starter

1. Display the map from page 74 of the students' book on the whiteboard. What does it show? Ask pupils to make statements about it. What overall patterns can they see?
2. Do you think some parts of (the local area) are better off than others? How can you tell? Do you think some parts of the country are better off than others? Why do you think this is?
3. Divide the board into two halves headed *wealthy areas* and *less wealthy areas* and ask pupils to come up and fill in characteristics of each, to make a graffiti wall.
4. Show images of wealthy and less wealthy areas. Ask pupils to rate them on a scale of 1–5, where 1 is very poor and 5 is very wealthy. Discuss what clues they used.

Ideas for plenaries

Plan plenaries for strategic points throughout the lesson, as well as at the end.

1 Suppose your area has a factory that needs unskilled workers, and they pay £7 an hour for a 35-hour week. How much will a worker earn in a week?

Suppose your area has a computer company that pays its skilled staff £40 an hour for a 35-hour week. How much will a worker earn in a week?

So if the average weekly earnings in an area are high, what does that tell you about the kind of employment in the area? If they are low, what does that tell you? Pupils could discuss in pairs and give feedback to the class.

2 From the map, what are the average weekly earnings in your area? (You could display the map.) Does everyone in the area earn within that range? Is this figure high or low, compared with other areas? Why do you think that is?

3 Will the pattern of earnings shown on the map be the same 50 years from now? (You could display the map.) Give reasons.

4 Do you think earnings vary across other countries too?

5 Do you think earnings vary from country to country?

6 Give pupils a few minutes to think up one question each, related to this unit. Any questions that the class (or you) can't answer could be set for homework.

Further class and homework activities

Suggestions 29 and 30 on page 103 of this book

Answers to 'Your turn'

1 £440

2 a under £350 a week

b No. This is the average figure. Some people will earn a lot more than £350 a week,, depending on their jobs.

c over £475 a week

d A high average weekly earning indicates that an area has plenty of skilled jobs to offer, with good pay. A low average weekly earning indicates that most of the available jobs are poorly-paid.
A is in a predominantly rural area with little industry. It depends largely on farming and tourism, and the pay in both of these can be low (and tourism in rural areas tends to be seasonal).
B is in the Greater London area; London is the centre of government, finance, business, and the media, with many skilled and highly paid jobs. It is also a major tourist centre all year round.

3 a Overall, average earnings are highest in the south east of England.

b Areas in the south west and north east of England, in Wales, in the east of Scotland, and around the edges of Northen Ireland are in the lowest earnings band.

4 Include: good farmland, oil (or other valuable mineral), beautiful countryside (attracts tourists), interesting history, museums and other tourist attractions, flourishing industry, plenty of companies offering highly skilled and highly paid employment, easy access (having a port, airport, good road and rail links), being a centre of government.

5 a **Y** seems a lot poorer. The shuttered shops look permanently shut. (Their shop signs have gone and there's a 'For sale' or 'To let' sign.) The pavement looks dirty, and the buildings look badly cared for. In **X**, on the other hand, the houses look new and well cared for, and the boats indicate an affluent area.

b The closed shops. When people in the area were better off the shopkeepers were able to make a living.

c Local factories may have closed down. So people are unemployed, which means they have less money to spend in the shops. Low morale and lack of money means people don't look after an area.

6 The order should be:

1 A new factory opens. It employs local people and pays them well.
2 So the local people have more money to spend.
3 So they buy more clothes and shoes and other goods.
4 So the local shops make more money.
5 So the shops get better, and other services (like restaurants and sports centres) open.
6 So the area becomes more attractive to live and work in …
7 … so more companies think about moving there.

7 Students' flow charts can be similar to that in **6**. They could include some or all of these: a successful tourist attraction brings in visitors; this encourages restaurants, cafes and tourist shops to open, as well as places offering tourist accommodation; it also encourages people to look after the area, to attract more tourists; the rise in tourism creates jobs for local people; so they have more money to spend; so the regular shops and services in the area improve; so other companies are attracted to the area, bringing further employment.

5.8

The UK in the world

About this unit

This unit is about the UK's links with other countries. Its memberships of the EU and the Commonwealth are shown on a world map. Other kinds of links are briefly reviewed. In 'Your turn' pupils explore some of the links, and then the idea of interdependence.

Key ideas

- The UK has many links with other countries.
- Some are political. For example it belongs to the Commonwealth of countries and the European Union.
- There are many other kinds of links too, including links through trade and tourism.
- The UK depends on other countries, and they depend on it. Countries are interdependent.

Key vocabulary

the Commonwealth of countries, the European Union (EU), the euro, trade, transnational corporations (TNCs), aid, treaties, interdependence

Skills practised in 'Your turn'

- Geography skills: comparing maps to identify and name countries
- Literacy skills: writing a paragraph about the UK's interdependence in the world
- Thinking skills: coming up with reasons and consequences; assessing relative importance; presenting evidence of interdependence

Unit outcomes

By the end of this unit, most pupils should be able to:

- explain what the Commonwealth of countries is, and name at least five members
- explain what the European Union is, and name at least five members
- give examples of the UK's links with other countries
- explain what interdependence means
- recognize that the UK and other countries are interdependent

Resources

For starters **1** and **2** and plenaries **1** – **3**: all images from the book are on *geog.1 resources and planning OxBox CD-ROM*

Ideas for a starter

1 Who in this class is an EU citizen? Hands up. Who belongs to the Commonwealth? Hands up. Who don't know? Hands up. (There will probably be a good many 'Don't knows' for one or other). Then move onto (or display) the map on page 76 of the students' book. You can ask the questions again for plenary **1**.

2 Display the map from page 76 on the whiteboard. Ask what it shows. Then ask pupils to give you at least six facts they have deduced from the map, including two about the UK.

3 Write a large heading on the board: the UK's links with other countries. Then ask pupils to come up and write in examples, to create a graffiti wall. (You could start them off with one or two, for example *We buy food from other countries* and *Our football teams play matches against teams from other countries*.)

Ideas for plenaries

Plan plenaries for strategic points throughout the lesson, as well as at the end.

1 Ask the questions from starter **1**. (You could display the map.)

2 Do question **4** in 'Your turn' as a plenary.

3 Do this before question **5** in 'Your turn'. Do a drawing like this one on the board. Then ask pupils to explain what interdependence means, and to give you examples of how the UK and other countries are interdependent.

4 Ask a few pupils to read out their answers for question **5** of 'Your turn'.

5 Each of these words shows a way the UK is linked to other countries. Unscramble!

1 LICTOPILA 2 AERDT 3 DAI 4 AEIETTSR
5 RTULECU 6 NAUGGELA 7 NCT 8 MRSTIOU

6 Ask the 'What if … ' question from the top of page 76 of the students' book.

Further class and homework activities

Interactive quiz for Chapter 5 on *geog.1 resources and planning OxBox CD-ROM*

Suggestions 31 – 33 on page 103 of this book

Assessment materials for Chapter 5 on *geog.1 assessment file & OxBox CD-ROM*

Review 'Your goals for this chapter' on page 61 of *geog.1* students' book

Answers to 'Your turn'

1 It is a group of 53 countries, including the UK, that have historical and some economic and social ties. 51 of them are ex-colonies of Britain. The 53rd country, Mozambique, is an exception. (It was a Portuguese colony. It was admitted to the Commonwealth in 1995, at the request of its Commonwealth neighbours.)

2 b This shows the complete list, divided into continents. Many of these countries are too small to show up on the map on page 76 but pupils may be interested in discussing them:

Commonwealth countries …

… in Africa
Botswana
Cameroon
Gambia
Ghana
Kenya
Lesotho
Malawi
Mauritius
Mozambique
Namibia
Nigeria
Seychelles
Sierra Leone
South Africa
Swaziland
Tanzania
Uganda
Zambia

… in South America
Guyana

… in North America (including Caribbean)
Antigua and Baruda
Bahamas
Barbados
Belize
Canada
Dominica
Grenada
Jamaica
St Kitts and Nevis
St Lucia
St Vincent and the Grenadines
Trinidad and Tobago

… in Europe
Cyprus
Malta
UK

… in Asia
Bangladesh
Brunei
India
Malaysia
Maldives
Pakistan
Sri Lanka

… in Oceania
Australia
Fiji
Kiribati
Nauru
New Zealand
Papua New Guinea
Samoa
Solomon Islands
Tonga
Tuvalu
Vanuatu

c Most are ex-colonies of Britain

2 a Any six from these:

Austria	Germany	Netherlands
Belgium	Greece	Poland
Bulgaria	Hungary	Portugal
Cyprus	Ireland	Romania
Czech Republic	Italy	Slovakia
Denmark	Latvia	Slovenia
Estonia	Lithuania	Spain
Finland	Luxembourg	Sweden
France	Malta	United Kingdom

b i Anyone with a passport of any EU country is an EU citizen

ii More flexibility about where to live and work; travelling a little easier; if they ran a business, it would give them access to a large market for their goods / services.

3 Students should be able to answere *yes* to both questions, with reasons drawn from the unit. **4** Answers will vary. **5** Make sure pupils undertand *interdependence* before they start writing.

5 Further suggestions for class and homework

Most of these suggestions are addressed to your pupils. Where research or further resources are needed, the internet will almost certainly provide the answer. (Eg *google* and choose *Web* or *Images*.)

It's the British Isles!

1 Tell me what you know Students do a spider map to summarise what they know about the physical and human geography of the British Isles already. First work with them to set up a frame for the spider map. For example:

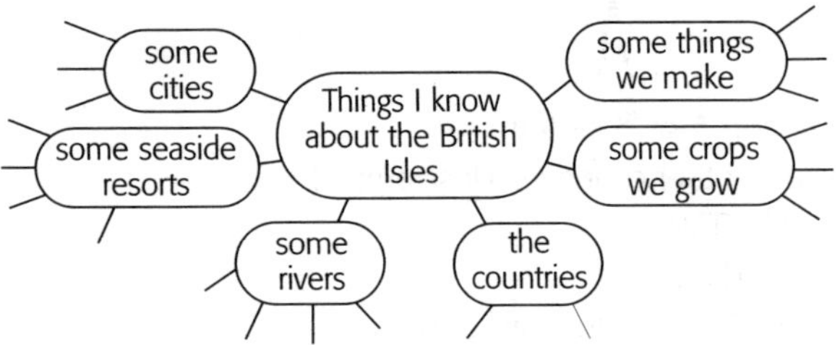

The spider map can be varied in content and extent to suit the class. They can add to it as their work on the UK progresses */**/***

Your island home

2 Once upon a time Tell the story of Britain's travels over the last 250 million years, as a long strip cartoon for the classroom wall! This would be a challenging group project. The aim is to get pupils excited about the story.
You'll need to give pupils guidance about where to do their research, and perhaps provide some simplified material. A good starting point would be a timeline showing where Britain was at different times relative to the Equator (guesswork!), when the dinosaurs appeared, when humans first appeared, when the British Isles split from the rest of Europe, and so on. The strip cartoon could have maps of the breakup of Pangaea interspersed with other drawings. Each cell could have say 40 words of text under it. **/***

3 Write a blurb You have been asked to write a blurb for a new book, or a magazine ad for a new film, telling the story of how the British Isles evolved to be where they are, and look as they do. Make it sound really exciting – in not more than 100 words. Choose an image to go with it. **/***

4 Photo sketch Find a postcard of a place in the British Isles, showing a landscape. Draw an annotated sketch from it. *

5 Contrasting landscapes Create a wall display: a map of the British Isles surrounded by postcards and pictures from magazines, travel brochures and other sources, showing contrasting landscapes. A leader line connects each image to the corresponding place on the map. *

It's a jigsaw!

6 Your mental map Ask pupils to draw a mental map of the British Isles, and mark in any borders they know about, and label the seas – with no peeking at books or wall maps. (Remind them of their work on mental maps in Unit 2.3.) This should produce some interesting results.
Agree a mark scheme. Students then use the map on page 139 of *geog.1* students' book, or an atlas or wall map, to score themselves.
Ask pupils to keep their maps. You can ask them to draw another one at the end of the topic, and see whether they have improved – see suggestion 3 below. */**/***

7 Polishing your mental map Set pupils the challenge of polishing their mental map of the British Isles. You could start with the outline and the seas. Explain what the goal is – that by the end of the topic they should be able to draw a *recognisable* map of the British Isles from memory, and that there will be prizes for the best, and for the most improved. (You can add bits to the mental map as the topic progresses.) For pupils with less skill in drawing maps, work out a short cut so that they can produce a simplified shape that still looks recognisable. */**/***

8 Know your region On an A4 outline map of the British Isles mark in the countries and nations, and then just your administrative region (eg South West), and the counties / unitary authorities within the region. Mark a dot to show roughly where you live. (Add this to the mental map.) *

9 Flags of the British Isles On an outline map of the British Isles, mark in the countries and nations of the British Isles, and their flags. *

10 Who's in charge? On an A4 outline map of the British Isles, mark in the countries and nations of the British Isles. Then mark in the capital cities of each country and region. Say whether they have National Assemblies or parliaments, and mark which one is the main parliament in the UK. (This could be combined with **9** above.) *

11 Count the shires Find out how many counties in England (or the UK) end in *-shire*. Mark them on an outline map. *

12 A bloody battle The border lines on the map of the British Isles are the outcome of many struggles. Find out about one big battle between any two nations, and say what the battle was about, and describe it as if you were there. Your history teacher might help you choose a battle. **

What's our weather like?

13 Weather map Cut out a weather map from a newspaper. Mark and name a place on it (not the place where you live). Write a weather report for that place, based on the map. *

14 Make your own weather symbols Write a list of words to describe the weather: hot, windy, frosty and so on.
Make up a symbol for each word. Use your symbols to draw a weather report for the weather in your area, for each day this week. (Or one day a week, for the whole term.) *

15 Weather calendar Draw a circle about 20 cm diameter on a sheet of paper. Divide it into 12 equal slices, like a cake. Label the slices with the names of the months, in order. In each slice, draw symbols to show what you think the weather is usually like that month. Add a key for the symbols. *

16 How good is the weather forecast ? Draw up a table like this:

Date	Weather forecast for tomorrow	Actual weather	Weather forecast score (out of 10)

Watch a TV weather report this evening. In your table, note what it says for your area. (You can use symbols.)
Tomorrow, note how the weather actually turned out, and give the weather forecast people a score out of 5.
(0 = they got it all wrong, 5 = they got it exactly right.)
Do this every day for a week. Work out the average score.
Note: this can be a class project. Pupils take turns to watch the weather forecast. **

Who are we?

17 Cultural contributions Does your area have a Chinese restaurant? A mosque? A stall that sells West Indian foods? A pizza place? Make a list of all the local features that show the influence of other cultures. See if you can group them under suitable headings. (For example one heading could be 'Places of worship'.) The local yellow pages will help. **

18 Research a group of in-migrants Choose one group of in-migrants for the 20th century. Find out where they came from, when, why, where they settled, and how they have contributed to life and culture in the UK. Write a report. You can illustrate it with pictures and maps. **

19 Research the invaders Choose a group of invaders (for example the Romans) and research them as in **18**. **

Where do we live?

20 Paper search List all the UK places mentioned in the 'home news' or sport section of a daily newspaper. Mark them on an outline map of the UK. **

21 Top ten cities Tell pupils it's time to add some cities to their mental map of the UK. Give out blank outline maps of Great Britain or the British Isles. Students mark in and label the ten largest cities, plus their own settlement if it's not one of the ten. They then familiarise themselves with the locations of these places. (For example by covering up labels and testing themselves or getting someone else to test them.) Test pupils and give prizes, or let pupils test each other. **

22 Place quiz Choose a city (or river or island or upland area) in the UK. Without naming it, write down 5 facts about it, to tell the rest of the class. The class has to identify it.
(This could be a game. Pupils take turns to present their facts. Award 1 point to the pupil who identifies a place first, and 1 to any pupil whose place is not identified. At the end of each turn, the 'winner' marks the place on a large outline map of the UK.) **

23 Make a place profiler Ask pupils to come up with a list of opposites to describe places – dull / interesting, ugly / attractive, quiet / noisy and so on. Using the most suitable pairs of words, they then draw up a set of scale lines, one below the other, to make a place profiler. This shows one:

ugly •——•——•——•——• attractive

To 'score' a place, pupils mark an X at their chosen point on each scale. Joining all the Xs gives the place profile.
This can be used for a local place, or for any images of places around the UK that the class has collected. Use a different colour for each place, and compare profiles. *

24 Population pyramid Give out three population pyramids for the UK (from the internet) over the last 200 years, or show a set from an atlas. Then ask some questions about them (or pupils make up questions for each other). **

25 Could it all be to do with coal? Students compare a map of the coal areas (from an atlas or the internet) with the population map on page 70 of *geog.1* students' book. They try to explain any correlation they notice. **/***

26 Is there a link with rainfall? Compare the population map on page 70 of *geog.1* students' book with the rainfall map on page 67. Notice anything? Explain! **

27 Population growth Give pupils these population statistics for the British Isles. The population figures are in millions.

Year	Pop	Year	Pop	Year	Pop	Year	Pop
1570	4.2	1600	4.8	1630	5.6	1670	5.9
1700	6.0	1750	6.5	1801	16.3	1811	18.5
1821	21.0	1831	24.1	1841	26.9	1851	27.5
1861	29.1	1871	31.6	1881	35.0	1891	37.8
1901	41.6	1911	45.4	1921	47.1	1931	49.0
1941	?	1951	53.3	1961	55.6	1971	58.9
1981	59.8	1991	61.3	2001	62.9		

(The figures up till 1801, the year of the first official census, are estimates.) Students draw a line graph, and comment. **

What kind of work do we do?

28 Soapy work? List all the characters in your favourite soaps, films or books who have jobs. Group their jobs into primary, secondary, tertiary and quaternary activities. *

Richer? Poorer?

29 Magic wand? Think of an area you consider poor. You are in charge. You plan to make it wealthier. What will you do? **

30 My Britain Write a report on your local area with headings like these: Where is it? Who lives here? What's the weather like? What kinds of jobs do people do here? and so on. ***

The UK in the world

31 The Commonwealth Games? Find out about them and design some exciting web pages about them. */**

32 Adopt an EU country Choose one EU country (not the UK) and find out at least six things about it. Tell the class. (Don't neglect the less well-known EU countries.) */**

33 Adopt a Commonwealth country Do as above, but this time for a Commonwealth country.) */**

6 Rivers

Helping you deliver the KS3 Programme of Study

This chapter addresses these areas of the Programme of Study:

Key concepts

Physical and human processes Explain how physical and human processes shape places, landscapes and societies. **Environmental interaction** Understanding that the physical and human dimensions of the environment are interrelated and together influence environmental change.

Key processes

Geographical enquiry Ask geographical questions; display information; analyse and evaluate evidence, presenting findings to draw and justify conclusions. **Graphicacy and visual literacy** Use maps at a range of scales, and photographs. **Geographical communication** Communicate knowledge and understanding using geographical vocabulary and conventions in both talk and writing.

The big picture

These are the key ideas behind this chapter.

- A river is rainwater flowing to the sea; it completes the water cycle.
- Rivers shape the land they flow over, by eroding, transporting, and depositing material.
- The result is the characteristic landforms found along the river.
- We use, and abuse, rivers, as they flow on their way to the sea.

A pupils' version of this big picture is given in the *geog.1* students' book opener for Chapter 6, and in *geog.1 resources and planning OxBox CD-ROM*, for the whiteboard.

The chapter outline

Use this, and their chapter opener, to give pupils a roadmap for the chapter.

6 **Rivers** As the pupils' chapter opener, this unit is an important part of the chapter; see page 11 for notes about using chapter openers

6.1 **The water cycle** How water circulates continually between the ocean, the atmosphere, and the land; and a closer look at how the rainwater reaches a river

6.2 **A river on its journey** The journey of a river from source to sea, and the River Coquet as an example

6.3 **Rivers at work** How rivers erode, transport and deposit material on their journey to the sea

6.4 **Landforms created by the river** How V-shaped valleys, waterfalls, meanders and oxbow lakes are formed

6.5 **Rivers and us** How we use rivers – and abuse them – on their journey to the sea

Objectives and outcomes for this chapter

Objectives	Unit	Outcomes
Most pupils will understand:		Most pupils will be able to:
• what the water cycle is, and that rivers are part of the water cycle	6.1	• draw a simple diagram representing the water cycle
• how rainfall reaches a river, during the water cycle	6.1	• draw a diagram to show how rainwater reaches and feeds a river
• that rivers have different parts and features, and each has a special name	6.2	• name, define and identify the different parts and features of a river (source, drainage basin, tributary, channel, bed, banks and so on)
• that rivers shape the land by erosion, transport and deposition of material	6.3	• describe how erosion, transport and deposition take place
• that these processes produce characteristic landforms along a river	6.4	• recognise a V-shaped valley, a waterfall, a meander and an oxbow lake, and explain how each was formed
• that we make a great deal of use of rivers, and also harm the living things in them, as they go on their journey to the sea	6.5	• give five ways in which we use rivers, and three ways in which we harm fish and other river life

These tie in with 'Your goals for this chapter' in the pupils' chapter opener, and with the opening lines in each unit, which give the purpose of the unit in a pupil-friendly style.

Opportunities for assessment

See the formal assessment materials for this chapter on *geog.1 assessment file & OxBox CD-ROM*. They include a level-marked assessment with success criteria and a feedback form, interactive assessments, a scored test, and a self-assessment form.

There are other opportunities for assessment too. For example, you could use some of the more extended 'Your turn' questions in the students' book, worksheets or longer learning activities from *geog.1 resources and planning OxBox CD-ROM*, or some of the 'Further suggestions for class and homework' at the end of this chapter.

Getting ready for this chapter

Some of the starters and plenaries suggested for this chapter may need resources prepared in advance. Check out the *Resources* section on the 'Help at a glance' pages that follow.

geog.1 resources & planning OxBox CD-ROM has all the photos and diagrams from the chapter, for whiteboard display, plus movies and interactive materials. You will find these very useful for devising your own starters and plenaries. In addition, *geog.world CD-ROM* is a rich source of further material, including interactive webfiles and skills lessons.

About the chapter starter

The photo on page 78 in *geog.1* students' book shows whitewater rafting on Sixmile Creek, in the Kinai Peninsula, Alaska, USA. The foam is a sign of rocky outcrops and ledges in the river bed – which means rock that's resistant to erosion. You can do whitewater rafting at several locations in the UK (most of them in Scotland).

6.1

The water cycle

About this unit

This unit presents the water cycle, and then focuses on the part that is most relevant to this chapter: how rainwater feeds the river.

Key ideas

- Water circulates continuously between the ocean, the atmosphere and the land. This circulation is called the water cycle.
- The water cycle has four stages:
  evaporation of water from the ocean to the air as water vapour
  condensation of the water vapour to form clouds
  precipitation (rain falling) from the clouds to the land
  flow of rainwater over and through the land to rivers, and hence back to the ocean.
- This is how rainwater reaches and feeds a river:
  - some runs over the ground to the river, as surface runoff
  - some infiltrates (soaks down into) the soil
  - some of this then flows sideways through the soil to the river, as throughflow
  - the rest trickles down to fill up cracks in the rock below, as groundwater
  - the groundwater flows slowly to the river, feeding it.

Key vocabulary

evaporation, condensation, precipitation, water cycle, infiltration, surface runoff, permeable, groundwater, impermeable, throughflow, groundwater flow

Skills practised in 'Your turn'

- Geography skills: copying and completing diagrams
- Literacy skills: finding the terms that match definitions; writing a dramatic radio report
- Thinking skills: coming up with explanations

Unit outcomes

By the end of this unit, most pupils should be able to:

- define the terms given in 'Key vocabulary' above
- explain what the water cycle is and draw a simple diagram to represent it
- draw a diagram to show how rainwater reaches and feeds a river

Resources

For starter **1**: a set of images of rivers of all sizes, from the Amazon to streams, on paper or in digital form
For starter **4** and plenaries **1**, **3** and **4**: a set of images of rivers of all sizes, from the Amazon to streams, on paper or in digital form
For plenary **6**: a pair of True/False cards, like referee cards, for each student (green for true, red for false)

Ideas for a starter

1. Show images of a range of rivers, from the Amazon to small local rivers. What do they all have in common? Where does the water come from? Where does it go to?
2. It rained today (or yesterday or ...). Where did the water come from? How did it get there? Where did it go to? Build up the water cycle on the board.
3. We're going to do the water cycle today. What do you know about the water cycle already?
4. Display the image from page 80 of the students' book. Ask them to explain to you what it shows. Keep saying 'Tell me more' until they've told you the full story.

Ideas for plenaries

Plan plenaries for strategic points throughout the lesson, as well as at the end.

1 Could we stop the water cycle? (You could display the drawing from page 80.)

2 Give me an explanation:
- Sea water is salty. Why isn't rain salty?
- There are no rivers in the Sahara desert.
- There are no rivers in Antarctica.

3 Which stages of the water cycle affect humans? (You could display the drawing from page 80 as an aid.) Which stages do we make use of? How? Pupils could work in pairs to create a spider map. (Note that Unit 6.5 is about how we use rivers.)

4 Look at (or display) the photo at the bottom of page 80 of *geog.1* students' book. Where do we get our tap water from? Does it go back to the water cycle? Pupils could discuss this in pairs and give their ideas to the rest of the class.

5 Write the term *Water cycle* down the side of your page. Now make an acrostic (where each letter of *Water cycle* starts a statement or word) about the water cycle. Some pupils will enjoy the challenge of writing statements.

6 Call out a set of 15 statements about what has been covered in the lesson, some true and some false. Pupils have to raise green or red cards, or shout *True* or *False*. Or ask pupils to make up one true or false statement each, and call them out in turn, and the rest of the class responds.

7 Write a paragraph on the board, with gaps in it, summarising what has been learned. Pupils have to fill in the gaps.

Further class and homework activities

Interactive activity for Unit 6.1 on *geog.1 resources and planning OxBox CD-ROM*

Worksheet 6A on *geog.1 resources and planning OxBox CD-ROM*

Suggestions 1 – 9 on page 116 of this book

Answers to 'Your turn'

1

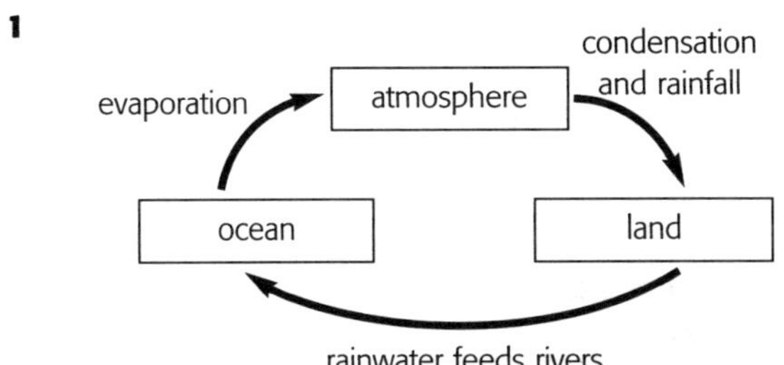

2 A = permeable, B = groundwater, C = water vapour, D = infiltration, E = precipitation, F = evaporation, G = condensation, H = impermeable

3 The missing labels are: 1 surface runoff, 2 throughflow, 3 groundwater flow

4 a It reaches impermeable rock at some point .

b It continues to be fed by groundwater. (But if the dry weather continues the groundwater level will fall.)

c There is no rain to replace the water flowing back to the ocean or sea. Without rain, the groundwater level will fall. So the river level will fall too.

d In very wet weather, groundwater levels, throughflow, and suface run-off all increase, feeding the river. Once the soil is saturated run-off takes over – and it is fast, so the river fills up very quickly.

5 Pupils could mention these and more: crops fail so people starve; vegetation everywhere dries up and withers; all the world's rivers eventually go dry; this means no water supply for our homes or factories; no water to drink or wash in or cook with; no steam to make electricity. We'd have to find a way to use sea water.

6.2 A river on its journey

About this unit

This unit presents a drawing of a river, with the parts and features named and labelled. It also shows the river's long profile. In 'Your turn' pupils apply what they learned from the drawings to answer questions about the River Coquet.

Key ideas

- Rivers have different parts and features, and each has a special name. See 'Key vocabulary' below.
- A cross-section along the length of a river is called its long profile. The long profile curves downwards like the side of a saucer, as the river flows down towards sea level.

Key vocabulary

source, mouth, watershed, drainage basin, confluence, tributary, flood plain, channel, river bed, river bank, long profile

Skills practised in 'Your turn'

- Geography skills: answering questions using the information given on a map; measuring length on a map; comparing a photo and a map, to answer questions
- Numeracy skills: working out the area by counting squares
- Thinking skills: coming up with reasons; using a spider map to list ways we use rivers

Unit outcomes

By the end of this unit, most pupils should be able to:

- define, name and identify the parts and features of a river given in 'Key vocabulary' above
- count squares to find area

Resources

For starter **2**: *A river's journey* movie on *geog.1 resources and planning OxBox CD-ROM*
For plenary **3**: a class set of maps (preferably in colour) showing a local river and its drainage basin; the Environment Agency may be able to supply a map to photocopy

Ideas for a starter

1 How many rivers can you name? As pupils call them out, write them on the board. Ask which are in the UK, and underline these. Then ask what all the rivers might have in common (apart from water). Starting on high land and flowing downhill are two charactertistics they share. (There are others.)

2 Show the movie *A river's journey*. This features the River Dart from source to mouth. Ask questions about the river and how it changes along its course.

3 Turn to the map of the British Isles on page 139 of *geog.1* students' book. Work out where each river below has its source, and where it flows to. Join it to the answers with wavy lines.

Rises in …	**River**	**Flows to …**
Pennines	Spey	English Channel
Grampians	Thames	Bristol Channel
Cotswolds	Severn	The Humber
Exmoor	Liffey	North Sea
Cambrians	Exe	Irish Sea
Wicklow Mountains	Trent	North Sea

Ideas for plenaries

Plan plenaries for strategic points throughout the lesson, as well as at the end.

1 Find the River Coquet on the map on page 139 of *geog.1* students' book. Where in the UK is it? Also find it on the OS map on page 31 of the students' book, and look at the photo of it, at Warkworth, on page 22.

2 Why are rivers all different lengths? Why are they all different shapes?

3 Give out maps showing a local river and its drainage basin. Pupils identify the source, tributaries, settlements along the river, and so on. They could work out the length of the river and estimate the area of the drainage basin. This could lead to a piece of writing describing the local river. (See suggestion 10 on page 116 of this book.)

4 Write *source, confluence, mouth, tributary, drainage basin, flood plain* on the board. Pupils have four minutes to study the drawing on page 82 of the students' book. Then they close the books, and draw a sketch map of an imaginary river with two tributaries, and label it using all the labels from the board. Pupils check each other's drawings.

5 Look at these strange words. Each is the combination of *two* parts of a river. Find each word and then explain what each one means:
a) SMOOUURTCHE (source mouth)
b) TWRAITBEURTSAHREYD (watershed tributary)

6 Show *A river's journey* movie from *geog.1 resources and planning OxBox CD-ROM,* if you did not use it as a starter.

Further class and homework activities

Interactive activity for Unit 6.2 on *geog.1 resources and planning OxBox CD-ROM*

Worksheets 6B, 6C and 6D on *geog.1 resources and planning OxBox CD-ROM*

Suggestions 10 – 21 on page 116 of this book

The Nile in *geog.1*, *Rivers* on *geog.world CD-ROM*

Answers to 'Your turn'

1 a Barrowburn
b ten (and two of these have their own tributaries)
c Shillmoor
d the North Sea
e i the field at A **ii** the field at C

2 a A drainage basin is the area of land from which rainwater drains into a river.
b i There are 80 squares either full or at least half full.
ii 720 square kilometres

3 80 km

4 a is correct. The long profile is usually steeper near the source. It flattens out near the mouth of the river.

5 It won't end up in the River Coquet since D is outside the Coquet's drainage basin. It will end up in some other river, not shown on the map, that includes D in its drainage basin.

6 a out towards the sea – so eastwards **b** Amble
c It is on the east coast, so it was easy to reach by boat from southern England or the continent; it is also near Scotland, where the Romans fought the Picts – so perhaps they used it as a place to bring in soldiers and army supplies.
d i A sheltered harbour has been built, which suggests a fishing history. In fact Amble is home to a fishing fleet.
ii The photo shows a marina, and sandy beaches. People on holiday also like to go fishing and windsurfing, and take boat trips, and Amble may offer these activities. (The OS map on page 31 of the students' book shows the marina, and a point for boat trips.)

7 Pupils could include these and more: walk on the beach, walk back along the river, swim, sail, sunbathe, row on the river, take a fishing trip, watch the fishermen landing catches, fly a kite, explore rockpools, explore Amble, eat (fish and chips?).

6.3

Rivers at work

About this unit

This unit is about the work of the river in eroding, transporting and depositing material. In 'Your turn' pupils use what they have learned to analyse photos.

Key ideas

- A river continually shapes and smooths its bed and banks by eroding, transporting and depositing material. So the river bed and banks are always changing.
- Erosion is where the river picks up material. Erosion is the result of a combination of processes: abrasion, attrition, hydraulic action, and solution. The faster it flows, and the more water it has, the faster the river can erode.
- Transport is where the river carries material away. Soluble material is transported in solution, the smaller particles as a suspension, and the rest bounces and rolls along the river bed. The faster it flows, and the more water it has, the more material the river can transport.
- As the river moves onto flatter land it loses energy, so it drops or deposits its load. It drops the heaviest material first.

Key vocabulary

erode, deposit, transport, abrasion, attrition, hydraulic action, solution, suspension, load, bedload, sediment

Skills practised in 'Your turn'

- Geography skills: analysing photos and drawing conclusions
- Literacy skills: matching words and definitions
- Thinking skills: coming up with reasons and explanations

Unit outcomes

By the end of this unit, most pupils should be able to:

- explain the terms given in 'Key vocabulary' above
- describe how erosion, transport and deposition take place
- recognise that erosion will predominate in the upper stretch of a river, and wherever it is flowing fast; and deposition predominates when it slows down
- recognise signs of fast flow, and deposition, from photos

Resources

For starter **1** and plenary **3**: all images from the book are on *geog.1 resources and planning OxBox CD-ROM*

For starter **2**: a photo of a mature river in a rural area, on paper or in digital form

For plenary **1**: a lump of rock, two smaller rough stones and two smooth pebbles (roughly egg-sized), a small bowl of water, a plastic cup, a sachet of coffee or sugar

For plenary **2**: a glass tank or glass baking dish or similar (preferably at least 30 cms long), enough water to fill it two-thirds full, some small stones and a couple of medium ones, a largish beaker of soil, a little sugar, and a spatula to get the water moving

Ideas for a starter

1. Use the map of the River Coquet, on page 75 of *geog.1* students' book, to set up a mystery. (You could display the map.) Say: Early this morning a fish in the North Sea swallowed a tiny fragment of Fred Smith's field. The field is at point A near Barrowburn, around 75 km away. Can anyone explain how this happened?
2. Show an image of a river. Do you think this river has always looked like this? Will it always look like this in future? Is it having any effect on the land it flows over?

Ideas for plenaries

Plan plenaries for strategic points throughout the lesson, as well as at the end.

1. Provide the resources listed on the opposite page for plenary **1**. Ask a pair of pupils to use these resources to demonstrate the roles of abrasion, attrition and solution in erosion. Other pupils ask them questions about these processes, related to rivers.

   Then ask pupils to think up a way to demonstrate hydraulic action (not necessarily in the classroom). For example directing a hose onto a bank of earth?
2. Provide the resources listed on the opposite page for plenary **2**. Ask a pair of pupils to use these resources to demonstrate load, bedload, suspension and solution, in the transport of material by rivers. Other pupils ask them questions about them, related to rivers.

   Then ask pupils to suggest a way to use the same materials to demonstrate deposition, and how heavier material is deposited first.
3. Look at page 78 in *geog.1* students' book. (You could display the photo.) What river process are these people enjoying? Why is the water white? (Rough rock below.) What does that tell you about that rock? (Resistant to erosion.)
4. Make up one question on any of the ideas or key words you learned in this lesson. Your teacher will nominate a person (X) for the hot seat. X then nominates three people in turn, to ask him/her a question. If X makes a mistake another pupil takes the hot seat.

Further class and homework activities

Interactive activity for Unit 6.3 on *geog.1 resources and planning OxBox CD-ROM*

Investigating a river on *geog.1 resources and planning OxBox CD-ROM*

Suggestions 22 – 25 on page 117 of this book

Answers to 'Your turn'

1 material is picked up – erosion
material is carried away – transport
material is dropped – deposition

2 a Erosion. The river seems to be in flood, with a lot of energy – and the more energy it has the faster it can erode. It is also transporting the material it erodes. There will be little or no deposition.

b i The fast-flowing water is pounding the banks and helping to break them up by hydraulic action. The water is dissolving any soluble material in the banks; this is called solution.

ii While they are being carried and bounced and rolled along, stones of all sizes are scraping material from the bed and banks. This is called abrasion. Stones are also banging into other stones and knocking bits off them, and wearing them away. This is called attrition.

3 a Depositing material

b It must be flowing slowly since it does not have enough energy to transport this material any further.

c Yes. Look at the flat land around the river. It is obvious that this will get flooded if the water level in the river rises much. There is also plenty of evidence of deposition, which takes place largely on flood plains, and where the river enters the sea.

4 When the river is in flood it is full of water and flowing very fast; so it has enough energy to pick up large heavy objects and carry them away.

5 a The river in the photo looks as if it's in flood, after the heavy rain. At the end of a very dry summer the water level will have dropped and the river will not be flowing nearly so fast, since it has been starved of rainwater. So you won't get all this white foam.

b Erosion will slow down, since the river is slower and has less water. If the water level falls really low, the river will deposit more and more material.

6.4

Landforms created by the river

About this unit

This unit explains how four landforms – V-shaped valley, waterfall, meander and oxbow lake – are formed. 'Your turn' helps to confirm what the pupils have learned.

Key ideas

- Rivers create distinctive landforms when they erode and deposit material – for example V-shaped valleys, waterfalls, meanders and oxbow lakes.
- A waterfall develops when a river flows over a layer of hard resistant rock with softer rock below.
- As a waterfall retreats a gorge will form. (But note that gorges are formed in other ways too – for example by fast downward erosion through soft rock.)
- A meander starts as a slight bend in the river. The bend develops further because the water has to flow faster round the outer curve, which then erodes faster. Material gets deposited along the inner curve where the water flows more slowly.
- A meander may get cut off and become an oxbow lake.

Key vocabulary

landform, V-shaped valley, downward erosion, waterfall, plunge pool, gorge, meander, oxbow lake

Skills practised in 'Your turn'

- Geography skills: drawing diagrams to show how a waterfall and a gorge develop; drawing a sketch of a river with a photo as stimulus
- Literacy skills: using the glossary
- Thinking skills: linking a landform to erosion, deposition or both

Unit outcomes

By the end of this unit, most pupils should be able to:

- define the terms given in 'Key vocabulary' above
- recognise a V-shaped valley, a waterfall, a meander and an oxbow lake, and explain how each was formed

Resources

For starter **1** and plenaries **3** and **4**: see *geog.1 resources and planning OxBox CD-ROM*
You can add other photos on paper or digital form, for example from *google images.*

For starter **2** and plenaries **1** and **2**: different samples of rock, from hard to soft.
The science department may be able to provide these. For example:

granite limestone sandstone chalk shale
→ getting softer

Ideas for a starter

1 With books shut, show the images of the waterfall, V-shaped valley and meanders from Unit 6.4 on the whiteboard (and any other images of river landforms you can). See if the class can name them. Ask for suggestions about how they were formed.

2 Show different samples of rock, named, and labelled from hard to soft. They are all rocks found in Britain. Do you think they will all be eroded equally easily? Might some be more resistant to erosion? Which might be the most resistant?

Lead on to the idea that erosion may be slower in some places, faster in others. This will affect how the river shapes the landscape. It can lead to different valley shapes, for example, and landforms such as waterfalls.

Ideas for plenaries

Plan plenaries for strategic points throughout the lesson, as well as at the end.

1. Ask a pupil to draw on the board how a V-shaped valley starts and gets wider. Then show a pair of rock samples, one hard and the other soft (eg granite and shale). In which rock do you think the V will widen faster? (Shale.)
2. Provide a pupil with labelled samples of hard and soft rock (eg granite and shale). The pupil has to demonstrate how a waterfall forms.
3. What's the landform in which Warkworth is built? (See the students' book pages 22 and 31, or display these images on the whiteboard.) Why was this settlement started here? Could it have been a bad idea?
4. Give /show pupils photos of river landforms. (You could display them.) They have five minutes to sketch one, with labels and annotations. Pupils swap, and check each other's sketches.
5. With books closed, copy down the statements and correct them where necessary.
   a) Oxbow lakes are found in mountains.
   b) Waterfalls develop where there is soft rock above hard rock.
   c) Downward erosion in a river valley creates a U shape.
   d) The correct name for a bend in a river is 'loop'.
   e) Rain and magnetism carry stones and soil down the sides of a river valley.
   f) As waterfalls erode the rock, gorges advance towards the river's mouth.
   g) Deposition occurs on the outside of a meander, where water flows more quickly.
   h) One day the oxbow lake will join up to the river again.

Further class and homework activities

Interactive activity for Unit 6.4 on *geog.1 resources and planning OxBox CD-ROM*

Worksheet 6E on *geog.1 resources and planning OxBox CD-ROM*

Suggestions 26 – 37 on page 117 of this book

Planning meanders on *geog.1 resources and planning OxBox CD-ROM*

Answers to 'Your turn'

1

Landform	Created by ...
V-shaped valley	erosion
waterfall	erosion
gorge	erosion
meander	erosion + deposition
oxbow lake	deposition

2 a narrow valley with very steep sides

3 a the soft rock

b Pupils should start with the drawing in the students' book. Subsequent drawings could look something like this:

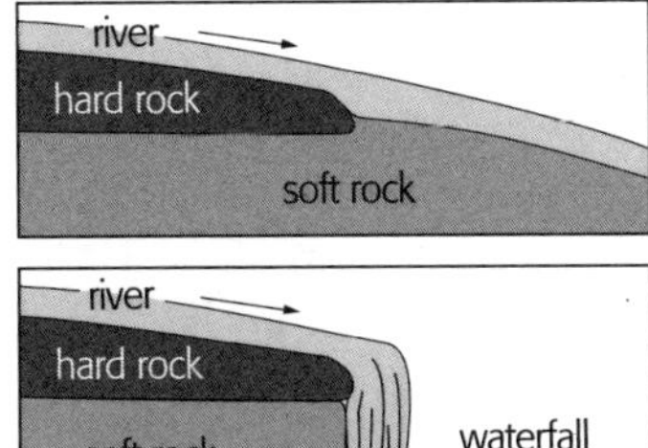

c A sequence as on page 86 is fine. Some pupils could try showing a part-frontal view of the gorge developing, as at the top of page 86. (Point this out to them.)

4 a Erosion. The water flows fastest around the outer bend.

b Deposition. The water flows more slowly around the inner bend, which means it has less energy. So it deposits material.

c One or both meanders could be cut off. The sketch could look like one of these.

i One meander cut off

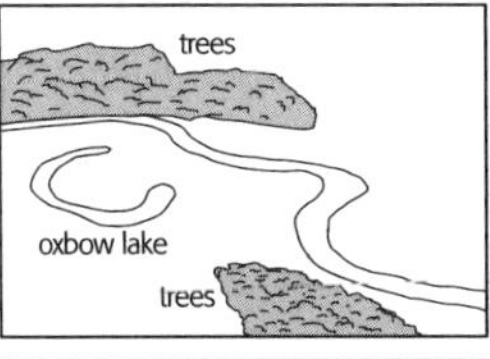

ii Both meanders cut off

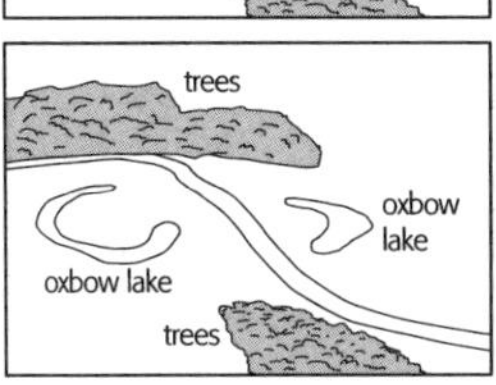

6.5

Rivers and us

About this unit

This unit is about how we use rivers – and often abuse them. In 'Your turn' pupils explore these, and their own connection with rivers.

Key ideas

- Water is both essential to life and and extremely useful substance – so we make a great deal of use of rivers as they flow on their journey.
- For example we use them as a source of our domestic water supply, for generating electricity, for washing and cooling things in industry, and for transport.
- We also abuse rivers, mainly by dumping things in them that harm, or kill off, the animals and plants that live in them. For one thing, we put our used water back into the river. We clean it up first, but it still contains harmful chemicals.

Key vocabulary

dams, electricity, water supply, industry, sewage works, algae, toxic, polluting

Skills practised in 'Your turn'

- Geography skills: 'reading' a drawing about how we use rivers
- Literacy skills: making up a conversation (between two fish)
- Thinking skills: summarising, using a spider map; presenting arguments; explaining; reacting to a point of view; thinking up an idea for a poster

Unit outcomes

By the end of this unit, most pupils should be able to:

- recognise that rivers are very important to us (even if we don't live near one)
- give at least five ways in which we use rivers
- give at least three ways in which we harm fish and other river life
- recognise that we will continue to put used water back into rivers – so we need to make sure it is well cleaned up

Resources

For starters **1** and **2**, and plenaries **1**, **2** and **5**: all images from the book are on *geog.1 resources and planning OxBox CD-ROM*

Ideas for a starter

1. With books closed, display the river drawing from page 88 of *geog.1* students' book. What do you think this drawing is showing? Start at the top right of the drawing and tell me as much as you can about it. (From here, move to page 88 in the book.)
2. With books closed, display the photo of the polluted river from page 89 of *geog.1* students' book. What do you think this shows? What might have caused it? How might this affect us?
3. Hold up a glass of clean water. Ask: Where did this come from? If pupils say 'A tap', ask 'But where before the tap?' and so on, until you arrive at 'A river'. (Let's assume your local supplies come from a river rather than an aquifer.) So why does it look so clean? Why is it safe to drink? And after you go to the toilet, where does the waste water from your body go? (Sewage works, then back to the river.)

Ideas for plenaries

Plan plenaries for strategic points throughout the lesson, as well as at the end.

1 Look at the boating photo on page 89. (Or you could display it.) Have you ever used rivers for leisure activities? Tell us about it.

2 Turn to the OS map on page 97 of the students' book. (Or display it. It's in the material for Unit 7.3.) It shows the town of Tewkesbury. They clean river water up for people's homes at the buildings labelled Wks. Fnd them, and explain why this spot was chosen for them.

3 Do you know where the water for your home comes from? Where is it cleaned up?

4 Pupils do a graffiti wall for all the stuff that goes down the drain from a home – washing up liquid, liquids from washing machines, dishwashers etc, bleach, fat, oil, bits of food, body waste. At the sewage works the waste is treated. Solid bits are removed. 'Good' bacteria clean up the liquid. But many chemicals can't be removed, and end up in the river. How would you like to be a fish, swimming about in those chemicals?

5 Waste water from our homes is cleaned up at sewage works. Turn to the OS map of Aylesbury on page 45. (Or display it. It's in the material for Unit 3.5.) See if you can find the sewage works for the town. (Hint: it's at the edge of town.) Give as many reasons as you can to explain why this spot was chosen for them.

6 Do you know where the sewage works for your area are?

7 Do question **1** in 'Your turn' as a plenary.

8 Who can come up with the best heading for the poster in question **6** in 'Your turn'? Set a time limit. Write the suggestions on the whiteboard and take a vote to find the best one

Further class and homework activities

Interactive quiz for Chapter 6 on *geog.1 resources and planning OxBox CD-ROM*

Suggestions 38 – 45 on page 117 of this book

Assessment materials for Chapter 6 on *geog.1 assessment file & OxBox CD-ROM*

Review 'Your goals for this chapter' on page 79 of *geog.1* students' book

Answers to 'Your turn'

1 False. Pupils will probably have washed this morning in a water supply pumped from a river, or a lake or reservoir fed by a river. They will have drunk treated river water, and eaten food cooked in it. This food may have come from crops irrigated by river water. Their body waste is treated in sewage works, and the liquid is carried away in a river. The electricity they use will have depended on river water (unless it was wind-generated).

Note that in some areas, the water supply is groundwater pumped up from aquifers. But overall, two-thirds of the UK's public water supply is from surface water (rivers, lakes, reservoirs).

2 a Pupils should include all the uses shown on page 88.

b This could provoke some discussion. For example, is the river's role in the electricity supply more important than its use as a drain for used water (from sewage works)?

3 Answers will vary, but the fish are likely to be vexed about pollution and fishing!

4 We all harm rivers whether we like it or not. We put chemicals down the drain every time we use soap, shampoos and detergents, and in our body waste. Many of these chemicals can't be removed at sewage works. They end up in the river, where they are pollutants. They promote the growth of algae, and harm fish.

We also put bleach and other disinfectants down sinks and toilets. These can kill 'good' bacteria at sewage works, and in the river.

This question could lead to a discussion of biodegradeable shampoos and detergents, which bacteria in the river can break down.

5 You might like to discuss these points with pupils:
- No matter how we dispose of used water, it will end up in a river in the end.
- If allowed to drain through the soil it will end up as groundwater (contaminated, unless treated first). This will flow to a river.
- But we use so much water (around 19 billion litres a day are supplied by the water companies in the UK) that draining it into the soil is not an option.
- Some pupils may suggest evaporating the used water away. What would we use to heat the water? What might be the effect of all that extra water vapour in the air?
- And if we keep taking water from rivers and not putting it back in quickly, what would happen the water levels in rivers?

6 You could explain to pupils that some outside drains (eg along the street) carry water into the normal sewage system, where it gets cleaned up (up to a point) at sewage works. But some carry it straight to the river, without it getting cleaned up on the way.

6 Further suggestions for class and homework

Most of these suggestions are addressed to your pupils. Where research or further resources are needed, the internet will almost certainly provide the answer. (Eg *google* and choose *Web* or *Images*.)

The water cycle

1 The illustrated water cycle Draw a circular flow chart to show the water cycle. Do drawings (for example of clouds and a river) to illustrate the different parts. Or cut out suitable photos from magazines and stick them around it. *

2 The adventures of Molly the water molecule You are Molly the water molecule. There you are, sitting on the surface of the Atlantic Ocean – and about to be evaporated! It will be the first step in a truly exciting journey.
Write the story of how you get from the ocean to a cloud, and then fall to land, and finally make your way back to the Atlantic Ocean, or perhaps the North Sea?
In your story, say where in the UK you fell, and how you reached a river. You can name the actual river you travelled in, and any towns or cities you passed through, on your way back to the sea.
Illustrate your story with a map of the route you took. Stick in pictures of places you got to – for example your cloud! **

3 The precipitation poster Precipitation can take several forms. Make a poster using pictures cut from papers or magazines, to illustrate the forms it can take. *

4 Cool clouds! Clouds are an important part of the water cycle, and they come in different styles. Find out about the different kinds of clouds and write a report. Illustrate it with a photo or drawing of each type of cloud. **

5 Cloud diary Using a digital camera, take pictures of the same piece of sky every day, for the rest of this project. Label the different kinds of clouds. **

6 Cloud poem Imagine you are a river. Write a poem about clouds, from the river's point of view! **

7 Ocean view The oceans cover about 70% of the Earth's surface, and hold about 97% of its water supply.
Give pupils an outline map of the world, on an A4 page. Pupils label the continents and oceans, and mark in the Equator. Then they plot their route for a sailing trip around the world, starting and ending in the UK, and visiting each ocean. They can go through the Suez Canal and Mediterranean on one leg of the journey. They can also stop off for food at different points. They name and label their starting port and stop-off ports. *

8 The water cycle and us Pupils create a colourful poster for the classroom wall about how we use the water cycle. *

9 Tell me more Pupils, working in pairs, find out more about one of these and do a short presentation to the class:
aquifers reservoirs dams hydroelectricity
You could ask them to prepare a visual aid. **

A river on its journey

10 Your local river Write a description of your local river. Include a map of the river from source to mouth. Show any tributaries. Mark in and label all settlements along the river, and any special features (eg industry, leisure facilities). Mark in the flood plain and the edge of the drainage basin if you can. The Environment Agency might help. ***/**/*****

11 Cities and their rivers in the British Isles Using an atlas, find 12 cities in the British Isles that are on rivers. Mark the rivers and cities on an outline map of the British Isles. *

12 Capital cities and their rivers Find 12 capital cities in the world that are on rivers. (Not more than 5 in Europe.) Mark the cities and rivers on an outline map of the world. *

13 Cities and rivers Why are so many important cities on rivers? Can you find any examples of important cities that don't have rivers running through them, and are not on the coast? (This could be combined with **11** or **12** above.) **

14 Sharing rivers Using an atlas, name 5 rivers that are shared by at least two different countries. Name the rivers and countries. Mark them on an outline map of the world. **

15 Adopt a river Choose any river in the UK. Draw a sketch map to show where it is, and which counties and towns it runs through. Now find out everything you can about it: its exact source, any historical events that took place on or along it, leisure activities on it, industry along it and so on. ***

16 Adopt an overseas river This time choose a river on another continent and find out all you can about it (as in **15**). Write a report for the class. (Tell pupils you want rivers from every continent. Or for every letter of the alphabet.) ***

17 Name this river! Choose a river from inside or outside the British Isles. Write down three facts about it – but keep its name secret. For example you could name the country, the high land where the river rises, and a town or city on it.
The class uses an atlas to identify the river, from these facts.
This could become a class game. Pupils take turns to present their facts. Award 1 point to the pupil who identifies a river first, and 1 to any pupil whose river is not identified.) **

18 Rivers for pleasure! Collect pictures to show leisure activities in and around rivers. Make a collage of them. *

19 Who lives there? Rivers are home to many different forms of wildlife. Find out about one wildlife species that lives in or beside British rivers, and write a report of at least 100 words about it. Don't forget drawings or photos. **

20 River story Find a story or a poem that has a description of a river in it. Bring it into school and read it to the class. **

21 Birth of a river? Do you think rivers change – or have we always had the same ones? Could new rivers be beginning somewhere, at this very moment? ***

Rivers at work

22 River poem You are a river – and you work ever so hard! Do you feel proud of yourself? Or are you a grumbler? Make up a poem about your life. Just one little snag – you must get the words *erode*, *transport* and *deposit* in! **

23 The story of Sid the Stone For as long as you can remember you had sat snugly in the river bank, listening to the water rushing past. Until one day ...
Write the story of how you were prised out of the bank by hydraulic action, and carried along on a journey. (Some pupils may be able to follow Sid's story right through until he ends up in sedimentary rock.) **/***

24 Design a demonstration Groups of pupils design a way to demonstrate *erosion*, *transport* and *deposition*. Pupils could vote on the best method – and then the winning group prepares and gives the demonstration. **/**

25 Can they cause problems? Could erosion and deposition by the river ever cause us problems? Explain. **/**

Landforms created by the river

26 Rivers on an OS map Draw a sketch map of a real river and its route, from an OS map. (Especially if it's a local river.) Mark in land height at different points along the river. Mark on features such as meanders, embankments, bridges, etc. **

27 The world's highest waterfall Which is the highest waterfall in the world? Find out, and write a leaflet to persuade tourists to visit it. Your leaflet must include a map! **

28 A very British gorge Do a short article for a geography magazine, about Cheddar Gorge. Say how it was formed. Don't forget a map showing where it is – and a photo? *

29 Britain's highest waterfall? Do a short article for a geography magazine, about High Force Waterfall. Say how it was formed. Add a map, and a photo if you can. **

30 The mysterious case of the disappearing rivers Britain has some disappearing rivers. One disappears at a spot called Gaping Gill. Put your detective hat on and find out more. Do a report for Scotland Yard saying why the river disappears, and where to. You can add a map and photos. **/***

31 Research some other river features These are three other river features: rapids delta estuary
Find out what each is. Write a description and add a drawing or photo. Give some real-life examples. **

32 Make up a river quiz Groups make up quizzes and quiz each other, with a prize for the winners. **

33 Odd-one-out Pupils prepare an odd-one-out to try out on other pupils, using what they learned in this topic. **

34 River crossword Pupils make up a crossword to try out on other pupils, using what they learned in this topic. **

35 A model river Pupils work in groups, to think up a way to create a 3-D model of a river and its drainage basin, with all the landforms they met. They produce an annotated sketch of the final design, saying what materials they will use and how they'll get the river to flow, for the demonstration. Pupils can vote on the best design – and produce it. **/***

36 Mind map Give pupils sugar paper to produce a mind map of rivers, using coloured markers. */**/***

37 River alphabet run Do an illustrated alphabet run for rivers, with something for each letter. */**/**

Rivers and us

38 Where do we get our water supply? We borrow water from the water cycle – but how? Pupils carry out an enquiry to find out where your local water supply comes from.
The Environment Agency and your water company may help. Perhaps someone will be willing to come into the class and give a talk. */**/***

39 Letter to a water company The class writes a letter to your water company, asking for details about where your water comes from, and where waste water is treated. */**

40 At the water works Find out exactly what's done to river water, to clean it up ready for us to drink. You could present your answer as an annotated drawing, or as a two-page article for a geography magazine, or even as a 3-D model. */**/***

41 What happens to our waste water? Our waste water gets returned to the water cycle – but how?
Pupils carry out an enquiry about what happens to the waste water that goes down the plug holes and loo. They should include a diagram of the stages in waste water treatment. Your water company may help – and might even send someone to talk to the class. */**/***

42 Who pays? Household gets a water bill. About how much is it, in your area? Is it fair to have to pay for water, which falls from the sky for free? */**/***

43 How much water do we use? A search on *google* for *water calculator* will bring up several. Choose one that's at the right level. (The one on the BBC news site may be suitable.) Pupils calculate the water use for their households. */**/***

44 Let's save water! The more water we use, the more harm we do to the environment. When there hasn't been much rain, rivers run low. Then we are competing with fish, water birds, and other water wildlife for river water. We win. They struggle to survive. So, how can we save water? Pupils prepare a leaflet with water-saving tips. (The internet will help.) */**/***

45 Who killed it? In 2007, the Yangtze River dolphin was declared extinct. Find out what happened to this gentle animal. Give your answer in the form of a PowerPoint presentation, or an illustrated children's story, or a speech to make at a protest meeting. */**/***

7 Floods

Helping you deliver the KS3 Programme of Study

This chapter addresses these areas of the Programme of Study:

Key concepts

Place Understand the physical and human characteristics of real places; develop geographical imaginations of places. **Space** Know where places and landscapes are located. **Environmental interaction** Understand that the physical and human dimensions of the environment are nterrelated and together influence environmental change. **Physical and human processes** Explain how physical and human processes shape places and landscapes. **Interdependence** Explore the social, economic, environmental and political connections between places. Understand the significance of interdependence in change, at all scales.

Key processes

Geographical enquiry Ask geographical questions; record information; analyse and evaluate evidence, presenting findings to draw and justify conclusions; solve problems and make decisions to develop analytical skills, and creative thinking about geographical issues. **Graphicacy and visual literacy** Use maps at a range of scales, photographs, and other geographical data (including OS maps and aerial photographs). **Geographical communication** Communicate knowledge and understanding using geographical vocabulary and conventions in both talk and writing.

The big picture

These are the key ideas behind this chapter.

- There have always been floods: they are a natural hazard.
- But we humans are causing more severe and frequent floods, by:
  - cutting down trees in drainage basins
  - extensive building in flood plains
  - causing, or at the very least accelerating, climate change, through burning fossil fuel
- We respond to floods in the short term by helping the victims.
- We respond to floods in the longer term by trying to prevent, or at least control, them.
- There are several ways to prevent or control floods, so that they do less damage – but the most effective way in the long term is to control land use in the flood plain.

A pupils' version of this big picture is given in the *geog.1* students' book opener for Chapter 7, and in *geog.1 resources and planning OxBox CD-ROM*, for the whiteboard.

The chapter outline

Use this, and their chapter opener, to give pupils a mental roadmap for the chapter.

7 **Floods** As the pupils' chapter opener, this unit is an important part of the chapter; see page 11 for notes about using chapter openers

7.1 **Tewkesbury under water** One girl's account of the floods in Tewkesbury, in July 2007

7.2 **What causes floods?** Explains what floods are, and looks at the factors that contribute to them

7.3 **So – why did Tewkesbury flood?** Pupils apply what they learned in Unit 7.2 to the floods in Tewkesbury

7.4 **Who helps in a flooding crisis?** An overview of our response to serious flooding, and the many organisations that help out

7.5 **Flooding: the consequences** Explores some of the short- and long-term consequences of the severe floods of 2007, in the UK

7.6 **Protecting ourselves from floods** Looks at different approaches to preventing and controlling floods, and ways to make homes flood-proof

Objectives and outcomes for this chapter

Objectives	Unit	Outcomes
Most pupils will understand:		Most pupils will be able to:
• what floods are, and what causes them	7.2, 7.3	• explain what a flood is, and give heavy rain as the main cause
• that some natural factors increase the risk of floods	7.2, 7.3	• give four natural factors that contribute to flooding, and for each, explain why
• that humans actions also contribute to the flood risk	7.2	• give two human activities that contribute to flooding, and for each, explain why
• that many organisations and people help out, when there are serious floods	7.1, 7.4	• give examples of five organisations that helped out, during the floods in Tewkesbury in 2007
• that serious floods have consequences for the whole country, not just the flooded areas	7.5	• give at least four countrywide consequences of the floods in the UK in 2007
• that serious flooding is expected to increase, in the UK	7.5	• recognise that global warming is expected to cause more serious flooding in the UK
• that we can take steps to prepare ourselves and our homes, when floods are on the way	7.1, 7.6	• list at least five steps to take, to prepare for floods; describe at least three design features that would help to make homes flood-proof
• that we can also take steps to protect our towns and cities from flood damage	7.6	• describe four approaches to protecting places from floods, and give examples

These tie in with 'Your goals for this chapter' in the pupils' chapter opener, and with the opening lines in each unit, which give the purpose of the unit in a pupil-friendly style.

Opportunities for assessment

See the formal assessment materials for this chapter on *geog.1 assessment file & OxBox CD-ROM*. They include a level-marked assessment with success criteria and a feedback form, interactive assessments, a scored test, and a self-assessment form.

There are other opportunities for assessment too. For example, you could use some of the more extended 'Your turn' questions in the students' book, worksheets or longer learning activities from *geog.1 resources and planning OxBox CD-ROM*, or some of the 'Further suggestions for class and homework' at the end of this chapter.

Getting ready for this chapter

Some of the starters and plenaries suggested for this chapter may need resources prepared in advance. Check out the *Resources* section on the 'Help at a glance' pages that follow.

geog.1 resources & planning OxBox CD-ROM has all the photos and diagrams from the chapter, for whiteboard display, plus movies and interactive materials. You will find these very useful for devising your own starters and plenaries. In addition, *geog.world CD-ROM* is a rich source of further material, including interactive webfiles and skills lessons.

About the chapter starter

The photo on page 90 of *geog.1* students' book shows the flooded town of Tewkesbury, in Gloucestershire, on July 24, 2007. The 900-year-old Abbey, on slightly raised ground in the centre of the photo, received only a little flood water. Tewkesbury was one of the places that suffered in the widespread flooding in the UK, in summer 2007, after weeks of heavy rain.

7.1

Tewkesbury under water

About this unit

This unit tells about the floods in Tewkesbury in July 2007. The account is in the form of diary entries. (These have been created from several personal accounts, with careful fact-checking.) In 'Your turn', pupils consider the damage floods can do to a home, and what to do in the event of a flood warning.

Key ideas

- Floods can bring a place to a standstill.
- They can do a great deal of damage to homes.
- There are several things you should do, to ensure personal safety and mimimize flood damage, when there's a warning that floods are on the way.

Key vocabulary

electric shock, gas leak, water treatment plant, insurance

Skills practised in 'Your turn'

- Literacy skills: identifying actions from an account, and recording them in a table; writing lists
- Thinking skills: giving reasons; ranking actions in order of importance; deciding what other actions could have been taken; making a list, from mental images; deciding on personal priorities in time of a flood

Unit outcomes

By the end of this unit, most pupils should be able to:

- describe the kinds of damage floods can do to homes
- explain how insurance works
- list at least five important things people should do to protect themselves and their homes, when a flood warning is given

Resources

For starters **1** and **2**: all images from the book are on *geog.1 resources and planning OxBox CD-ROM*

Ideas for a starter

1. Display the photograph of Tewkesbury and the surrounding area, from page 90 of the students' book. Ask pupils to suggest a suitable newspaper headline to go with it. Discuss the headlines.
2. Display the photograph of the flooded home, from page 92 of the students' book. How did this place get to be like this? What's the man doing?
3. With all other books closed, and no introduction, select a pupil to read out the first (or first two) diary entries from page 92 of the students' book. Then pass the book on for a couple of other pupils to read out, until the story is complete.
4. Ask: Have any of you had your home flooded? Tell us about it.

Ideas for plenaries

Plan plenaries for strategic points throughout the lesson, as well as at the end.

1 What do you think might have been the worst thing about those floods for:
Ellen? Ellen's mum? Ellen's dad? You, if you were there?
(You could choose pupils to act out the first three characters.)

2 Do you think events like this could happen to you, where you live? Explain.

3 What's an electric shock? How could you get one? What might it do to you? So how could you get one from flood water?

4 Ask pupils to read the panel about insurance on page 93. Then say: I want to insure the contents of my home. How do I go about it? About how much might the contents of an ordinary family home be worth? (Try £25 000 to £50 000?) Later, my home gets flooded and lots of things get ruined. What do I do now?

5 Choose five pupils to present their action plans from question **4** of 'Your turn' to the class. Ask pupils to vote on the best one. Why was it the best?

6 Work in pairs. Write a list of all the things you would have to do after a flood. Try to think of at least eight things. Ellen's story, and the photo on page 92, will help you. Arrange them in order of urgency, with the most urgent first. (Later, pupils can compare their lists with the Environment Agency's list. See suggestion 6 on page 132 of this book.)

Further class and homework activities

Worksheet 7A on *geog.1 resources and planning OxBox CD-ROM*

Suggestions 1–7 on page 132 of this book

Answers to 'Your turn'

1 a Students should list all these:

Action	Reason
puts sandbags outside door	try to keep water out
buys food	in case marooned
buys torches	for when electricity switched off
moves things upstairs	in case water comes in
gets camping gas stove out	back-up for cooking
charge mobile phones	in case of emergency
turn off gas	in case leak
turn off electricity	water conducts electricity

b This should provoke some thought. Turning off the electricity and gas should be very high on the list. These actions remove two immediate sources of danger.

2 The Environment Agency suggests these extra preparations:
- raise heavy things (fridges, sofas) on blocks to try to prevent flood water damage
- roll up carpets if possible
- put plugs into sinks and weigh them down, to prevent flood water backing up
- turn off water at mains

3 Some pupils will say they live in an upstairs apartment. Tell them to imagine it's on the ground floor. Anyone living in or with a basement has extra problems!

4 Answers will vary. Students with pets will need to make sure these are safe.

What causes floods?

About this unit

This unit explains what floods are, and gives the factors that contribute to flooding. Pupils explore these factors in 'Your turn'. (Climate change is not mentioned until Unit 7.5.)

Key ideas

- Floods occur when a river receives more water than its channel can hold. So the water overflows the banks.
- Floods are usually the result of heavy rain, or melting ice or snow.
- Other factors contribute to flooding:
  - impermeable rock in the drainage basin (rain can't soak through)
  - many tributaries (so the total area drained by the rivers may be very large)
  - very wet soil (no more rain can soak through, so it runs quickly over surface)
  - steep slopes down to the river (rain runs down slopes and quickly swells the river)
  - loss of trees (trees help to prevent flooding, because their leaves catch some rain and their roots take in lots of water)
  - built up areas (in the flood plain, and, more widely, in the drainage basin; rain can't soak through concrete so it runs into drains and reaches the river quickly)
  - the flat flood plain (the water easily washes over the river banks).
- Most of those factors contribute to flooding by promoting surface run-off, which fills the river quickly. (Infiltration, throughflow and groundwater flow are slower.)

Key vocabulary

flood, flash flood, impermeable, tributaries, built-up area, flood plain

Skills practised in 'Your turn'

- Geography skills: interpreting a diagram and a drawing
- Thinking skills: arranging sentences in a logical sequence; drawing a spider map to summarise; classifying factors; coming up with explanations; problem-solving

Unit outcomes

By the end of this unit, most pupils should be able to:

- define the terms given in 'Key vocabulary' above
- explain what a flood is, and give heavy rain as the usual cause
- give four natural factors that increase the flood risk, and for each, explain why
- give two human activities that increase the flood risk, and for each, explain why

Resources

For starters **1** and **2**, and plenaries **1** and **3**: all images from the book are on *geog.1 resources and planning OxBox CD-ROM*
For starter **3**: a watering can or similar, water, and a range of different outdoor surfaces

Ideas for a starter

1. With books closed, display the diagram from page 94. Ask pupils to try and work out what it is showing, step by step from left to right.
2. With books closed, display the diagram from page 95. Tell pupils it's about factors that contribute to flooding. See how many they can identify, with no text to help them.
3. Outside, get pupils to demonstrate the different rates of infiltration on different surfaces – grass, gravel, soil, rock, steep slope, tarmac – and help them make the connection between infiltration and flooding.
4. What do you think causes floods? Where do you think you're more likely to be flooded: near the mouth or a river, or near its source? Why do you think so?

Ideas for plenaries

Plan plenaries for strategic points throughout the lesson, as well as at the end.

1 Use starter **2** as a plenary, if you have not used it as a starter.

2 Use question **2** in 'Your turn' as a plenary. Invite pupils to add to a spider map on the whiteboard.

3 Do this after question **3** in 'Your turn'. Turn to the photo of Warkworth on page 22 of the students' book. (Or display it on the whiteboard. It's in the material for Unit 2.4.) Do you think it's in a flood plain? Give evidence for your answer.

   Then turn to the OS map on page 31. (Or display it. It's in the material for Unit 2.8.) Do you still think the same?

4 Ask pupils to present their solutions for question **4b** to the class. Pupils could vote for the one they think best.

5 If no-one lived on the flood plain, would there still be floods? Would they do damage?

6 All pupils stand up. Each in turn makes a statement about floods and flooding, then sits down. (You can decide whether to reject repeat statements – or you could have the class point out repeats.)

7 What was the most interesting thing you learned today?

Further class and homework activities

Interactive activity for Unit 7.2 on *geog.1 resources and planning OxBox CD-ROM*

Worksheet 7B on *geog.1 resources and planning OxBox CD-ROM*

Suggestions 8 – 12 on pages 132 – 133 of this book

Flash flood in Boscastle in *geog.1*, *Coping with floods*, on *geog.world CD-ROM*

Answers to 'Your turn'

1 The correct order is:

Heavy rain falls for a long period. The ground gets soaked. Infiltration slows down. More rain runs over the ground and into the river. The river fills up with water. The water rises over the banks.

2 a, b Students should use the factors given on page 95.

Natural	Human
heavy rain	loss of trees
impermeable rock	built-up areas
very wet (soggy) soil	blocked drains
steep slopes	living in the flood plain
tributaries	
the flat flood plain	

'Living in the flood plain' overlaps with 'built-up areas' but ask pupils to write both. All built-up areas along rivers and tributaries contribute in some measure to flooding, but it's the built-up areas in the flood plain that bear the brunt of the floods, and where flooding becomes a major issue.

Don't forget blocked drains. These can play a big part in flooding.

c the human factors

3 a Flat land along the river, that the river will naturally flood when it has too much water. Flood plains are usually found in a river's middle and lower sections, not in the upper section where the land is steep.

b the correct choice is **ii**

c the correct choice is **ii**

4 a i nobody lives at X

ii lots of people live around Y

iii few homes at Z

b Students might suggest building a high wall along the river. Ask them what the advantages and disadvantages of this would be. (You will come back to flood defences in Unit 7.6.)

7.3 So – why did Tewkesbury flood?

help at a glance

About this unit

This unit gives the background for the Tewkesbury floods: a news report, a rainfall map for May – July 2007, a map of a drainage basin, and an OS map for Tewkesbury. Pupils explore these, applying what they learned in Unit 7.2 to find out why Tewkesbury flooded.

Key ideas

These are a repeat of ideas met in Unit 7.2:

- Heavy rain is the main cause of flooding.
- Other factors contribute: for example prolonged wet periods, the number of tributaries that feed a river, the relief of the land.

Key vocabulary

(none new)

Skills practised in 'Your turn'

- Geography skills: analysing three different types of map for clues; using and giving OS grid references; comparing a photo with an OS map; deducing camera direction
- Reading a news report and a guidebook description
- Thinking skills: coming up with reasons

Unit outcomes

By the end of this unit, most pupils should be able to:

- describe what Tewkesbury is like
- give at least three reasons to explain why it flooded in July 2007
- recognise that if a settlement is built beside a river, on its flood plain, then it's at risk of flooding; so the real problem is not the floods, but where we've built

Resources

For starter **2** and plenaries **1**, **2** and **4**: all images from the book are on *geog.1 resources and planning OxBox CD-ROM*
For starter **4** and plenary **6**: numbered slips of paper (with consecutive numbers from 1 up to the number of pupils in the class), in a bag from which pupils can draw them

Ideas for a starter

1. With other books closed, ask a pupil to read out text A on page 96 of *geog.1* students' book. Then ask another pupil to read out text E on page 97.
2. Turn to (or display on the whiteboard) the photo of Tewkesbury from page 90 of the students' book. Ask: What factors do you think contributed to all this flooding? You could write pupils' answers on the board.
3. Use the Environmental Agency website to show the flood risk assessment for Tewkesbury. Select *Floods* at the home page and then write *Tewkesbury* in the *Flood map* box. Ask pupils to suggest reasons for the high risk zones.
4. At the start of the class, each pupil draws a slip of paper with a number on, out of a bag. Tell them that you'll be calling out numbers later, to check on what they've learned. (See plenary **6**.)

Ideas for plenaries

Plan plenaries for strategic points throughout the lesson, as well as at the end.

1. Do question **1** of 'Your turn' as a plenary. Display map B and ask: What does this map show? About how much of the UK got more rain than average? What about our area? What about Tewkesbury? And point out the darker patch north of Tewkesbury. How much rain did it get? The rain there affected Tewkesbury. Why?
   (The answer should be clear from map C. That area is within the drainage basin of the Avon, which carried its flood water to Tewkesbury.)
2. Do question **2** of 'Your turn' as a plenary. Display map C and ask: What does this show? Which are the two main rivers? Then ask question **2**. (Request a tributary count!)
3. After question **5**, do starter **3** as a plenary, if you haven't used it as a starter.
   Ask pupils to compare the Environment Agency map with the photo on page 90.
   Was this an *extreme* flood for Tewkesbury? What is your evidence?
4. Turn to the OS map on page 32 of the students' book. (Or display it, from the material for Unit 2.9.) Is Alton Towers likely to flood? Why do you think that? Check on the Environment Agency website to confirm. (Look for Alton in Staffordshire and scroll north on the map.)
5. Use the Environment Agency website to check out the flood risk for the school area, and other local places. Compare with the map for Tewkesbury used in the starter.
6. Call out numbers randomly (from the set you gave out earlier). Make a variety of requests. For example ask chosen pupils a question related to floods and flood risk. Ask them to make up sentences to show they understand different terms (such as *flood plain*). Ask pupil X to make up a question for pupil Y, and so on. Have fun!

Further class and homework activities

Interactive activity for Unit 7.3 on *geog.1 resources and planning OxBox CD-ROM*

Worksheet 7D on *geog.1 resources and planning OxBox CD-ROM*

Suggestions 13 – 1 on page 133 of this book

Answers to 'Your turn'

1 It had between twice and over three times (2 to 3.2 times) more rain than average, between 1 May and 22 July, 2007.

2 It is at the confluence of two rivers, the River Severn and the River Avon. Between them, these rivers have a great many tributaries, collecting rainwater from the land around them. All this is carried towards Tewkesbury – which puts Tewkesbury at risk of flooding.

3 a It will have made the ground soggy (saturated with water) so infiltration will have practically ceased. So further rain will run *over* the land (surface runoff) and quickly swell the rivers.

b Water from the Cambrian Mountains will run down the steep slopes quickly, and swell the River Severn. (Map B shows that the mountains also had heavier rainfall than usual in the May – July period.) You could ask pupils to point out the Cambrian Mountains on the map on page 62 of the students' book.

c With the ground already saturated, and the rivers swollen, the extra heavy rain on 20 July was enough to trigger the flooding, which reached Tewkesbury that evening.

4 a Mostly flat (contour lines far apart, and in places very far apart); so pupils should be able to deduce that Tewkesbury is in the flood plain.

b It will have played a big part in the flooding. On flat land the water will just spill out over the river banks and flow everywhere (like when you spill water on a flat floor).

5 a It's right on the banks of the River Severn. (Note *Severn Way* on the map.)

b The contour lines show that it is on higher ground – high enough to have escaped the flooding.

6 a i Pupils shouldn't have too much trouble finding the Abbey, the large church near the centre of the photo.

i It's at 891324.

b They appear to be caravans. This would be the caravan park in square 8832.

c Most of the roads appear to be flooded at some point.
For example the roads in 8932 are completely submerged.
Help pupils to identify and follow the roads in the photo using features such as the Abbey, caravan park and marinas.
Note that the road running from the roundabout in square 8932 to the junction in 8933 is the High Street. The road going past the Abbey is called Church Street.

d Pupils should be able to identify at least the marinas.

7 a top of photo is north east **b** top of photo is north

7.4 Who helps in a flooding crisis?

About this unit

This unit looks at the different groups and organisations that helped the flood victims, during the Tewksebury floods.

Key ideas

- The Meteorological Office (Met Office) produces weather forecasts.
- The Environment Agency looks after the rivers in England and Wales. Its work includes assessing flood risk, arranging for flood defences, and giving flood warnings.
- The Met Office and Environment Agency work closely together, to try to predict floods.
- When severe flooding occurs, many organisations and groups swing into action, to help people. For example the police, fire brigade, Coastguard Agency, local council, Red Cross. (All have emergency plans for dealing with disasters.)
- *Gold Command* is the name given to the control centre for dealing with a disaster. It is usually set up in the police headquarters for the area, since the police take overall charge in a civilian disaster (unless it's a fire, and then the fire brigade does). The Gold Command unit decides what needs to be done, and co-ordinates the efforts of the police, fire brigade, army, ambulance service and Coastal Agency.

Key vocabulary

the Environment Agency, the Met Office, Gold Command

Skills practised in 'Your turn'

- Geography skills: interpreting arrows that link photos
- Literacy skills: choosing to match definitions; writing interview questions
- Thinking skills: selecting to match criteria, choosing the most important

Unit outcomes

By the end of this unit, most pupils should be able to:

- explain the terms given in 'Key vocabulary' above
- name at least five groups or organisations that help out during flooding
- give examples of the kind of work they do

Resources

For starters **1** and **2**: all images from the book are on *geog.1 resources and planning OxBox CD-ROM*

Ideas for a starter

1. With books closed, display the photo of the soldier from page 98 of the students' book. Ask: Who is he? What's in the cases? Which country might this be? What kind of situation? Decline to explain the photo, and ask pupils to open their books.
2. With books closed, tell pupils you will step through a set of photos, without speaking. Their job is to look carefully, and be ready to tell you what's going on at the end. Then display all the photos for Unit 7.4, one after the other. (When pupils guess it's about flooding, you could ask for further information about each photo: what kind of help is being given, whether the people could be put into groups, and so on.)
3. Suppose there was an extreme flood in this area. Who would come to help us?
4. What kind of help do people need, when there's a flood? Pupils call out suggestions, or come up and write them on the whiteboard to make a graffiti wall.
5. These help when there's serious flooding. But who are they? (Some have two words.)

   clopie   myar   iref gabider   edr soscr

Ideas for plenaries

Plan plenaries for strategic points throughout the lesson, as well as at the end.

1 There's one kind of help that several of the groups are offering. What is it? Why is it so important?

2 What if the floods were so extreme that hardly anyone could get in to help?

3 The emergency services (like the police and fire brigade) have emergency plans to cope with disasters. What kind of disasters might these be, besides floods?

4 Ask several pupils to give you their answers for question **3** in 'Your turn'. Discuss with the class. You could take a show of hands to see which group, if any, has emerged as clear winner. (Ask a pupil to keep a tally on the board.)

5 Did you find question **3** difficult? If so, why? What might have made it easier?

6 When they have completed question **4** in 'Your turn', pupils swop questions with a partner, and take it in turn to be the interviewer and interviewee.

7 Which group would you most like to be part of, for helping out in floods?

8 What surprising thing did you learn today?

Further class and homework activities

Interactive activity for Unit 7.4 on *geog.1 resources and planning OxBox CD-ROM*

Flooding in the Kruger National Park on *geog.1, resources and planning OxBox CD-ROM*

Suggestions 16–21 on page 133 of this book

Answers to 'Your turn'

1 The arrows show who works closely with whom. The two most important groupings are the Met Office/Environment Agency and the emergency/rescue forces working under Gold Command.

2 a Met Office, forecasting heavy rain
Environment Agency, issuing flood warnings
local council workers, giving out sandbags (and they help to put up other temporary flood barriers where available)

b Choose two from:
local council workers (clearing up)
insurance companies (assessing and settling claims)
government (flood relief payments to flooded areas etc)
Environment Agency (reviewing the floods, and their response).

c Choose from: local churches, clubs, Red Cross, local shops and businesses. (Schools may get compensation for use of premises?)

d Most individuals are paid, except for volunteers from church groups, the Red Cross, local clubs, and staff from schools and businesses that are helping outside their paid work time.

e fire brigade, police, Coastguard Agency

f army, RAF (Royal Air Force)

g the Red Cross

h insurance companies

3 Answers will vary. The Environment Agency is a good choice, since we depend on it to identify areas at risk, and to issue flood warnings. If people get timely warnings they can prevent some flood damage (and keep themselves safe). The Met Office also has a critical role. Encourage debate.

4 You could start pupils off by reminding them to think of 'Who, What, How, Why, Where, When' questions.

7.5

Flooding: the consequences

About this unit

This unit moves beyond the floods in Tewkesbury to look at the wider flooding in the UK in summer 2007, the total damage it did, and some consequences. In 'Your turn', pupils explore these consequences, and classify them in different ways.

Key ideas

- Severe flooding has consequences for all of us, even if we don't live in a flooded area. For example, when the government gives money to help a flooded area, it has less to spend on other things.
- It's predicted that flooding will become more frequent, and more severe, in the UK, thanks to global warming.
- As a result, there are several big issues we need to think about, as a society. For example, should we stop building in flood plains? Should everywhere at risk of flooding get flood defences? And how will we pay for these?

Key vocabulary

consequences, global warming, infrastructure, insurance premiums

Skills practised in 'Your turn'

- Thinking skills: classifying consequences in many different ways, including short- and long-term; reflecting on whether this was difficult to do, and why; identifying consequences that might affect pupils themselves in the future

Unit outcomes

By the end of this unit, most pupils should be able to:

- explain the terms given in 'Key vocabulary' above
- give examples of different ways of classifying the consequences of flooding, including short-term and long-term
- give at least four countrywide consequences of the floods of summer 2007
- recognise that global warming is expected to increase serious flooding in the UK
- understand that this would mean having to spend billions on flood defences

Resources

For starter **2** and plenary **6**: see *geog.1 resources and planning OxBox CD-ROM*
For plenary **4**: a pair of True/False cards for each pupil (green for true, red for false)

Ideas for a starter

1. Whose families have been affected by flooding, like the floods in 2007? Hands up! Depending on your area, few or no pupils may raise their hands. Tell them that we have all been affected, even if indirectly. Then see if they can suggest why.
2. Show the movie *Flooding in Sheffield, 2007*. Tell pupils to watch closely, because they will be asked questions later. (See plenary **2**.)
3. Draw a money bag on the board, with the heading *Flooding costs money!* Ask the class why flooding costs money. Create a spider map of the answers, with the money bag in the middle. Then ask: Who pays? Answer: we all do, directly or indirectly, as they will see in the lesson.

4. Plenary **1** could also be used as a starter.
5. In this lesson I want you to be aware of the kind of thinking you have to do. I'll ask you about it later. (See plenary **8**.)

Ideas for plenaries

Plan plenaries for strategic points throughout the lesson, as well as at the end.

1 This is to make sure pupils understand the term *consequences*. Write a number of short sentences on the board. Ask pupils to pick out a cause and matching cosequence. For example: *She was really tired. The sunlight was very bright. The kite flew off. So they lost the match. So she did badly in her driving test. Their two best players got sent off. It was really windy. He put his sunglasses on*. Then ask pupils for their own examples of sentences containing a cause and consequence.

2 To follow on from starter **2**: Split the class into two halves. Ask one half to summarise the short-term consequences of the floods, for Sheffield. Ask the other half to summarise the long-term consequences. Pupils should use both what they saw in the movie *and* learned in the lesson. Set a time limit.

3 Students work in pairs and make a mind map about the consequences of flooding.

4 Can you think of anyone who benefits from flooding, in any way?

5 Give the class a couple of minutes to write two statements for this unit on a scrap paper. Both could be true, both false, or one true and one false. Collect the statements. A pupil reads them out in random order. The class holds up *True* or *False* cards or calls out *True* or *False*.

6 Show the movie *Flooding in Sheffield, 2007*, if you did not use it as a starter. Invite comments.

7 What would you say were the three key things you learned today?

8 So, how would you describe the kind of thinking you had to do in this lesson? Did you find it difficult or easy? Did you enjoy it?

Further class and homework activities

Floods in Bangladesh on *geog.1 resources and planning OxBox CD-ROM*
WS 7C and 7E on *geog.1 resources and planning OxBox CD-ROM*

Suggestions 22 – 25 on page 133 of this book

Answers to 'Your turn'

1 The early settlers chose sites with flat land for farming, and near rivers, to use as a source of water for drinking and washing, and as a transport route. They could fish in them too. In other words, they chose to settle on flood plains.

Later, some of the rivers would provide water for driving looms and mills, and later again, for steam-driven factory machinery. So, thanks to their locations near rivers, many of the early settlements grew into busy towns and cities. And they are still on flood plains …

2 a Two from: grief, stress, precious things lost.

b Tourism down, other business losses.

c Two from all the rest: crops lost, rise in food prices, insurance premiums up, government had less to spend on other things, conflict over building on flood plains, demand for flood defences.

d Grief, stress.

e Four from: loss of income from tourism, loss of earnings in other businesses, rise in food prices, insurance premiums up, government had less to spend on other things, new flood defences will have to be paid for somehow.

f The conflict over building on flood plains, which is rumbling on, will affect planning decisions, and therefore people's lives. Demand for flood defences has a social as well as financial aspect. Some pupils may identify the impact on tourists, and on people wanting to go to the cinema, pubs etc, as social consequences, which is fine.

3 a This shows one possible set of answers.

Consequences of flooding in 2007

Short term	Long-term
rise in food prices	grief (for dead people)
crops lost	precious things lost forever
stress	government had less to spend on other things
tourism down	insurance premiums up
other business losses	conflict over where to build
	demand for more flood defences

b Pupils are likely to have found **a** difficult, given how little they know about economic matters. In addition the choice is not always clear-cut. For example a business loss could be terminal if the business is already shaky. And some losses of precious personal things could be forgotten within a few months. Pupils are unlikely to know that insurance premiums tend to stay up once they rise – and particularly for flood-prone areas. This exercise will give plenty of scope for class discussion.

4 Government spending decisions as a result of the floods, higher insurance premiums, the conflict over building on flood plains, and the demand for more flood defences, may affect us all in some way, into the future (even if we don't live near rivers).

7.6 Protecting ourselves from floods

help at a glance

About this unit

This unit looks at four approaches to flood control. In 'Your turn' pupils explore the four approaches. Then they evaluate and score some proposals for flood defences in Tewkesbury.

Key ideas

- There are four main approaches to preventing or controlling floods:
  - control the water level (dams, pumping stations)
  - build barriers to keep water out or in (embankments, flood walls)
  - make the river's channel larger, to hold more water (dredge it)
  - control land use around the river (prevent further building, plant trees).
- Preventing floods is an expensive business.

Key vocabulary

dam, pumping station, embankment, flood barrier, temporary flood barrier, street drains

Skills practised in 'Your turn'

- Geography skills: interpreting a drawing, a diagram, and photos; comparing an OS map and photos to assess proposals for flood defences
- Thinking skills: comparing approaches; evaluating proposals and giving them a score; making a suggestion for flood defences; evaluating design features and picking out the two best; suggesting other design features

Unit outcomes

By the end of this unit, most pupils should be able to:

- define the terms given in 'Key vocabulary' above
- describe the four approaches to preventing or controlling floods
- recognise that a method of flood control may suit one place but not another
- recognise that controlling and preventing floods can cost a lot

Resources

For starter **1** and plenary **5**: marker pens and sugar paper
For starters **2** – **4** and plenaries **2** – **4**: all images from the book are on *geog.1 resources and planning OxBox CD-ROM*

Ideas for a starter

1. Group pupils into threes or fours (with books closed). Give each group a marker pen and sugar paper, and ask it to think of ways to prevent flooding. The groups share their ideas with the whole class. (You could display the photo from page 90 of *geog.1* students' book as an aid, during this activity.)
2. Look at the photo on page 22 of *geog.1* students' book. (Or you could display it. It's in the material for Unit 2.4.) Imagine you are in charge of this place. The river is starting to have serious floods, thanks to global warming. How will you respond? What would the disadvantages be, in what you plan to do? (See also plenary **4**.)
3. With books closed, display the drawing from page 102 of the students' book. What does it show? See how much pupils can deduce without text. Then they open their books at page 102. Ask five pupils to read out the text on the panels.
4. With books closed, display the diagram of the flood-proofed house from page 103 of the students' book. Look at each adaptation in turn. Ask pupils what its purpose is. Give clues and ask questions, to prompt thinking.

Ideas for plenaries

Plan plenaries for strategic points throughout the lesson, as well as at the end.

1. Divide the class into groups. Each group takes one approach to flood control, and thinks out the advantages and disadvantages. Feedback is given to the whole class.
2. Look at the upper photo on page 103 of the students' book. (Or display it.) How does a temporary flood barrier work? What will happen after the water recedes?
3. Look at the lower photo on page 103 of the students' book. (Or display it.) The river bank has been built up. Do you think this is enough to prevent these buildings from flooding?
4. Use starter **2** as a plenary. Pupils can apply the ideas they have met in the lesson.
5. Pupils work in pairs to make a 'flood defence' mind map.
6. Use pupils' answers for question **5b** to compile a list of suggestions on the whiteboard. Take a vote to choose the top two?

Further class and homework activities

Interactive activity for Unit 7.6 on *geog.1 resources and planning OxBox CD-ROM*

Interactive quiz for Chapter 7 on *geog.1 resources and planning OxBox CD-ROM*

Worksheet 7F on *geog.1 resources and planning OxBox CD-ROM*

Suggestions 26 – 28 on page 133 of this book

The Three Gorges Dam in *geog.1, Coping with floods*, on *geog.world CD-ROM*

Assessment materials for Chapter 7 on *geog.1 assessment file & OxBox CD-ROM*

Review 'Your goals for this chapter' on page 91 of *geog.1* students' book

Answers to 'Your turn'

1 a A = dam; B = pumping station; C = embankments; D = flood walls. See page 102 for what they do.

b The river bed is being dredged. This will deepen it, so the river channel can hold more water.

2 a Controlling the water level. Dams and pumping stations are large, strong structures that cost a lot.

b Controlling land use. The wildlife can live undisturbed.

c Controlling land use. You won't need dams, embankments, etc if you stop people building on the flood plain. (But they have to build somewhere.)

d Controlling land use. The river keeps its natural look.

e Controlling land use. You wouldn't have to worry about flood defences if you kept a safe distance from the river, and left the land along it for things like parks and golf courses. (But the reality is that many important places in the UK have rivers running beside or through them, so are vulnerable to flooding. We can't move them all away. So we have to employ a variety of flood defences.)

3 A Too late on the river's journey to protect Tewkesbury. The forest will indeed help soak up water around it – and it will restore itself if it gets flooded. But it will have very little impact on the gallons of flood water rolling down the river. (Look at the photo on page 90.) Large forests further back in the drainage basin, to help soak up rain *before* it reaches a river, would be much better. Score 1 or 2?

B Terrible idea. When you build a dam, the water gets trapped in the valley behind it. (Look at the dam on page 102 of the pupils' book.) Here there's no valley, just flat land. The water would spill out everywhere, behind the dam wall. Score 0.

C What about the view of the river, enjoyed by the local people, and tourists, and caravan owners? A tall wall would hide it from view. Score 0.

D Sounds like a good idea. They can be taken down again, so won't spoil the view. (But they will need to be a lot taller than the ones on page 103 of the students' book.) Storing the barriers at the council offices is also a good idea since the offices are near the river, and the council workers can put them up when a flood warning comes through. (They will take up quite a lot of storage space.) The barriers will protect only part of Tewkesbury though. As the photo on page 90 shows, flood water can come in at other places. So this is not the complete solution. Score 4?

E To prevent Tewkesbury flooding, they would need to be truly enormous concrete structures, like huge reservoirs, built into the flat ground. (Look at all that flood water in the photo on page 90.) They would not help the view around Tewkesbury! No, it is too late in the rivers' journeys for storage basins. Score 1 or 2?

F Try telling that to the people of historic Tewkesbury! Score 0.

4 Permanent flood walls all around it could be the best answer. Appearance is not really an issue here, and it's a key building to protect.

5 Answers will vary. Encourage pupils to be creative in **b**. You could ask them to sketch their ideas.

7 Further suggestions for class and homework

Most of these suggestions are addressed to your pupils. Where research or further resources are needed, the internet will almost certainly provide the answer. (Eg *google* and choose *Web* or *Images*.)

Tewkesbury under water

1 Interview Mr Adams You are a TV reporter. You have interviewed the man in the photo (page 92 of the students' book) about the floods, for the local TV news. We will call him Mr Adams. Write a full transcript of the interview. In this form:
Interviewer: 'Mr Adams, tell me ....'
Mr Adams: 'Well, the first thing I knew ....'
Say where the interview took place, and add directions for the TV editor. For example when to show Mr Adams, when to cut to pictures of the damage, and when to cut back to you. **

2 Flooding at home What if your home were flooded to a depth of 0.5 metres? Crawl around on the floor, at home, to investigate what would be damaged. Write a list.
(If you don't live on the ground floor, pretend that you do.)
Then see if you can divide your list up into different types of damage. For example: very serious, dangerous, easy to fix, not important. *

3 After the flood A flood has ruined your home.
The water was 0.5 metres deep. Now it has drained away but left a layer of mud everywhere. And the smell!
Take one room in your home and describe how it looks now, after the flood. *

4 What to do when there's a flood warning Design a leaflet telling people what to do when there's a warning that floods are on the way. It must be very clear, and simple, and show just the important points.
(You can get information to help you from the Environment Agency website at www.environment-agency.gov.uk.
Select *Flood* from the home page, and then look at the menu down the side. Or you could write to the nearest Environment Agency office, for leaflets. **

5 Flood warning! You receive a phone call from the local flood warning centre. The river is rising and your area will flood. *It is not safe to stay in your home. You have one hour to get ready to leave.*
What you will do in that hour? Write a list of the things you will do – but remember, it's only an hour! *

6 What to do after the flood Design a leaflet telling people what to do when they return home after a flood. Again it must be very clear, and simple.
For help, try the Environment Agency website at www.environment-agency.gov.uk or write to the nearest Environment Agency office, for leaflets. **

7 Insured? Access an insurance company's website, and display it to the class via the whiteboard. Fill in all the details for house contents insurance, and get a quote.
Then ask pupils to explain to you how insurance works – and why insurance companies can make large profits. **

What causes floods?

8 Do your own flooding sketch This is a very valuable exercise for summarising and confirming the factors that contribute to flooding. Pupils who are less confident about drawing could begin by tracing the drawing on page 95 of *geog.1* students' book, and adding to it as required.
a First, draw an aerial sketch of a river, like the one on page 95 of *geog.1* students' book. Centre your drawing in the middle of a large sheet of paper, leaving room to add notes all around it. (Or you can paste it onto a larger page later.) Draw in pencil first, so that you can rub out if you need to. Later, when you are happy with it, you can colour your drawing in. It should show:
– the source (the starting point of the river – look at page 80 in the students' book)
– the drainage basin, and the watershed (label this)
– three or four tributaries
– meanders in the flood plain
– a lot of building in the flood plain, close to the river, and other towns or villages in the drainage basin
– some forests, but not many (most have been cut down)
b It has been raining very hard for days, so next add these to your drawing:
– heavy rain clouds, and rain (do the rain lightly in pencil)
– flooding in the flood plain, where the built-up area is.
c Now add notes all around your drawing to explain why the river has got so full, and where all the water is coming from. Add notes about anything in the drainage basin that might have contributed to the flooding.
d Finally, mark in at least one place where there are floods, but where this is not really a problem.

9 Play Taboo Divide the class into paired teams to play this game – perhaps 4 or 5 in a team. There are two parts to the game. Each team follows the instructions below.
a First, choose the taboo words.
– Choose 6 key flood words. Make a card for each.
– At the top write the key word, and in a different colour add five words that you'd want to use, if you were explaining the key word to someone else. (These become the taboo words.)
b Now play the game.
– Swap all your cards with another team – but not your opposing team. (No team should have the cards it prepared.)
– Now, play the game with your opposing team. Each team takes turns. To play, a student chooses a card, hidden from the rest of his or her team, and then gives verbal clues, *but without using any of the taboo words*, to help the rest of the team guess the key word. The team has just one minute to guess, but can make any number of guesses in that time.
– Meanwhile the opposing team must keep an eye on the clock *and* make sure that no taboo words are used. (So the opposing team must see the card that was chosen.)
c Then the teams reverse roles. **

10 Make up a flood quiz Groups make up quizzes and quiz each other, with a prize for the winners. **

11 Make up a flood crossword Groups make up crosswords, then swop and complete them. **

12 Global warming and floods So far we have looked at several factors that contribute to flooding. They are all factors connected with a river's drainage basin. There is one other factor that is likely to contribute in a massive way to flooding, in the future, and affect all drainage basins. That factor is global warming.
Work with pupils to come up with an enquiry question about the causes and effects of global warming. Then pupils carry out the enquiry.
(If pupils need help in tackling an enquiry, see *How to carry out an enquiry* in *geog aid* of *geog.world CD-ROM*.
This skills lesson is suitable for whole-class delivery, using an interactive whiteboard or projector.) ****/*****

So – why did Tewkesbury flood?

13 Tell me more about Tewkesbury ... Do some research on Tewkesbury and prepare a two-page unit about the town, like the units in *geog.1* students' book, for a travel magazine. Give some of the town's history, and say what visitors can see there. Add a map or two, and photos. ****/*****

14 Building in the flood plain? You are in charge of planning for Tewkesbury. Mr Jamison, a developer, has applied for permission to build a new hotel in the Walton Cardiff area of the town. The proposed hotel would be at 909323 on the OS map. (See page 97 of the students' book.) You have discussed his application with your team, and now you are writing to Mr Jamison with your decision, and your reasons. What will you say? (Check the Environment Agency flood risk map for Tewkesbury before you reply. See if you can download the map and include it with your answer.) ******

15 Everybody out! Tewkesbury is at serious risk of flooding. Global warming could make floods more frequent, and more serious. It's time to air your views on the subject.
a Write a letter to the Tewkesbury Chronicle suggesting that everyone just moves out of Tewkesbury. Give your reasons – but keep them brief, otherwise the editor will edit them.
b Now write a letter from an angry reader of the newspaper, in reply to yours. ***/**/*****

Who helps in a flooding crisis?

16 The Environment Agency Find out more about it, and the different kinds of work it does. Where is it based? Write a one-page leaflet about it (on the computer?). You could add a drawing or photo of a river. Check out the EA website: www.environment-agency.gov.uk) ******

17 Flood warnings The Environment Agency issues flood warnings in England and Wales. Find out what the different levels of warning are, and how they reach the public.
Then do a clear, simple, colourful leaflet about them.

18 How serious? Floods are described as 1 in 10, 1 in 100, 1 in 200 and so on. What does it all mean? Find out and explain to the class. *******

19 Is your home at risk? Is your home at risk of flooding? Check it out on the Environment Agency flood map. ******

20 The Red Cross One of the organisations that helped in Tewkesbury has branches all over the world: the Red Cross. It is called the Red Crescent in some countries. Find out more about it and the work it does, and write a report. ******

21 You are Gold Commander You are Gold Commander at Gold Command at Gloucester, during the floods in 2007. You're the top cop, organising how the police, army, navy, fire brigade, ambulance service and Coastguard Agency will work together. Suddenly a report comes in that the Mythe water treatment plant at Tewkesbury has been flooded. That's bad news. Who will you call first? What will you say? Make up the phone conversation. ******

Flooding: the consequences

22 It's all our fault? *The real truth about floods is this: We have built in the wrong places, and now we are paying the price.* That is the first sentence of your letter to a national newspaper, about the floods that caused widespread damage across the UK in 2007. Complete the letter! ***/**/*****

23 Paying the price Flood defences will cost billions. So we may have to pay higher taxes, or higher water bills. One group of pupils prepares a presentation about taxes: what they are, and how the tax system works. The other group finds out about water bills, and prepares a presentation. Some pupils may welcome the chance to use PowerPoint. ***/**/*****

24 Report on another flood Research a recent flood in another country. Write a two-page unit about it. You can use Unit 7.3 in *geog.1* students' book as your model. Add a map, and photos. If possible, create your unit on the computer, using a desk-top publishing package. ****/*****

25 A Bangladesh enquiry Bangladesh suffers severe flooding most years. Help pupils think up an enquiry question about this. They then carry out the enquiry. A section comparing the floods in Bangladesh and the UK would be useful. ***/**/*****

Flood control

26 Flood control in your area Draw a sketch of your nearest river using an OS map, and mark the areas where flooding occurs. For this, use the flood map on the Environment Agency website. Then find out what (if anything) has been done to control flooding, and mark this on your sketch map too. You could take photos of embankments or other flood barriers, if there are any nearby. (Contact the Environment Agency office for your area, for further information.) *******

27 Design a house to cope with floods Imagine you live on a flood plain, in an area that suffers heavy flooding.
Design a house that will cope well with floods. For example you may want to think about where to store things during floods, and whether you should have carpets. Will you build on stilts? What about a house that turns into a boat? ***/**/*****

28 No more flood defences Hold a short class debate on the motion: *We can't be certain there will be more flooding, so we should not build all these expensive flood defences.*

8 Sport

Helping you deliver the KS3 Programme of Study

This chapter addresses these areas of the Programme of Study:

Key concepts

Place Understand the physical and human characteristics of real places. **Space** Understand the interactions between places and the networks created by flows of information, people and goods. **Interdependence** Explore social, economic, environmental and political connections between places. **Environmental interaction** Understand that the physical and human dimensions of the environment are interrelated and together influence environmental change; explore sustainable development and its impact on environmental interaction. **Physical and human processes** Explain how human processes shape places, landscapes and societies.

Key processes

Geographical enquiry Ask geographical questions; record and display information; analyse and evaluate evidence, presenting findings to draw and justify conclusions. **Graphicacy and visual literacy** Use maps at a range of scales, photographs, and other geographical data (including OS maps and aerial photographs) **Geographical communication** Communicate knowledge and understanding using geographical vocabulary and conventions in both talk and writing.

The big picture

These are the key ideas behind this chapter.

- Sport has strong links with geography – through the environments and locations in which it is played, the flow of sports teams and players, and the flow of sports goods.
- Sport is big business. For example hundreds of thousands of people depend on football for a living, and the top clubs earn, and spend, millions.
- Not everyone enjoys the benefits. Most sports kit is made in poor countries with low wages – and some of the people who make it are exploited.
- Sports venues can have a big impact on their surroundings. Many factors need to be considered, in choosing their locations. The choice can cause conflict.
- Sports venues can be used to regenerate an area. The Olympic Park in east London is an example.

A pupils' version of this big picture is given in the *geog.1* students' book opener for Chapter 8, and in *geog.1 resources and planning OxBox CD-ROM*, for the whiteboard.

The chapter outline

Use this, and their chapter opener, to give pupils a roadmap for the chapter.

8 **Sport** As the pupils' chapter opener, this unit is an important part of the chapter; see page 11 for notes about using chapter openers

8.1 **Geography and sport** What has sport got to do with geography? This unit explores that question

8.2 **The football business** Why football is big business, and how the big clubs earn

8.3 **Liverpool FC is moving home** A case study: Liverpool FC is moving from its Anfield stadium to a new one just across the road, in Stanley Park

8.4 **Who are the losers?** A case study about football manufacture in Pakistan

8.5 **London 2012** The Olympic Park is being built in the Lower Lea Valley in London; we look at the plan for the Park, and the long-term aim of regeneration

8.6 **Making the Olympics sustainable** One feature of London's winning bid was its commitment to sustainable development; here we explore the plans for that

Objectives and outcomes for this chapter

Objectives	Unit	Outcomes
Most pupils will understand:		Most pupils will be able to:
• that sport has strong links with geography	8.1	• give four examples of sports that usually depend on the natural environment, and four that usually depend on built venues in towns and cities
• that football connects people and places all around the world	Ch 8 opener	• give examples of ways in which football links people and places all around the world
• that football is big business for many clubs	8.2	• give at least five ways in which big football clubs earn money
• that many factors must be considered, when choosing the location for a new football stadium, and that the choice may cause conflict	8.3	• give at least three factors to consider, when choosing a location for a football stadium; give at least two ways in which a stadium will affect an area (one positive, one negative)
• why most sports kit is made in poorer countries	8.4	• explain why football kit is made in poorer countries, and how this can lead to people being treated unfairly
• that the Olympic Games are not just a multi-sport event: they are a catalyst for regeneration	8.5, 8.6	• describe ways in which the 2012 Olympic Park will help to regenerate a run-down area of London
• that the idea of sustainable development can be applied to the Olympic Games	8.5	• give at least four ways in which the Olympic Park will be an example of sustainable development

These tie in with 'Your goals for this chapter' in the pupils' chapter opener, and with the opening lines in each unit, which give the purpose of the unit in a pupil-friendly style.

Opportunities for assessment

See the formal assessment materials for this chapter on *geog.1 assessment file & OxBox CD-ROM*. They include a level-marked assessment with success criteria and a feedback form, interactive assessments, a scored test, and a self-assessment form.

There are other opportunities for assessment too. For example, you could use some of the more extended 'Your turn' questions in the students' book, worksheets or longer learning activities from *geog.1 resources and planning OxBox CD-ROM*, or some of the 'Further suggestions for class and homework' at the end of this chapter.

Getting ready for this chapter

Some of the starters and plenaries suggested for this chapter may need resources prepared in advance. Check out the *Resources* section on the 'Help at a glance' pages that follow.

geog.1 resources & planning OxBox CD-ROM has all the photos and diagrams from the chapter, for whiteboard display, plus movies and interactive materials. You may find these very useful for devising your own starters and plenaries. In addition, *geog.world CD-ROM* is a rich source of further material, including interactive webfiles and skills lessons.

About the chapter starter

The photo on page 104 of *geog.1* students' book shows the Paraguayan footballer Roque Santa Cruz playing for Backburn Rovers, and the Brazilian footballer Alex (or Alex Rodrigo Dias da Costa) playing for Chelsea, in a Premier League match in London in September 2007. The result: a goalless draw.

8.1

Geography and sport

About this unit

This unit shows photographs of different sports – and in 'Your turn' pupils explore the link between sport and geography.

Key ideas

- There are many links between sport and geography.
- For one thing, some sports depend mainly on the natural environment (physical geography). Others depend on venues we build for them, usually in towns and cities (human geography).
- Also there is a continual flow of athletes and teams, moving between countries around the world, and competing against each other.

Key vocabulary

natural features, natural environment, venues (see the glossary at the end of this book)

Skills practised in 'Your turn'

- Geography skills: drawing a sketch map of the UK, and attempting to mark sports venues on it, in roughly the right places
- Thinking skills: matching sports to natural environments, or to built venues; surmising the effect of weather on different sports; naming some international sports events; deciding whether there is a link between sport and geography, and giving reasons

Unit outcomes

By the end of this unit, most pupils should be able to:

- give examples of links between sport and geography
- give four examples of sports that usually depend on the natural environment
- give four examples of sports that usually depend on built venues in towns and cities

Resources

For starters **1** and **2**, and plenaries **1**, **2** and **4**: all images from the book are on *geog.1 resources and planning OxBox CD-ROM*
For starter **4**: a cricket bat, rugby ball, tennis racquet, or similar item (but not a football)

Ideas for a starter

1. Use question **1** as a starter. (You could display the photos.) Ask pupils to identify the sport in each photo. Then carry on with the rest of the question.
2. Display just one photo from the unit, for example the photo of the climber or surfer. Ask: What's this got to do with geography?
3. Which is your favourite sport? Ask a pair of pupils to do a tally chart for the class and then draw a bar chart for the results, on the board. (There could be a *None* bar on the chart for pupils who dislike sport.) Ask for comments on the results.
4. Hold up a cricket bat or similar sports item made overseas. Ask: What's this got to do with geography? The answer is that it was made in another country, where wages are lower.

Ideas for plenaries

Plan plenaries for strategic points throughout the lesson, as well as at the end. Most of the questions in 'Your turn' will work well as plenaries.

1 Do question **2** in 'Your turn' as a plenary. (You could display the photos.)

2 Do question **3** in 'Your turn' as a plenary. (You could display the photos.) Elicit from pupils that 'artificial' environments are created for some sports, eg dry ski slopes.

3 Are there any sports venues in your area? Natural or built? If built, why are they located where they are?

4 Do question **4** in 'Your turn' as a plenary. (You could display the photos.)

5 Pupils compare their answers for question **5a** in 'Your turn'. Ask for comments on any difficulty they had with question **5b**. Remind them about polishing their mental maps. (They could mark their places on a sketch map of the UK for homework.)

6 When pupils have completed question **7** in 'Your turn', compare *Yes* and *No* responses around the class.

7 Did you enjoy today's lesson? Why? Could all lessons be like this? Why?/Why not?

Further class and homework activities

Worksheets 8A and 8B on *geog.1 resources and planning OxBox CD-ROM*

Suggestions 1 – 9 on page 148 of this book

Investigating a sport on *geog.1 resources and planning OxBox CD-ROM*

The World Cup in *geog.1*, *Football!*, on *geog.world CD-ROM*

Answers to 'Your turn'

1 a A = motorsports (Formula One) B = tennis C = skiing
D = (dinghy) sailing E = cycling (Tour de France)
F = rock climbing G = surfing H = cricket I = sprinting

2 These *usually* depend on the natural environment:
C – skiing needs snow and slopes
D – sailing needs sea (or rivers) and wind
F – rock climbing needs steep rock
G – surfing needs the sea and large waves.
But note that you can also ski on artificial ski slopes, climb on artificial climbing walls, and sail on reservoirs.

3 a In the photos, built venues are being used only in A, B, H and I. But venues get built for most of the other sports too: velodromes for cycling, artificial ski slopes, and climbing walls. And people can sail on reservoirs, although these are not primarily for that purpose.

b Built venues are likely to be in towns and cities, where people can reach them easily – except for Formula One, for which venues are likely to be on the edge of, or outside, a town or city, since this noisy and dangerous sport needs plenty of space. (An exception is the Monte Carlo Grand Prix, held on the streets of Monte Carlo.)

4 Most sports and sporting events are affected by the weather.
A – in wet weather you need to use special tyres
B, H – rain will stop play, in tennis and cricket
C – rain will melt snow: not good for skiing
D – it could make sailing more exciting
E – cycling events like the Tour de France continue in spite of cold, wind and rain, but these conditions make cycling more difficult, and cause crashes
F – cold, wind and rain make rock climbing more dangerous
G – wind and rain don't affect surfers much; in cold conditions you'd wear a wet suit
I – runners carry on regardless.

5 Some of many possible suggestions:
A, Silverstone; B, Wimbledon; C, Aviemore, in the Cairngorms in Scotland; D, the Solent (the channel between England and the Isle of Wight; E, Manchester Velodrome (the UK's national cycling centre); F, Ben Nevis in Scotland or Snowdonia in Wales; G, Newquay in Cornwall; H, Lords or the Oval in London, Old Trafford in Manchester; I Lindford Christie Stadium in London, Sport City in Manchester, National Indoor Arena in Birmingham, Don Valley Stadium in Sheffield

6 Some examples:
A – any Grand Prix event
B – Wimbledon
C – the Winter Olympics, every four years
D – round-the-world yacht racing, or the Isle of Wight Regatta
E – the Tour de France
F – climbing Everest (or other top mountain)
G – the Association of Surfing Professionals (ASP) World Tour, or the British Surfing Association Championships, or the Triple Crown of Surfing
H – the cricket World Cup
I – the Olympics, or the Commonwealth Games.

7 Some links between sport and geography:
- some sports depend largely on natural features, and the natural environment, as above
- some are weather-dependent
- many sports are linked to specific places and venues
- locations for built venues are chosen for geographical reasons
- people from all over the world travel to top competitions to compete or watch.

(Also, from the chapter opener, some pupils may remember to add that sports goods may be imported from other countries.)

8.2

The football business

About this unit

This unit looks at the ways big football clubs earn money. In 'Your turn' pupils explore these, and consider whether having better players, or moving to a bigger, better stadium, would help. This prepares the way for the stadium case study in Unit 8.3.

Key ideas

- Football is not just a game. It is big business. (This is also true of some other sports.)
- The top clubs earn millions of pounds a year. They also spend a lot.
- It's not just the clubs that earn money from football. Cafés, pubs, merchandise manufacturers and many other businesses gain too.

Key vocabulary

catering, merchandise, TV fees, conferences, private viewing boxes, sponsorship

Skills practised in 'Your turn'

- Literacy skills: writing a paragraph to explain
- Thinking skills: matching photos to text items; assessing the consequences of having better players, or a better stadium; coming up with examples; arranging text into a logical argument, to complete a flow chart

Unit outcomes

By the end of this unit, most pupils should be able to:

- explain the terms given in 'Key vocabulary' above
- list at least five ways in which big clubs earn money
- recognise that having better players, and a bigger, better stadium, could help a club earn money

Resources

For starter **3**: an example of replica strip, or other merchandise bought from a football club; or access a club's online shop

For starter **4**: all images from the book are on *geog.1 resources and planning OxBox CD-ROM*

For starter **5**: around 25 'banknotes' – Monopoly money or just card – and a money pot
For plenary **1**: the website of any top football club (checked in advance for ease of use)

Ideas for a starter

1. Name a really well-paid player. Where does the club get the money to pay him?
2. Which is your favourite football team? A pair of pupils do a tally chart for the class, then draw a bar chart for the results, on the board. (It may need a *None* bar.)
3. Show an example of club merchandise, or display a club's online shop. Ask why a club wants to sell these things – and why people want to buy them.
4. Display the photos from page 108 of the students' book, one at a time. Ask pupils what's going on in each one. (This will help them with question **1** in 'Your turn'.)
5. Put the set of banknotes on the desk. Ask: How do football clubs earn money? Pupils come up in turn, lift one banknote, give one answer, and put the banknote in your money pot. Answers should not be a repeat of someone else's.
   When pupils have run out of suggestions, ask: What do clubs spend money on? This time pupils come up, each give one answer, and each take one banknote from the pot. Discuss what might happen if a club ends up with no money in the pot. How could it get some in a hurry? (Find a tycoon?)

Ideas for plenaries

Plan plenaries for strategic points throughout the lesson, as well as at the end.

1. For after question **1** of 'Your turn': Access a top football club's website. (Check it out in advance for ease of use.) Review the sections, then focus on the ones that are about finance and corporate issues.
2. As well as clubs earning money, individual players can earn a lot of money too, on top of their salaries. What examples can you give me?
3. Do you think it's fair that clubs can 'buy' and 'sell' players?
4. Do you think it's fair that British clubs can 'buy' players from other countries?
5. Write a list of jumbled words on the board, about ways a club makes money.
   For example:
   thamc scettik trancegi carmenshedi
   With books closed, pupils have to unscramble them. Against the clock?
6. Who owns your favourite football club? Pupils could research this for homework.

Further class and homework activities

Worksheets 8C and 8D on *geog.1 resources and planning OxBox CD-ROM*

Interactive activity for Unit 8.2 on *geog.1 resources and planning OxBox CD-ROM*

Suggestions 10 – 15 on pages 148 – 149 of this book

Investigating a sport on *geog.1 resources and planning OxBox CD-ROM*

Ski time in *geog.1, Football!*, on *geog.world CD-ROM*

Answers to 'Your turn'

1

Way to earn money	**Could the club earn more from this by …**	
	having better players?	**moving to a bigger, better stadium?**
1 sell match tickets	yes	yes
2 sponsorship	yes	yes
3 TV fees	yes	yes
4 rent out rooms for conferences	no	yes
5 sell merchandise	yes	yes
6 catering	yes	yes
7 rent out private viewing boxes	yes	yes

In most cases, better players will help draw in larger crowds, and attract a higher level of sponsorship. But people wanting conference facilities will be looking for good facilities, not good players.

Moving to a bigger better stadium will help in all kinds of ways. Larger capacity means more ticket and merchandise sales, and more opportunity for sponsorship. (Eg Emirate Airline's sponsorship of Arsenal's Ashburton Grove stadium.) The club can include modern conference facilities, gyms, creches, and all kinds of other facilities.

2 Could include: pubs, restaurants and cafés, chip shops, people who make and sell merchandise, coach and taxi firms and other transport companies, TV and radio companies who broadcast the matches, the companies who sponsor the club and players, the fans (who gain a great deal of enjoyment).

3 This is the text for flow chart boxes 2 – 6:

2 … so it wins more and more matches …

3 … which means it sells more tickets and more merchandise.

4 This also means it makes more money from TV and sponsorship.

5 So the club gets richer and richer …

6 … so it can afford more of the world's top players.

4 Pupils could include some or all of the following points.

Football is big business. For the big clubs, it is largely about making money. A larger stadium means a club can sell more match tickets, and food and drink, and merchandise. It will have more private viewing boxes to rent out. It will also be able to make more money from other ventures, such as conference facilities. It can use the money to help it compete with other clubs, including by buying in top players. Then the more successful its players are, the more sponsorship, and TV fees, it will attract. So it will make even more money.

Liverpool FC is moving home

help at a glance

About this unit

This unit is about Liverpool FC's move from its Anfield stadium to a new one just across the road, in Stanley Park. In 'Your turn', pupils suggest location requirements for a new stadium, and score Stanley Park on each; they suggest where in the park to place the new stadium, and ways to redevelop the old one; and they write to a newspaper.

Key ideas

- You need to consider the special requirements for a football stadium, when choosing a location for it.
- When a club moves out, the old stadium becomes a brownfield site. It can be redeveloped. Ideally this will be an example of sustainable development.

Key vocabulary

location, redevelop, regenerate, sustainable development (see the glossary at the end of this book)

Skills practised in 'Your turn'

- Geography skills: reading an OS map; comparing an OS map with a photo; drawing a sketch map (see note for question **4** in 'Answers for Your turn'); marking in a suggested site for the new stadium and its access road(s)
- Literacy skills: writing a letter to a newspaper about the plans for the new stadium
- Thinking skills: coming up with reasons; suggesting requirements for the location for a new football stadium; choosing the exact site for the new stadium; making suggestions for sustainable redevelopment of the old stadium; thinking about the proposed the new stadium from the point of view of a local person

Unit outcomes

By the end of this unit, most pupils should be able to:

- give at least three location requirements for a football stadium
- give at least two ways in which a football stadium will affect an area (one positive, one negative)
- give examples of conflicts that can arise, over the location of a new football stadium

Resources

For starter **4** and plenaries **1** and **3**: all images from the book are on *geog.1 resources and planning OxBox CD-ROM*

Ideas for a starter

1 You have to choose a site for a new secondary school. What will you need to think about? Write pupils' (sensible) suggestions on the board. Give prompts. For example: 'Is it easy to reach by public transport? Is there room for playing fields?'
Explain that these are *location requirements*. Do you think a jail would have the same location requirements? What about a football stadium?

2 A new football stadium is to be built in your area, just down the road from your home. Pupils note good and bad points about this, on the board – one colour for good, another for bad.

3 What can you tell me about Liverpool FC? Pupils add to a spider map on the board.

4 With books closed, display the photo from page 111 on the whiteboard. Ask pupils to guess where it is. (Clue: two football stadiums. Further clue: city beginning with L.) Tell me everything you see in the photo.

5 Keeping all other books closed, choose two pupils to read out the text panels at the top of page 110. After each, discuss what it's about.

Ideas for plenaries

Plan plenaries for strategic points throughout the lesson, as well as at the end.

1. (If starter **4** not used.) Look at the big photo on page 111 of *geog.1* students' book. (You could display it.) What does it show? Pupils each give one sentence about one thing they notice, trying not to repeat what others have said.
2. Look at the park where the new stadium will go. A greenfield site or a brownfield site?
3. Look at the OS map on page 111 of the students' book. (You could display it.) Tell me as much as you can about the area. And give me your evidence!
4. Choose pupils to explain these terms: redevelop sustainable development.
5. a) Draw a 'sustainable development' diagram on the board, like the one on page 83 of this book. Discuss the terms at the end of the 'legs'. Then divide pupils into small groups for the next part.
   b) From what you know about it so far, what score would you give the proposed new stadium in Stanley Park, for sustainability? (For example, give a score out of 10 for each leg, then add the scores.)
   c) Discuss the scores. Do groups agree? Would the Liverpool FC manager give a different score? What about Len Williams (the letter writer)?
   d) What other information would pupils like to have, to give a fairer score?
6. Choose pupils to read out their letters for question **6** of 'Your turn'. Invite comments.

Further class and homework activities

Worksheet 8E on *geog.1 resources and planning OxBox CD-ROM*

Football moving home on *geog.1 resources and planning OxBox CD-ROM*

Suggestions 16 – 19 on page 149 of this book

Answers to 'Your turn'

1 Mainly to get a bigger stadium, so that the club can bring in more money. A modern stadium will help sell tickets, and will probably help the club attract top players

2 a From the map and photo, it's clear that there isn't room to expand on the Anfield site. The old stadium is flanked on three sides by houses, which are built quite close to it.

b Anfield has strong links with the local area, going back to 1892. It has many local fans. These links would be broken if the club moved out of the city. It would be harder for local fans to get to the new stadium, and most would be very upset by the move.

3 Other questions for the first column of the table could include:
Easy access by car?
Space for parking cars and coaches?
Space to build other facilities?
Will the public transport be able to cope?
How much will the land cost?
Will we get planning permission?
Will the local people object?
(Pupils won't be able to give scores for all items, from the text. They can put question marks in their table.)

4 It will add greatly to the value of this exercise if pupils draw the park roughly to scale. (And say three times the size shown in the OS map.) So they could measure the park on the OS map, use the scale to work out its real-life dimensions, and draw it (roughly) to a larger scale. Pupils could also look at Walter's mental map on page 20 of their books, to remind themselves of some park features.

They will also need a feel for the distances and dimensions involved. So compare the dimensions of the park, and the stadium, with some local distances and dimensions: for example the length of the front of your school. Pupils can use the (estimated) dimensions given for the stadium to work out where it will fit on their sketch maps.
Some questions for pupils to think about:

- Would it make sense to build near the existing car park?
- Is it best to avoid the cemetery side of the park?
- There are boating ponds, tennis courts and a bandstand in the upper part of the park, and many paths. There is also a small school, not marked on the OS map (but see Walter's map). Is it best to avoid these?
- Will you need to knock down any houses? You can buy them from their owners and then demolish them. (The houses along the park, opposite the current stadium, have in fact been demolished to make way for the new stadium.)

5 a You will need to talk through the three strands of sustainable development with the pupils – and particularly if they have not done Unit 3.8 already.

b Possibilities are: flats (with long-term season ticket holders given priority?); overnight accommodation for fans coming for big matches, who would love to spend a night in the old grounds; leave part unchanged as a memorial, with guided tours; have an interactive museum with archives of photos, footage etc, and a cinema dedicated to football; workspaces for local small businesses, especially new start-ups; a fitness centre for elderly people (who might be unwilling to go to one in the new stadium). Pupils may come up with better ideas.

6 Point out that the letter-writer is not necessarily against the new stadium. Pupils can use the letter on page 110 of the students' book as a model.

8.4

Who are the losers?

About this unit

This unit introduces the idea of fair trade (to be picked up again in *geog.3*). It looks at the production of hand-stitched footballs in Sialkot in Pakistan. Pupils meet Omar, a stitcher (whose 'story' is based on reports by Oxfam and other organisations). In 'Your turn', pupils explore the supply chain, and where the money goes.

Key ideas

- The sports goods industry (like many others) gets goods manufactured in poorer countries, where wages are lower, in order to reduce costs and increase profits.
- 75% of the world's hand stitched footballs are made in and around the city of Sialkot in Pakistan. Football stitching is hard work and the pay is very low.
- The stitchers receive only a very small fraction of the final price of the football.

Key vocabulary

vicious circle, profit, supply chain (see the glossary at the end of this book)

Skills practised in 'Your turn'

- Numerical skills: simple calculations; calculating percentages; drawing a pie chart
- Thinking skills: predicting consequences; arranging text to form a logical argument; coming up with suggestions

Unit outcomes

By the end of this unit, most pupils should be able to:

- explain the terms given in 'Key vocabulary' above
- explain why companies get footballs, and other sports goods, made in poorer countries
- state that football stitchers receive only a small fraction of what a customer pays

Resources

For starter **1**: a leather football; a piece of stiff leather; a strong needle and strong thread
For starter **2**: eight role cards, each with a label for one role listed below; they could be on thread to hang around pupils' necks; 50 squares of paper to represent £50
For starter **3** and plenary **2**: see *geog.1 resources and planning OxBox CD-ROM*

Ideas for a starter

1. Hold up a leather football. Ask: Which do you think is the hardest work – sewing the ball or kicking it? Point out the number of seams, and that they are sewn by hand.

   Offer the piece of leather, a strong needle and some thread. Ask for volunteers to sew some stitches. (Careful.) Discuss how difficult this is. Ask pupils to imagine doing it for 12 or 14 hours a day, day after day, and for around £2.60 per day.

2. Assign roles to eight pupils to match the table on page 113 of the students' book: football stitcher; factory owner; supplier of materials; supplier of other services to the factory; shipper to the UK; British sports goods company; sports shop; customer.

   First, the eight pupils arrange themselves in logical order, with prompting from the class, and act out the *supply chain*. For example the supplier of materials passes a bit of leather to the factory owner, who passes it to the stitcher; the stitcher passes a finished football to the factory owner who passes it to the shipper, and so on.

   Now give the customer £50 to buy a football. The customer gives this to the shop, the shop pays the supplier £31, and so on, to match the table. For the 50ps, divide a piece of paper in two. Invite comments about where the money goes. Is it fair?

3. With books closed, display the first photo from page 112 of the students' book, and Omar's photo from page 113. What's the connection? Which person do you think is working harder? Which do you think works longer hours?

Ideas for plenaries

Plan plenaries for strategic points throughout the lesson, as well as at the end.

1 With books closed, ask a pupil to read out Omar's story. Then discuss.

2 (Similar to starter **3**.) Display the first photo from page 112 of the students' book, and the photo of Omar from page 113. How are these two people connected? Which person do you think is working harder? Which works longer hours?

3 Who puts most work into the football, along that football supply chain?

4 Who is the main winner, in that football supply chain? Who is the main loser?

5 Who has the least power, in that football supply chain? Who has the most power?

6 The German company Adidas provides sports goods. (It provides the strip for the Chelsea team – see page 104 of the students' book.) Where do you think it gets its sports goods made? (In Cambodia, Vietnam, Indonesia, Thailand and other Asian countries.) Why do you think this is?

7 The same eight pupils, or eight different pupils, could act out the situations given in question **3** of 'Your turn'. This could be very powerful.

8 Question **5** of 'Your turn' could become group work. Divide the class into groups with these roles: customer, shop, sports goods company, factory owner, stitcher. Each group discusses what could be done to make the situation more fair, and whether it really wants this to happen. Then representatives from each group get together and see if they can come up with a joint solution. Will there be winners? Who? Will there be losers? Who? (Note: there are already Fairtrade footballs. See suggestion 21 on page 149 of this book.)

9 Do you think our football clubs should do something about the low pay for stitchers?

10 Ask pupils what they think *supply chain* means. Discuss it for footballs. Are there supply chain for other things? (For example for the milk you buy in supermarkets?)

11 Do you think it's fair when our standard of living is at the expense of other people's?

12 What has this topic got to do with geography?

Further class and homework activities

Worksheet 8F on *geog.1 resources and planning OxBox CD-ROM*

Suggestions 20 – 22 on page 149 of this book

Answers to 'Your turn'

1 5769 days (nearly 16 years)

2 This table gives the percentages and angles for the pie chart:

Item	Percentage	Angle in pie chart
shop	20	72
supplier	62	223.2
shipping and transport companies	3	10.8
factory owner	10	36
supplier of materials	3	10.8
stitcher	1	3.6
other factory costs	1	3.6

c The British supplier gets the largest share, and the stitcher the smallest.

3 a They may get thrown out – and have trouble finding other jobs, in which case they could starve. (No social security.)

b The British company might decide to go elsewhere.

c The shops might try to find a cheaper supplier. Otherwise they will charge their customers more.

d Many people in Sialkot would lose their jobs and would probably be unable to find other jobs.

e Many people would lose their jobs as the machine took over.

4 The order should be:

2 … so he has even less chance to go to school …

3 … so he can't learn new skills (like reading and writing) …

4 … so he can't get a better job …

5 … but every year food and clothes cost a little more …

5 The obvious thing is to pay the stitchers more. But discuss the implications of this. The diagram at the bottom of page 112 will help. Also discuss who has the most power to change things. Could it be the customer?

8.5

London 2012

About this unit

This unit is about the Olympic and Paralympic Games that London will host in 2012. One aim of London 2012 is the regeneration of the Lower Lea Valley. In 'Your turn' pupils consider the work needed to get the site ready for the games, answer questions based on a map of the Olympic Park, and consider who'll benefit, and who may lose out.

Key ideas

- The Olympic and Paralympic Games are not just the world's top multi-sport event. They are also an opportunity to regenerate an area.
- The site chosen for the London 2012 games is a neglected area in the Lower Lea Valley in east London.
- In any development project there will be winners – and there may be some losers.

Key vocabulary

Olympic and Paralympic Games, regenerate, contaminated (see the glossary at the end of this book)

Skills practised in 'Your turn'

- Geography skills: finding information from a map; measuring linear distances on a map
- Thinking skills: giving a reason; identifying who may benefit and who may lose out, in the 2012 Olympics

Unit outcomes

By the end of this unit, most pupils should be able to:

- say where in London the Olympic Park will be
- recognize that the Olympic and Paralympic Games can lead to regeneration
- describe ways in which the 2012 Olympics will help to regenerate a run-down area
- recognize that London 2012 will bring benefits – but that some people will feel they have lost out, and not everyone is in favour

Resources

For starters **1** and **2**, and plenaries **1** and **2**: all images from the book are on *geog.1 resources and planning OxBox CD-ROM*
For plenaries **4** and **5**: see *geog.1 resources and planning OxBox CD-ROM*

Ideas for a starter

1. With books closed, display the lower left image from page 114 of the students' book (an artist's impression of the Olympic Park in 2012). Without saying what it is, explain that this site will host a major event. Can anyone guess which one? Where is the site? Then use the maps on page 114 of the students' book to show where the Olympic Park is located.
2. With books closed, display the map from page 115 of the students' book (the Olympic Park). Without saying what it is, ask: What do you think this shows? Where do you think it is located?
3. What does *London 2012* mean? (You could display the logo from *google images*.)
4. Draw the Olympic circles on the board. This is a clue to what this lesson is about. Can you guess? And what can you tell me about the Games?

Ideas for plenaries

Plan plenaries for strategic points throughout the lesson, as well as at the end.

1. Pupils look at the map on page 115 of the students' book. (Or you could display it.) When you call out their names, pupils make one statement about it – trying not to repeat what someone else has said.
2. Pupils look at the map on page 115 of the students' books. (Or you could display it.) Ask questions like these: What goes on in the media centre? Why is there a sponsors' village? Why security checks? What's a velodrome? What goes on in the aquatics centre? Where are the car parks? Why? Where will *you* head for, if you visit the Olympic Park?
3. About how big is the Olympic Park, in square kilometres? How did you estimate this?
4. Discuss the 'Did you know?' facts on page 115 of the students' book.
5. Name another sporting event (local or otherwise). Then draw two columns. In one show groups that may benefit as a result of the event. In the other, show groups that may lose out.
6. Show the movie: *The London Olympics: Are people pleased?*
7. Show the movie: *The London Olympics: How will people be affected?*

Further class and homework activities

Worksheet 8G on *geog.1 resources and planning OxBox CD-ROM*

Suggestions 23 – 25 on page 149 of this book

Answers to 'Your turn'

1. The world's top multi-sport event, originally modelled on the Olympic Games of Ancient Greece, that were held in the village of Olympia, near Mount Olympus. They are held every four years. Nearly 200 countries can take part. (199 countries have National Olympic Committees.)
2. The equivalent games, for athletes with disabilities.
3. Because it takes so long (and costs so much) to prepare for them.
4. Pupils should list at least some of these:
   arranging for the money that's needed (where will it come from?)
   getting planning permission buying the land from its owners
   giving them alternative sites? knocking down existing buildings
   cleaning up the contaminated soil (it gets dug up and washed)
   laying power supplies to the site roads into the site for builders
   designing the venues and other buildings getting builders in
   project managing the building bus, train and road links to the site
   accommodation for athletes places for athletes to train
   transport around the site for officials and athletes car parking
   places to eat places to shop (for merchandise) ticket offices
   toilets litter disposal security for everyone
5. Pupils can use the map and map key to list the different ways to get to the Olympic Village, and the stations that serve it.
6. Pupils should understand that 'as the crow flies' means the straight-line distance.
   - **a** about 500 metres, measured from the centre of the National Rail icon. (For comparison, ask pupils to name somewhere that's about 500 metres from the school gates.)
   - **b** About 1100 metres, or 1.1 km, measured to the nearest point of the stadium. (Will the athletes walk everywhere?)
7. Encourage pupils to think broadly here.
   - **a** All these will benefit:
     construction companies, designers and architects involved in building the site, and all the workmen they employ on short-term contracts; transport companies such as National Rail; taxi firms; catering, cleaning, and security staff, employed during the Games; journalists, newspapers and TV stations (plenty to write and broadcast about, and TV can attract high-level advertising during Games slots); sponsors (world-wide exposure); the companies who provide the on-site food; companies who make Olympic Games merchandise; people who design and print tickets, Park maps, and other material; hotels in and around London, where all the visitors will stay; firework companies (for opening and closing ceremonies); companies that make uniforms (for guides etc); athletes (chance to meet top-level competition and perhaps win glory); Olympic officials (chance to travel etc); visitors (they will see exciting events); TV viewers who like sports; schools around the country (sports development encouraged) and so on. And also the commuters who will benefit from the improved transport links in the future; and estate agents and houseowners in the area, since house prices will go up as the area improves. (See Unit 8.6 too, for what will become of the Park after the Games.)
   - **b** People who may feel they have lost out:
     the people and companies who were moved off the site to make way for the Olympic Park; those Londoners who didn't want the Olympics and have to pay more council tax because of them; people who hate non-stop sport on TV; commuters in London who will have to cope with even more crowded transport during the Games, charities that would have won Lottery funding if it weren't for the Games, other important services that the government could have spent the money on, and so on.
     (See Unit 8.6 for more about funding.)

8.6

Making the Olympics sustainable

help at a glance

About this unit

This unit is about one aspect of London's Olympic bid: the commitment to sustainable development. It gives ways in which the planners intend to make the Olympic Park sustainable. In 'Your turn', pupils explore these, and how different people might benefit. They identify some short- and long-term benefits. And then they respond to a cynic.

Key ideas

- Sustainable development is development that brings economic, social and environmental benefits.
- The aim is to make the Olympic Park a truly sustainable development.
- Here are some of the main ways this will be achieved:
  - through cleaning up a neglected and contaminated site and its waterways
  - by providing power for the Park from renewable sources
  - by ensuring that the buildings can be used after the games, for homes and business
  - by ensuring excellent public transport links, to cut down car use during the games, and later.

Key vocabulary

sustainable development, economic, social, environmental, infrastructure, National Lottery, council tax, recycle (see the glossary at the end pf this book)

Skills practised in 'Your turn'

- Literacy skills: explaining a term in own words
- Thinking skills: identifying features that will benefit different individuals; picking out short- and long-term economic, social and environmental benefits; responding to the statement that the Olympic Games are a huge waste of money

Unit outcomes

By the end of this unit, most pupils should be able to:

- explain what sustainable development means
- give at least four ways in which the Olympic Park will be an example of sustainable development
- give examples of short-term and long-term economic, social and environmental benefits, from the 2012 Olympics

Resources

For starters **1** and **2**: all images from the book are on *geog.1 resources and planning OxBox CD-ROM*
For plenary **6**: see *geog.1 resources and planning OxBox CD-ROM*

Ideas for a starter

1. With books closed, display the photo of the building being demolished, from page 116 of the students' book. Say it's connected to the Olympic Games. In what way? Then ask pupils to guess how much it will cost to host the Olympic Games.
2. Point out the photo of the train on page 116 of the students' book (or display it). It's one of the new trains being laid on for the Olympics. It's called the Javelin. Why? Why is it needed? (A 'Did you know?' on page 115 gives a clue.) Do you think they'll stop using it after the games are over?
3. Draw a 'sustainable development' diagram on the board, like the one on page 83 of this book. Ask pupils to come to the front of the class, and explain what the terms at the end of the 'legs' mean.

Ideas for plenaries

Plan plenaries for strategic points throughout the lesson, as well as at the end.

1 Do starter **3** as a plenary, if not used as a starter.

2 Ask six pupils to read the text in panels A to F aloud, to the class. Other pupils' books are closed.

3 Look at panel A. Which do you think is the most important item in it, for making the Olympic Park sustainable? Go around the class for answers. Repeat for each panel. (Or combine with **2** and ask the question after the pupil has read out the text.)

4 The 2012 Olympics will cost £9 billion to host. Ask a pupil to come to the board and write that number in full. (£9 000 000 000) Does everyone agree?

5 Draw a money bag on the board. Add some arrows and labels as shown. Then invite pupils to add more. What if hardly any money came in? Would it matter?

6 Use the interactive activity for Unit 8.6 as a plenary.

Further class and homework activities

Interactive activity for Unit 8.6 on *geog.1 resources and planning OxBox CD-ROM*, if not used as a plenary

Interactive quiz for Chapter 8 on *geog.1 resources and planning OxBox CD-ROM*

Suggestions 26 – 28 on page 149 of this book

Assessment materials for Chapter 8 on *geog.1 assessment file & OxBox CD-ROM*

Review 'Your goals for this chapter' on page 105 of *geog.1* students' book

Answers to 'Your turn'

1 It's important to ensure pupils understand the idea of sustainability and its three strands, before they start on the other questions.

2 **a** C1, C3, C4 and probably D1 **b** C6

c D3 **d** any or all of D2, 4, 5

e any of D, and E1, E4 **f** A1 and 4

g B 2 and 3, and E2 and 3, since through these measures the Park aims to minimize its contribution to global warming (which is affecting people all over the world, including in Kenya)

3 Some suggestions:

Economic

Short term: earnings for all the companies and workers directly involved in building the site, running the services during the Games, and so on; and for all those indirectly involved (hotels, merchandise manufacturers, transport companies and so on).

Long term: earnings from increased tourism to the UK in the future; earnings for the businesses who set up in the Park, and the people who will work in them; a financial boost to the surrounding area, which is likely to attract more businesses as a result of the improvements (including for transport) carried out for the Games.

Social

Short term: enjoyment of the Games, for participants, visitors, and TV viewers; tickets won't cost too much so lots of people can enjoy at least one visit to the Games; a sense of excitement in London; people from all over the world gather, and meet each other.

Long term: the improved transport links to the area will make life better for commuters; the Olympic Park may turn out to be a great place to live and work; the Games will give a long-term boost to sport in the UK as well as providing top-class venues for us all to enjoy; people in the UK may be encouraged to take more exercise and become healthier, thanks to the Games.

Environmental

Short term: people will arrive by public transport, bike or on foot, minimizing pollution during the Games; the huge amount of waste that will be generated will be recycled, and not fill up landfill sites.

Long term: transformation of a run-down contaminated site to a clean one that looks good and is a healthier place for humans and wildlife. Waterways all cleaned up. Use of renewable energy in the Park will continue into the future.

8 Pupils should have enough information from the unit to respond. Encourage them to think about it and make up their own minds. (Make it clear that they don't have to respond in favour of the Games.)

This would be a good topic for a class debate. Pupils could do further research into the cost of the games.

8 Further suggestions for class and homework

Most of these suggestions are addressed to your pupils. Where research or further resources are needed, the internet will almost certainly provide the answer. (Eg *google* and choose *Web* or *Images*.)

Geography and sport

1 Chart your preferences What is your favourite sport?
a) Each pupil stands up, names his or her favourite sport, then sits down again. (Encourage them to come up with a sport, rather than say 'None' – but all answers should be recorded.) All pupils keep a tally. You may need to show an example.
b) Then pupils draw up a bar chart. If a large number of sports are given, they should draw thin horizontal bars.
c) Next, pupils draw a pie chart for the same results. (The angle per pupil will be around 12° so it will be possible to show a slice for all sports mentioned.)
d) Finally, pupils write a paragraph commenting on the results. For example: *For over half the class, the favourite sport was ____. ____ pupils preferred team sports.*
Pupils could create the graphs by hand, or in Excel. They could add images of the different sports to their report. ***/****

2 So you don't like football? What is your favourite sport? What geographical questions could you ask about it? Brainstorm some questions – then find out the answers! ******

3 Today's sporting events From a newspaper, note down at least 20 sporting events in the UK today, and where. Mark and name the locations on an outline map of the UK, and add labels to say what the events are. (Or use events from last weekend. Note – not more than 4 from any one sport.) ***/****

4 Overseas players and coaches Many Premier League players and coaches come from outside the UK. Stick an outline map of the world in the centre of a larger piece of paper. Colour and label the countries that overseas players and coaches come from. Then write their names and Premier League clubs in boxes around the map. Colour-code these to match their home countries, and link them to the countries by leader lines. (This could be done for either men's or women's Premier League clubs, or both.) ***/****

5 Top athletes in other sports Pupils can modify **4** for their chosen sport. For example choose cricket players from overseas in British cricket teams, or choose their favourite athletes and 'map' them. ***/****

6 Getting to the match Your favourite football team is playing at Wembley Stadium. (Or somewhere else quite a distance from where you live.) You can travel to the match by car, train or coach.
Plan your route for each form of transport, and draw a sketch map for it. Then work out which journey will be: fastest; shortest in distance; cheapest. (For a car journey, think about petrol costs. And think about whether you'll need to stay away overnight. That will be an added cost.)
Pupils could work in groups for this, with each group researching one method of travel to a given fixture, and pooling the results. *******

7 It doesn't have to be football! Pupils can modify **6** for any event in their chosen sport, within the UK. The event should be a reasonable distance from pupils' homes.

8 A match abroad Your favourite football club is playing abroad – and you are going to the match! You can choose the location. (It must be in Europe.) Find out the different ways to get to the city / town and how much each will cost.
Show the routes on a map, and say which route is fastest / shortest in distance / cheapest. *******

9 Not football! Modify **8** for other sports. For example it could be a cricket tour, the World Cup final in rugby, a skiing holiday. Show the routes on a map, and say which route is fastest / shortest in distance / cheapest. *******

The football business

10 Football-related jobs Pupils list all the jobs *within* a football club in one column. For example player, football manager, coach, secretary, cleaner. And then jobs that depend indirectly on fooball in a second column: football reporter, football strip manufacturer, coach driver, and so on. They underline those in the tertiary sector in one colour, secondary in another, and primary (if they come up with any) in a third. Invite comments on the results. ***/**/*****

11 Jobs in your sport Give examples of 20 jobs linked to your favourite sport (if not football). Classify as in **10** above.

12 Why companies sponsor teams Companies pay out lots of money to sponsor football teams. Ask pupils to draw a flow chart to explain why. Or give them this flow chart to complete, using the list in italics below it. ***/**/*****

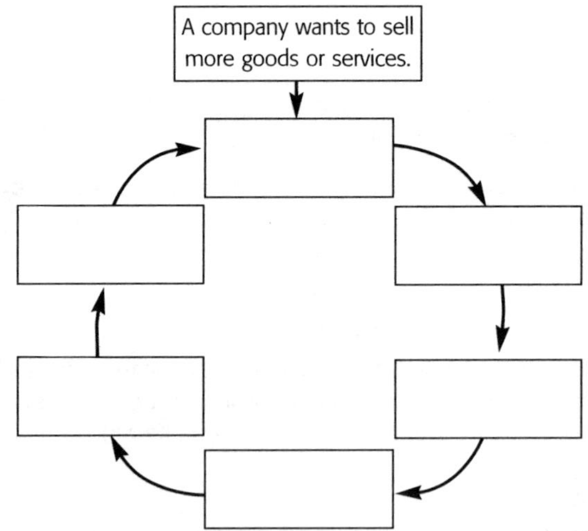

The missing text:
So the sponsor is happy.
So it wins more matches.
So they buy more of its goods or services.
So it sponsors the team.
So the fans at the match, and watching it on TV, see the sponsor's name.
Meanwhile the club uses the money to buy better players.

13 Why is TV willing to pay so much for football? The TV companies compete to pay millions for the rights to screen football matches. Why? Pupils see if they can come up with a flow chart to explain. ****/*****

14 The ethics of strip change Many football clubs change their strip frequently – and charge their fans high prices for replica strip.
a You are a mum or dad, tired of the pressure to buy new replica strip, and tired of the high prices. Write a letter to the Football Association to complain about it. Your letter must be at least 150 words long. ******
b You work for the FA, dealing with complaints from the public. Write a polite reply. ******
Pupils could work in pairs on this, to write both letters.

15 Policing football The police are kept busy on match days. Find out from the local police what preparations they make for match days. (Invite a policeman in to give a talk?) *****

Liverpool FC is moving home

16 Location requirements
a Do a spider map to show location requirements for a football club. Now do the same for:
a secondary school a youth club a dry ski slope
a windfarm a police station a petrol station
a nuclear power station a bank a jail an airport
b Pick out two that have very similar requirements.
c Pick out two that have very different requirements.
You could share out **a** among the class. ***/**/*****

17 On Anfield's doorstep What's the area like, around the Liverpool FC stadium?
a Describe it, using the photo and OS map on page 111 of the students' book
b You are head teacher in the school at 3693 on the OS map. Write to the chairman of Liverpool FC, asking for special privileges for the pupils in your school, since it is on the club's doorstep. (For example season tickets? Use of training grounds? Special sports coaching? Sponsorship for school events? Anything else you can think of? Within reason …) ******

18 Your local stadium Find your local stadium (or the stadium of your favourite club) on a 1: 50 000 OS map. Draw a sketch map and add important features about the location – main roads, train and bus stations and so on. Find out details about the stadium – how many people it can hold, how old it is and so on. (The club can provide details.) Finally write a report about it. ******

19 The effects of a stadium How does your local stadium affect the area and the people who live near it? Brainstorm the kinds of people you would ask about this (for example local residents, pub owners, police). Which different groups of residents would you ask, to get a full picture? (Age / sex.) How would you collect and record the information? Draw up a questionnaire. Then if possible contact/ interview people, and write a report. (See *How to carry out an enquiry* in *Skills kit* on *geog.world CD-ROM*.) ******

Who are the losers?

20 Better than school? Omar works very hard for little pay.
a 100 years ago, you too might have been at out at work – in a factory, or down a mine, or up a chimney. Find a description of children at work and read it out. (Try *David Copperfield* or *Hard Times* by Charles Dickens, *Lark Rise to Candleford* by Flora Thompson or *The Water Babies* by Charles Kingsley. Or ask your English or History teacher for suggestions.) ******
b Why did conditions change, for children in the UK? Find evidence to back up your answer. (History teacher?) *******

21 Find out about Fairtrade footballs Do an internet search on Fairtrade footballs. Report to the class. ****/*****

22 Check your clothing! Pupils check labels on their own clothing, including school uniform, to see where items were made, and do a tally chart for them. They pool the results for the class, and draw a bar chart showing number of items per country. (Or, even better, do a located bar chart, with the countries shaded and labelled on an outline world map, the bars standing in their countries, and a 'scale' for the bars.) Then they try to explain any patterns they find. ***/**/*****

The 2012 Olympics

23 You are a top athlete from Ancient Greece You took part in Games in Olympia. And you were champion. Tell us about it. Pupils can use the library or internet for research about the Ancient Olympics. ***/****

24 The modern Olympic Games They have been going since 1896. Find out which countries played host each year. (Ignore the Winter Olympics.) Shade and label them, and give the year(s) they were host, on an outline map of the world. ***/****

25 Getting to the Beijing Olympics, 2008 Pupils have tickets for events – and bravely decide to travel overland, by road and rail. Plot a route from the UK. ****/****

Making the Olympics sustainable

26 Making your school more sustainable What could be done to make your school a more sustainable organisation? Give us your ideas. Sketches and digital photos welcomed. ******

27 But what about the flights? Around 17000 athletes and officials will attend the 2012 Olympics. Most will fly here. Many visitors will fly in too. Their planes will use jet fuel, which gives carbon dioxide when it burns.
a Find out how airline travel contributes to global warming.
b Write a letter to the International Olympics Committee about whether the Olympics can ever be truly sustainable.
c See if you can suggest a solution to this dilemma. *******

28 An Olympics acrostic Write SUSTAINABLE OLYMPICS down a page. Then write 19 sentences about the 2012 Olympics, using the letters of those words as the first letters of your sentences. (Or you could use just SUSTAINABLE.) ***/****

9 Our restless planet

Helping you deliver the KS3 Programme of Study

This chapter addresses these areas of the Programme of Study:

Key concepts

Place Understand the physical and human characteristics of real places; develop geographical imaginations of places. **Space** Know where places and landscapes are located. **Scale** Make links between scales, to develop understanding of geographical ideas. **Physical and human processes** Explain how physical processes shape places, landscapes and societies.

Key processes

Geographical enquiry Ask geographical questions; record and display information; analyse and evaluate evidence, presenting findings to draw and justify conclusions. **Graphicacy and visual literacy** Use maps at a range of scales, photographs, and other geographical datas. **Geographical communication** Communicate knowledge and understanding using geographical vocabulary and conventions in both talk and writing.

The big picture

These are the key ideas behind this chapter.

- The hard outer part of the Earth is cracked into big slabs, which we call plates.
- Plates are always on the move, dragged by convection currents in the hot soft rock below them.
- Plates can push into or pull away from each other, or slide past each other. All these movements cause earthquakes, and some cause volcanic eruptions.
- So the earthquake and volcano sites around the Earth form a pattern, which matches the pattern of plate edges.
- Earthquakes and eruptions cause a great deal of damage, and loss of life.
- We can't stop them. All we can do is help the survivors in the short term, and look for ways to protect people from these hazards in the long term.
- This costs a lot of money. So poorer countries generally cope less well than richer countries with these hazards, and may depend on richer countries for help.

A pupils' version of this big picture is given in the *geog.1* students' book opener for Chapter 9, and in *geog.1 resources and planning OxBox CD-ROM*, for the whiteboard.

The chapter outline

Use this, and their chapter opener, to give pupils a mental roadmap for the chapter.

9 **Our restless planet** As the pupils' chapter opener, this is an important part of the chapter; see page 11 for notes about using chapter openers

9.1 **A slice through the Earth** The layers in the Earth, and a closer look at the crust

9.2 **Our cracked Earth** Plates, and their link with earthquakes and volcanoes

9.3 **How are the plates moving?** The different kinds of plate movements, and how they cause earthquakes and eruptions – and can even make mountains grow

9.4 **Earthquakes** What they are, the Richter scale, and the damage earthquakes do

9.5 **Earthquake in Pakistan** Case study: the earthquake that destroyed the town of Balakot, in northern Pakistan, in 2005

9.6 **Tsunami!** Case study: the tsunami in the Indian Ocean in 2004

9.7 **Volcanoes** The structure of volcanoes, and the damage eruptions can do

9.8 **Montserrat: living with an active volcano** Case study: how life on a Caribbean island changed forever, in 1995, when a sleeping volcano awoke

9.9 **Coping with earthquakes and eruptions** Our short- and long-term responses

Objectives and outcomes for this chapter

Objectives	Unit	Outcomes
Most pupils will understand:		Most pupils will be able to:
• that the Earth is made up of different layers	9.1	• name and describe the three layers that make up the Earth
• what the Earth's plates are, and why they move	9.2	• explain what a plate is and why it moves; name at least five plates; draw a simple labelled cross-section of a moving plate
• that plate movements result in earthquakes and volcanic eruptions	9.2, 9.3	• explain that earthquake and volcano sites occur along plate edges; describe the three ways in which plates move relative to each other; explain why each causes earthquakes, and some cause eruptions
• what earthquakes are, and what damage they do, and why	9.4, 9.5	• explain what causes earthquakes, and why everything shakes; give examples of earthquake damage; explain what the Richter scale tells us
• what tsunami are, and what damage they do	9.6, 9.7	• explain what causes a tsunami, and why it can affect many countries; describe the damage it can do
• what volcanoes are, and what kinds of damage eruptions do, and why	9.8	• draw a labelled cross-section of a volcano; list the products from eruptions, and the damage they do
• that we have similar kinds of response to earthquake and volcano disasters	9.8	• give three examples each of short- and long-term responses to earthquake and volcano disasters
• that poorer countries may find it more difficult to cope effectively with such disasters	9.9	• explain why poorer countries may find it harder to cope with these disasters, and protect people

These tie in with 'Your goals for this chapter' in the pupils' chapter opener, and with the opening lines in each unit, which give the purpose of the unit in a pupil-friendly style.

Opportunities for assessment

See the formal assessment materials for this chapter on *geog.1 assessment file & OxBox CD-ROM*. They include a level-marked assessment with success criteria and a feedback form, interactive assessments, a scored test, and a self-assessment form.

There are other opportunities for assessment too. For example, you could use some of the more extended 'Your turn' questions in the students' book, worksheets or longer learning activities from *geog.1 resources and planning OxBox CD-ROM*, or some of the 'Further suggestions for class and homework' at the end of this chapter.

Getting ready for this chapter

Some of the starters and plenaries suggested for this chapter may need resources prepared in advance. Check out the *Resources* section on the 'Help at a glance' pages that follow.

geog.1 resources & planning OxBox CD-ROM has all the photos and diagrams from the chapter, for whiteboard display, plus movies and interactive materials. You will find these very useful for devising your own starters and plenaries. In addition, *geog.world CD-ROM* is a rich source of further material, including interactive webfiles and skills lessons.

About the chapter starter

Page 118 of *geog.1* students' book shows the abandoned town of Plymouth, on the Caribbean island of Montserrat, in 1997. In the background is the Soufriere Hills volcano. Plymouth was once the capital of Montserrat, with a population of around 3500. It was evacuated in 1995, when the volcano grew active. Since then, the town has been buried and burned by ashfalls and pyroclastic flows. In 2008, thirteen years later, the volcano was still active, and Plymouth, like much of the island, still out of bounds.

9.1

A slice through the Earth

About this unit

This unit is about the Earth's structure. It shows the different layers that make up the Earth, and then focuses on the lithosphere, and the convection currents in the soft rock below it. 'Your turn' gives pupils the chance to summarise what they have learned.

Key ideas

- The Earth is made up of three different layers: crust, mantle and core.
- The crust (that we live on) is solid; the core is partly solid, partly liquid; and much of the mantle is soft like butter, and even runny in places.
- There are two types of crust: **continental crust** (forms the continents, and is mainly granite); **oceanic crust** (lies under the oceans, and is mainly basalt).
- The crust and the upper part of the mantle form a hard layer called the lithosphere. This floats on the soft hot rock in the mantle.
- The convection currents in this soft hot rock are responsible for changing the face of the Earth, as you'll soon see.

Key vocabulary

crust, mantle, core, oceanic crust, continental crust, granite, basalt, trench, lithosphere, convection current   (see the glossary at the end of this book)

Skills practised in 'Your turn'

- Geography skills: drawing and labelling a cross-section
- Numeracy skills: simple calculations
- Thinking skills: filling in a table using information from the text

Unit outcomes

By the end of this unit, most pupils should be able to:

- explain the terms given in 'Key vocabulary' above
- name and describe the three layers that make up the Earth
- draw a simple diagram to show continental and oceanic crust, the lithosphere, the soft rock below it, and convection currents

Resources

For all starters, and plenary **7**: all images from the book are on *geog.1 resources and planning OxBox CD-ROM*
For starter **4**: a creme Easter egg, or other spherical chocolate with a runny centre; a plastic knife to open it with
For plenary **4**: samples of granite and basalt, roughly the same size

Ideas for a starter

Turn to the image of the Earth on page 4 of *geog.1* students' book for all these starters. (Or you could display it. It's in the material for Chapter 1.)

1. We know what it's like on the outside of the Earth. What do you think it's like inside? Write pupils' ideas on the board. Say you'll come back to them later. (See plenary **8**.)
2. Imagine you dig a tunnel down inside the Earth, under the school. What do you think it will be like at a depth of: 1 m ? 10 m ? 100 m ? 1 km ? 1000 km ? 6000 km ? Close your eyes and do a mind movie. Will you meet any animals on the journey?
3. You dig a hole straight through the Earth, passing through the centre. How deep will it be? Guess. (About 12 800 km. Or 20 times the distance from London to Edinburgh.)
4. Hold up a creme Easter egg or a spherical chocolate with a runny centre. Ask: Who can tell me what this and the Earth have in common? Open it up.

Ideas for plenaries

Plan plenaries for strategic points throughout the lesson, as well as at the end.

1. How do you feel about living on top of soft and melted rock? Do you think this rock has any affect on our lives? (You can come back to this one in later lessons.)
2. About the mantle: Can you think of any materials you eat that are hard when they are cold, but get softer when they're heated, and can even go runny? (Butter, chocolate, toffee? Candle wax is a non-edible example.)
3. The deepest hole so far is only just over 12 km. Name a place 12 km from here. So how do we know so much about inside the Earth? (From studying earthquake waves, and meteors from other planets. The speed and direction of earthquake waves are affected by the materials they pass through, and their temperatures.
4. Pass around samples of granite and basalt to show continental and oceanic crust. Ask pupils which they think is which, and to describe any differences. Does one feel any heavier (denser) than the other?
5. What's the difference between the crust and the lithosphere?
6. Make up a set of answers – or ask pupils to make up an answer each on a strip of paper. For example: *It's mainly liquid iron*. Pool the answers. The class has to guess the questions.
7. Display the photo of boiling rock from page 108 of the students' book. What do you think makes it so hot inside the Earth? (Some heat is still left from when the Earth formed; some is produced when unstable 'radioactive' atoms inside the Earth break down naturally.) This could also be a homework project. See suggestion 3 on page 170 of this book.
8. Return to pupils' comments on the board, from starter **1**. Ask pupils to say which can be ticked, and which need to be crossed out or corrected. (There will probably be some you won't have met in the unit. For example pupils may have suggested 'quiet'. In fact the Earth is full of sound waves – the *P* component of seismic waves – but these are outside the audible range for humans.)
9. With books closed, pupils call out a list of words from today's lesson. A pupil writes them on the board. The person who calls out a word then has to define it (or you nominate another pupil to do this).

Further class and homework activities

Interactive activity for Unit 9.1 on *geog.1 resources and planning OxBox CD-ROM*

Suggestions 1 – 5 on page 170 of this book

Answers to 'Your turn'

1

Layer	Made of ...	Solid or liquid?	How thick?
crust	rock	solid 8–65 km	
mantle	rock	outer part solid, inner part soft, and melted in places	2900 km
core			
– outer	iron and nickel	liquid	2220 km
– inner	iron and nickel	solid	1260 km

2 a Up to 6445 km (the crust varies from 8 to 65 km in thickness). That's about 7 times the length of Great Britain (from John o' Groats to Land's End).

b 322.25 hours. If you cycle 8 hours a day that's just over 40 days. Pretty strenuous cycling!

3 The missing labels, from left to right, are:

ocean
oceanic crust made of basalt
upper mantle
continental crust made of granite
the crust and upper mantle together form the lithosphere

9.2

Our cracked Earth

About this unit

This unit is about the Earth's plates. It starts with a map of earthquake and volcano sites around the world, to show how these form a pattern. This pattern is then explained by plate theory. 'Your turn' helps to familiarise pupils with the idea of plate movements.

Key ideas

- Earthquakes are caused by sudden rock movements.
- Volcanoes are where liquid rock erupts from the Earth's surface.
- The Earth's hard surface (the lithosphere) is cracked into huge slabs called plates. These float around on the soft rock below, dragged by convection currents.
- Earthquakes occur at plate edges, where the plates push into or slide past or pull away from each other. Volcanoes also occur at or close to plate edges.
- So a map of the Earth's main volcano and earthquake sites matches the plate map.

Key vocabulary

earthquake, volcano, plate, lithosphere, convection current, Ring of Fire (in *Did you know?*) (see the glossary at the end of this book)

Skills practised in 'Your turn'

- Geography skills: answering questions based on maps; drawing a diagram of a plate
- Numeracy skills: a calculation involving a change of units (km to cm)
- Thinking skills: coming up with reasons; predicting future changes

Unit outcomes

By the end of this unit, most pupils should be able to:

- define the terms given in 'Key vocabulary' above
- describe in general terms the pattern of earthquake and volcano sites around the world, and explain that this pattern is the result of plate movements
- explain what plates are, and name at least five of them
- explain what makes plates move
- draw a simple labelled cross-section of a moving plate (to show the structure of a plate, the soft rock below the plate, and a convection current in the soft rock)

Resources

For starter **2**: a hard-boiled egg, and something to tap the shell with, to crack it
For starter **3** and plenaries **1** and **2**: see *geog.1 resources and planning OxBox CD-ROM*
For plenary **3**: a 3-D relief map of the ocean floor (chosen from *google images*)
For plenary **4**: online access in the classroom, to show an animation for plate movements (type in *animation plate movements* in *google*; check in advance for level)

Ideas for a starter

1. Write the headings *Earthquakes* and *Volcanoes,* one on each half of the board. Then ask: What do you know about earthquakes? What do you know about volcanoes? Write down words or phrases to summarise pupils' responses. Could these be grouped in any way? For example: *causes consequences locations*?
2. Hold up an egg (hard-boiled, but don't say). Ask: What has this and the Earth got in common? Then tap on the shell and crack it. (Make sure the cracked pieces are not too small.) Ask: Now what else do it and the Earth have in common?
3. Use the interactive activity for Unit 9.2. Ask pupils to suggest answers. Reveal clues.

Ideas for plenaries

Plan plenaries for strategic points throughout the lesson, as well as at the end.

1 Turn to (or display) the map on page 110 of the students' book. Ask pupils to describe the pattern of earthquake and volcano sites. Each gives one fact, which should not be a repeat of an earlier one. Prompt pupils to notice where most earthquakes and volcanoes are, and whether there are more on land, or in the ocean. Facts can include negatives such as: *There are no volcanoes down the east coast of North America.*
Encourage pupils to look at the political map on pages 140 – 141 of *geog.1* students' book, to give more detail. For example, to name countries in high-risk areas.
This could also be a written exercise. See suggestion 6 on page 170 of this book.

2 Use the interactive activity for Unit 9.2, if you have not used it as a starter.

3 Display a 3-D relief map of the ocean floor from *google images*. Pupils see if they can identify plate edges, by comparing it with the map on page 111.

4 Display an animation of the Earth's plates. Type in *Earth plates animation* in *google*. Check them in advance, to find one the right level for KS3.

5 Use questions **1** and **2** in 'Your turn' as plenaries.

6 Use questions **4** and **5** in 'Your turn' as plenaries. (See the note about question **4** in the answer section below.)

7 Tell me the three *key* facts you learned today. Pupils discuss and agree on them. (Eg There are plates. They are moving. The movement causes earthquakes and volcanoes.)

8 Give pupils, working in pairs, three minutes to discuss what they've learned. Warn that you'll ask for feedback when the time is up. Then ask questions, some straight and some with a twist. For example:
- What are plates?
- What's our plate called?
- Why is London getting further from New York?
- Why are Europe and Asia on the move together?
- What's the difference between the crust and the lithosphere?
- Which do you think are the three most important things you learned today?

9 Choose a pupil to be in the hot seat. Another pupil asks him or her a question about what they've learned in today's lesson. Then nominate two different pupils (4–6 pairs in total). There's one golden rule: questions can not be repeated!

Further class and homework activities

Suggestions 6 –10 on page 170 of this book

Answers to 'Your turn'

1 a A shaking of the Earth's crust. It is caused by a sudden rock movement.
b A volcano is where lava (melted rock) erupts out through the Earth's surface..

2 a Eurasian **b** North American
c Indo-Australian **d** Pacific, or Nazca
e Nazca **f** Pacific

3 The drawing should be like the one in the middle of the strip on page 123, but with the crust, mantle and lithosphere labelled.

4 The Earth's hard surface is cracked into big slabs called plates. These are continually moving. Their movement causes earthquakes and volcanoes along and near the plate edges. So earthquakes and volcanos tend to lie along lines that match the plate edges.

5 It is not near a plate edge. But note that it used to be! Edinburgh sits on the remains of an extinct volcano, the mountains in North Wales are the remains of a volcanic plateau, and there are volcanic rocks throughout the UK.

6 484 million years! (Some pupils will need to be reminded that 1km = 1000 m and 1 m = 100 cm)

How are the plates moving?

About this unit

This unit describes the three ways in which the Earth's plates move, relative to each other, and shows how plate movements result in earthquakes, volcanoes, and mountain building. 'Your turn' gives pupils the chance to apply what they have learned.

Key ideas

- The Earth's plates can move apart, push into each other, or slide past each other.
- All plate movements cause earthquakes. But they give volcanoes only where they cause rock to get pushed down towards the mantle. This rock then melts and rises.
- When two continental plates push into each other, rock gets pushed and squeezed up to form fold mountains.

Key vocabulary

plate, magma, earthquake, volcano, fold mountain (see the glossary at end of this book)

Skills practised in 'Your turn'

- Geography skills: interpreting a map of the Atlantic Ocean floor; copying and labelling a plate diagram
- Thinking skills: explaining a set of facts by comparing maps

Unit outcomes

By the end of this unit, most pupils should be able to:

- define the terms given in 'Key vocabulary' above
- describe the three ways in which plates move relative to each other
- explain that all plate movements cause earthquakes, and why
- say which ones also give volcanoes, and why
- explain how fold mountains are formed, and name a range of fold mountains

Resources

For starter **1** and plenaries **3** and **7**: see *geog.1 resources and planning OxBox CD-ROM*

For starter **2** and plenary **4**: three ceramic tiles, identical except one has blackened sides

For plenary **1**: a sample of basalt rock

For plenary **2**: online access in the classroom, to show an animation for sea floor spreading (type in *animation sea floor spreading* in *google*; check in advance for level)

Ideas for a starter

1. Use the interactive activity for Unit 9.3 as a starter.
2. Hold up two tiles. Say that they represent plates, floating on soft rock. They are millions of sq km in area, and weigh billions of tonnes. Let them touch along one edge, then pull them apart. What will happen in the gap? Explain that when they move, the pressure on the soft rock in the gap drops. So this soft rock melts and rises. (When pressure falls, so do melting points.) The gap in effect becomes a volcano. Do you think there'll be earthquakes when the heavy plates move?

   Ask: In what other ways could the tiles move? Show that they can push into each other, and slide past each other.

   Swap one tile for one with blackened sides. This plate has oceanic crust. It's heavier than the other plate, which has continental crust. Show the two plates pushing into each other. One will start to sink at the edge. Which one do you think it will be? (Heavier materials sink.) What might happen to the rock when it sinks into the hot mantle? (It heats up and melts. So you get a volcano nearby.)
3. As for **2** but draw them on the board, and add the convection currents.

Ideas for plenaries

Plan plenaries for strategic points throughout the lesson, as well as at the end.

1. Show pupils the sample of basalt. The ocean floor is made of basalt. Where did it come from? The ocean floor has some very new, young, basalt. Why?
2. Display an animation of sea floor spreading. Type in *animation sea floor spreading* in *google*. Check them in advance, to find one the right level for KS3.
3. Do question **1** of 'Your turn' as a plenary. You could display the map (or a larger one from *google images*) and ask more questions. For example: Where will the newest basalt be, on this map? Over time, the basalt in the middle of the ridge is pushed out. Why? Where does it go? As you move out from the ridge, the basalt gets older. Why?
4. Plates are moving apart in places, creating new crust. But the Earth is not getting larger. Why not? (Because in other places, crust is being pushed down into the Earth, or squeezed upwards. Ask two pupils to demonstrate this using the tiles.)
5. For a reprise, draw a table like this one on the board (but without the answers, written in here in italics). Write the options *yes*, *no*, and *will do if it pushes crust down* beside the table. Pupils come up and write in one answer each, until the table is complete.

Plate movement	Does it make new crust?	Does it push crust up or down?	Does it cause earthquakes?	Does it cause volcanoes?
pulling apart	*yes*	*no*	*yes*	*yes*
pushing into each other	*no*	*yes*	*yes*	*will do, if it pushes crust down*
sliding past each other	*no*	*no*	*yes*	*no*

6. Will a map of the Earth look the same 50 million years from now? Discuss. Then you could display the map found at http://www.scotese.com/future.htm.
7. Show the movie *Underwater volcano.* Discuss it. Remind pupils that there are more volcanoes under the ocean than on land.

Further class and homework activities

Worksheet 9C on *geog.1 resources and planning OxBox CD-ROM*

Suggestions 11 – 15 on page 170 of this book

Answers to 'Your turn'

1 a There are four: North American, South American, African, and Eurasian **b** basalt

c Plates are moving apart, and magma is rising between them, creating the ridge, and new ocean floor.

d Yes. Any plate movement means large masses of rock are shifting, so you get earthquakes.

e Wherever plates are moving apart under the ocean. Eg between the Nazca and Pacific plates, and between the Antarctic and Indo-Australian plates. (Note: there will also be ridges where plates moved apart *in the past*.)

2 The drawing should look like the one on the right. Note that several potential earthquake sites are marked. (Earthquakes will occur anywhere rock gives way under pressure.)

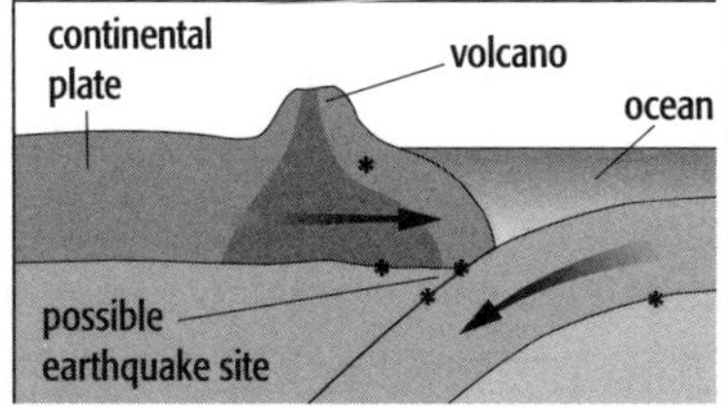

3 a Peru is near the boundary between the Nazca plate (ocean crust) and the South American plate (continental crust). The Nazca plate is sliding under the South American plate, causing earthquakes and volcanoes. (See the drawing at the bottom of page 124 of the students' book.)

b Iran is on the Iranian plate. This plate is under pressure from plates on all sides. But the crust is continental crust, so rock is being pushed up to form fold mountains.

c Italy is close to a meeting point between three plates that are pushing against each other. Heavier oceanic crust is sliding under the continental crust, causing earthquakes and volcanoes.

d Japan lies where the Eurasian, Philippine and Pacific plates are pushing into each other. This causes earthquakes in Japan. The heavier Pacific plate is sliding under the others, and this gives rise to volcanoes. Japan has more than 70 active volcanoes.

The islands of Japan are in fact volcanoes created by these plate movements. The volcanoes started on the ocean floor and grew taller and taller. In time they grew out of the water, giving Japan.

9.4

Earthquakes

About this unit

This unit explains what earthquakes are, introduces the Richter scale, and summarises the damage that earthquakes can do. In 'Your turn' pupils define terms, give an 'eye-witness' account of earthquake damage, and apply what they've learned, to different situations.

Key ideas

- Earthquakes are caused by sudden rock movement, when rock under strain gives way.
- The strain energy that has been building up in the rock is released, and spreads in all directions as seismic waves.
- These waves shake the Earth as they travel through it. Structures standing on the Earth's surface get shaken in turn, and may collapse.
- The magnitude of an earthquake is the amount of energy it releases.
- Magnitude is measured on the Richter scale. An increase of 1 unit on this scale represents a 10-fold increase in the amplitude of the waves (their height on a graph), and around a 30-fold increase in released energy – which means a lot more damage.

Key vocabulary

earthquake, seismic wave, focus, epicentre, aftershocks, seismometer, magnitude, Richter scale, tsunami (see the glossary at the end of this book)

Skills practised in 'Your turn'

- Literacy skills: giving definitions; writing an 'eye-witness' account of earthquake damage, using a photo as stimulus
- Thinking skills: drawing conclusions about earthquake damage from a diagram; coming up with explanations

Unit outcomes

By the end of this unit, most pupils should be able to:

- define the terms given in 'Key vocabulary' above
- explain what causes earthquakes, and why everything shakes
- explain what the Richter scale is, and that the higher the Richter number, the more damage an earthquake can do
- give examples of earthquake damage

Resources

For starter **1**: a chair and string; a rough surface to drag the chair over (eg concrete)
For starter **2**: a heavy brick; two sheets of coarse sandpaper; sticky tape; strong elastic
For starter **3**: sugar paper and coloured marker pens
For starter **4** and plenary **2**: see *geog.1 resources and planning OxBox CD-ROM*
For plenaries **4** and **5**: a pair of True/False cards for each pupil (green = true, red = false)

Ideas for a starter

1. Stand a chair on a rough surface. Pull it along by a loop of string tied to a leg; it will jerk along even when the pull is constant. Pupils observe and describe the motion. Explain that the sudden jerking of a huge mass of rock, when plates move, causes earthquakes.
2. Cover a heavy brick with sandpaper, taped in place. Loop a length of elastic around the sides. Place it on a second sheet of sandpaper and pull on the elastic. Watch what happens as the tension mounts. (The stretch in the elastic indicates 'strain'.)
3. Pupils work in pairs to create a spider map on sugar paper, showing what they know already about earthquakes. (They will return to their spider maps in plenary **6**.)
4. With books closed, display the photo from page 127. What do you think happened here?

Ideas for plenaries

Plan plenaries for strategic points throughout the lesson, as well as at the end.

1 It is important to generalise the sequence on page 126 of *geog.1* students' book

Point out that *any* rock that's being pushed or pulled will store up strain energy. But at some point it will suddenly give way at a fault, moving with a jolt and releasing the stored strain energy. The released energy causes shaking or earthquakes.

Also point out that the two masses of rock shown in the sequence could be any size. They could be the edges of plates millions of km in area, and weighing billions of tonnes. The forces could be pulling them apart, or making them slide past each other, or dragging one underneath the other. Or they could be rock masses some distance from the edges, but still affected by plate movements.

You could sketch other possibilities on the board. For example plates sliding past each other, as shown on the right.

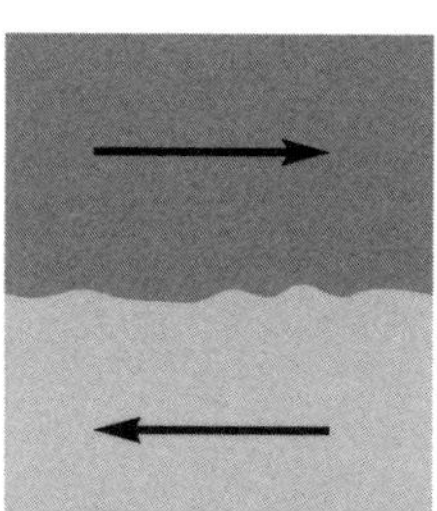

The plates lock like teeth, so strain builds up. They will suddenly lurch free, setting off an earthquake.

2 Show the movie *Earthquake*.

3 Questions **1** and **2** in 'Your turn' could be used as plenaries.

4 Call out 10 statements about earthquakes, some true and some false. For example:
Earthquakes occur only along plate edges.
The epicentre is directly below the focus.

Pupils have to raise green or red cards, or shout out *True* or *False*. Where a statement is false, nominate a pupil to correct it.

5 As for **4**, but give each pupil a number (from 1 up to the number of pupils in the class). Ask pupils to make up one T/F statement each. Then call out a number, and that pupil reads his or her statement to the class. Pupils raise cards in response.

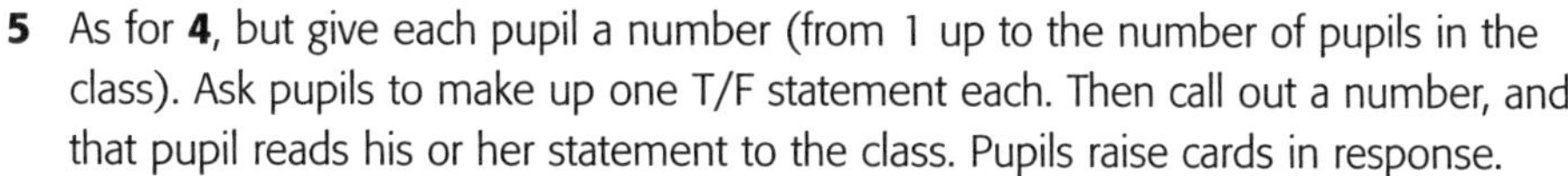

6 Pupils who did starter **3** return to their spider maps, and add anything else they have learned, in a different colour. They then come up with ways to group the information. (For example under *Cause, Effect, Size, Location*?) They could group by underlining in different colours, and add a colour key.

Further class and homework activities

Interactive activity for Unit 9.4 on *geog.1 resources and planning OxBox CD-ROM*

Worksheets 9A and 9D on *geog.1 resources and planning OxBox CD-ROM*

Suggestions 16 and 17 on page 170 of this book

Earthquake! in *geog.1, Plates, earthquakes and volcanoes*, on *geog.world CD-ROM*

The Kobe earthquake in *geog.1, Plates, earthquakes and volcanoes*, on *geog.world CD-ROM*

Answers to 'Your turn'

1 When enough tension builds up in a rock it will suddenly give way, like an elastic band snapping. The result is a (sudden) earthquake.

2 For definitions see the back of this book, or pages 142–143 in *geog.1* students' book.

4 a At A, since it is nearer the epicentre.

b At B, since buildings can collapse and kill people.

c A lot more damage, since it releases a lot more energy.

d 30 times

e At 5 am, since people will be asleep. By 10.30 am, many will have left for work and school. That does not mean they are out of danger. But they will have more chance to protect themselves if they are awake, for example by moving away from windows, and following the emergency earthquake drill.

5 a Chile is near the edge of the South American plate, close to where the heavier Nazca plate is sliding under it. So Chile has volcanoes, and many earthquakes.

b Chile is a long, narrow country. Its cities and towns are all close to the coast and therefore to the plate edge. So they would be badly affected by a large earthquake at the plate edge. Chile is also a poor country, so many homes may have been badly built. In addition to the damage caused by shaking, the earthquake also set off a tsunami, which destroyed homes along the coast.

c The earthquake set off a tsunami in the Pacific Ocean which travelled across the ocean, and drowned people in Japan. (It also drowned people in Hawaii and did extensive damage in Hawaii and Japan, and some damage on the west coast of the USA.)

9.5

Earthquake in Pakistan

About this unit

This unit is about the earthquake that destroyed the town of Balakot, in northern Pakistan, on 8 October 2005. Yasin's story is based on news reports: most of the schools collapsed, while classes were going on. A map shows the cause of the earthquake. In 'Your turn' pupils explain why it happened in simple words, write a diary entry for a survivor, and consider the likelihood of further earthquakes in the region.

Key ideas

- The boundary between the Indo-Australian and Eurasian plates runs up through Pakistan and across northern India.
- The Indo-Australian plate is pushing hard into the Eurasian plate. So the rock along the boundary is under great strain. It has many cracks (faults) in it, and there is a high risk of earthquakes.
- The death toll and devastation in Balakot were enormous, because buildings and other structures could not cope with being shaken. They collapsed, crushing people.

Key vocabulary

quake-proof (see the glossary at the end of this book)

Skills practised in 'Your turn'

- Geography skills: reading and interpreting maps
- Literacy skills: explaining in simple words; writing an empathic diary entry, with a photo as stimulus; writing a plan, in bullet points
- Thinking skills: giving reasons and explanations; coming up with a plan to protect people from earthquakes

Unit outcomes

By the end of this unit, most pupils should be able to:

- explain the term given in 'Key vocabulary' above
- explain why parts of Pakistan, Kashmir, and northern India are, and will continue to be, at high risk of earthquakes
- describe the effect of the earthquake on Balakot
- explain the part that poor building work played in its destruction
- say that Kashmir is split up and controlled by three countries: Pakistan, India, and China

Resources

For starter **2** and plenaries **3** and **7**: see *geog.1 resources and planning OxBox CD-ROM*
For plenary **5**: 10 or 12 toy bricks, dominoes or draughts pieces; a flat piece of wood, at least 1 cm thick, and A4-sized or larger (a breadboard or similar would do)

Ideas for a starter

1. Who can tell me where Pakistan is (without looking at a map)?
2. With books closed, display the map from page 129 of *geog.1* students' book. What does it show? Which of these countries might be at high risk of earthquakes? Why?
3. With class books closed, read out, or choose a pupil to read out, Yasin's story. Discuss it.

Ideas for plenaries

Plan plenaries for strategic points throughout the lesson, as well as at the end.

1 Ask six pupils to read out the earthquake factfile from page 128 of the students' book, a section each. This should help the class to grasp the enormity of the damage.

2 Why was Balakot at high risk of earthquakes? Ask a pupil to explain. Interrupt part-way through, and ask another pupil to continue.

3 If you did not use starter 2: display the map from page 129 of *geog.1* students' book. What does it show? Why was Balakot at high risk of earthquakes? Do you think other parts of Pakistan are at risk? Why? From this map, which other countries may also be at risk? (The map on pages 140 – 141 of the students' book may help.)

4 Write on the board, in large letters: *Earthquakes don't kill!* Ask: Is that true? What was the *real* cause of all the deaths? (Collapsing buildings.) Can we prevent earthquakes? Can we improve buildings?

5 Build a short column from toy bricks or similar, to represent a building, on a flat piece of wood. Ask a pupil to demonstrate what happens when a badly-built building gets shaken during an earthquake. Then ask pupils to suggest how the building could be made quake-proof. (This could lead to further work. See suggestion 19 on page 170 of this book.)

6 We talk about making buildings quake-proof. In fact 'quake-resistant' is a better term. Why do you think this is? (Because no building can withstand the most serious earthquakes without at least some damage.)

7 Many countries are at high risk of earthquakes, because of plate movements. Italy is one of them. Show the movie *Earthquake in Italy.*
(For homework, pupils could try to find out why Italy is earthquake-prone. See suggestion 21 on page 171 of this book.)

Further class and homework activities

A mystery on *geog.1 resources and planning OxBox CD-ROM*

Suggestions 18 – 23 on page 171 of this book

Answers to 'Your turn'

1 Pakistan is in Asia. It shares borders with Iran, Afghanistan, and India. It has a coast on the Arabian sea.

2 Kashmir is disputed territory. Pakistan and India both claim it. Part of it is now controlled by Pakistan, part by India, and part by China. The earthquake was in the Pakistanl part.

3 The explanation could go something like this: Pakistan and Kashmir lie across two giant slabs of rock that are pushing into each other. They are pushing so hard that the rock is under great pressure. So it has lots of cracks in it. One day, the pressure got too much at a place in Kashmir, and a huge mass of rock shot upwards at a crack. This made the ground shake. It was an earthquake!

4 You could start your pupils off by asking them what they see in the photo, and what the woman is doing, and why.

5 It's true that Balakot was an old and historic place. However, the area is at high risk of earthquakes. We can't prevent them. So it would be asking for trouble to rebuild it on the same spot.

6 The plates continue to push into each other. (Experts can tell this using GPS – the global positioning system that uses a set of satellites to detect movement from space.) So more strain is building up in the rock that India, Pakistan and Kashmir lie on. So there will certainly be more earthquakes – but the experts can't say when.

7 Encourage pupils to think about things like these:
- iidentify all the places at high risk of earthquakes; geologists can help with this
- order the buildings in these places to be strengthened, to help them cope with shaking
- make sure new buildings are as quake-proof as possible
- make sure important public buildings (schools, hospitals and so on) are especially sturdy
- bring in tough building laws, making it illegal for people to put up weak buildings
- make sure any new towns are built away from faults
- make sure people are trained in what to do when there's an earthquake (including special earthquake classes in schools)
- make detailed plans about what to do when an earthquake occurs
- arange that doctors, soldiers, helicopters, tents, medical supplies, tinned food supplies, and so on, will be on standby

There is one snag with all this: it will cost a lot. Pakistan is not a wealthy country.

9.6

Tsunami!

help at a glance

About this unit

This unit is about the devastating tsunami in the Indian Ocean, on 26 December 2004. It explains what a tsunami is, and describes the damage this one did, with eye-witness accounts from four people. In 'Your turn', pupils are asked to explain some facts about the tsunami, and come up with ideas for a tsunami warning system.

Key ideas

- Tsunami are waves set off in the ocean, by an earthquake in the ocean floor. The waves travel out in all directions.
- Out in the ocean they travel fast, but are not high. As they approach shallow water they slow down, and a wall of water piles up, sometimes as high as 30 metres.
- When they hit land, these powerful waves can do enormous damage.

Key vocabulary

tsunami, earthquake, epicentre (see the glossary at the end of this book)

Skills practised in 'Your turn'

- Geography skills: interpreting a map; interpreting photos
- Thinking skills: giving reasons and explanations; coming up with ideas for a tsunami warning system

Unit outcomes

By the end of this unit, most pupils should be able to:

- explain what a tsunami is, and what causes it
- explain why it can affect many countries
- describe the damage it can do

Resources

For starter **3** and plenary **5**: all images from the book are on *geog.1 resources and planning OxBox CD-ROM*
For plenary **1**: twelve small slips of paper, numbered 1 to 12

Ideas for a starter

1 Ask: Suppose there was a big earthquake in the ocean floor. What do you think it would do to the water?
2 Ask: Can anyone tell me what a tsunami is? What causes it? Can you tell me anything else about it? Pupils write answers on the board, perhaps in the shape of a high wave, or around a drawing of a high wave.
3 With books closed, display the photo from the top of page 130, and ask questions about it. What do you think is happening here? Who are these people? What are they doing here? Where is this place? Why is this happening?

Ideas for plenaries

Plan plenaries for strategic points throughout the lesson, as well as at the end.

1 At the start of the class, give out twelve slip of paper, numbered 1 to 12, one to each of twelve pupils. Then the pupils read out the text in the corresponding boxes on page 130 of the students' book. Ask them to say *15 minutes after the earthquake* and *two hours after the earthquake* instead of + *15 minutes*, + *2 hours* and so on.

2 Do question **1** of 'Your turn' as a plenary.

3 Do question **2** of 'Your turn' as a plenary.

4 Ask four pupils to read out the eye-witness accounts on page 131 of the students' book.

5 Point out (or display) the photos at the top of page 131. Look at the first one. If you were on a beach and saw the water being sucked away like this, what would you do?

6 Select pairs of pupils to present their ideas for a warning system to the rest of the class. Ask for comments.

Further class and homework activities

Interactive activity for Unit 9.6 on *geog.1 resources and planning OxBox CD-ROM*

Suggestions 24 and 25 on page 171 of this book

Answers to 'Your turn'

1 It's caused by an earthquake in the ocean floor. (And the earthquake is caused by plate movements.)

2 a Many countries border the Indian Ocean. The waves travelled across the ocean in all directions, and reached over a dozen of them. (Some countries were safer because they were sheltered by others.)

b Some countries were futher from the epicentre than others, so it took longer for the waves to reach them.

c Indonesia was very close to the epicentre. Somalia was thousands of kilometres away. The waves lost energy as they travelled, so they did less damage in Somalia.

d The waves may be only a metre high out at sea, and in many ocean-going boats you would not notice this. They slow down and grow taller in the shallower water at the coast.

e The Philippines were sheltered from the tsunami by Thailand and Indonesia. (Students should check the map on pages 140–141 of the students' book.)

3 It's natural to want to help people who have suffered a natural disaster – and especially when they are poor, and clearly can't help themselves. (Most of the affected countries are poor.)
This disaster was especially horrifying because of the large numbers of deaths, and the huge devastation.
In addition, many people around the world wanted to help because they had relatives in the stricken countries, or had been on holiday in those countries.

4 There could be several reasons.
The edge of the Pacific Ocean is a high risk area, on the edge of the Pacific plate.
The Pacific Ocean is vast (it covers almost a third of the earth), and many countries border it. Many of them are wealthy: the USA, Canada, Australia, and Japan, for example, with important coastal cities (such as Tokyo) to protect.
In addition the USA has military bases in the Pacific to protect.
So these countries had the money, expertise, and strong incentives, for setting up a warning system.

5 This could be an interesting challenge for pupils. Help them deduce that there are two parts to it: first, how to detect an earthquake in the ocean floor, and second, how to warn those countries at risk. (Each country in turn has to warn its coastal settlements.) Floating seismometers, satellites, and solar-powered sirens might all contribute?

9.7

Volcanoes

About this unit

This unit looks at the structure of a volcano, and describes the materials that may be thrown out during an eruption. In 'Your turn', pupils draw a diagram of a volcano, study a photo of a landscape devastated by volcanic activity, arrange products of eruptions in order of danger, and write an e-mail with a photo as stimulus.

Key ideas

- Volcanoes are where magma (melted rock) erupts through the Earth's crust. Once out, the magma is called lava.
- Magma can be thin and runny, or thick and sticky (viscous).
- Thick sticky magma causes the most dangerous eruptions because it can't escape from a volcano easily; the pressure builds up until the magma explodes out.
- Explosive eruptions produce particles of all sizes, from dust to blocks of rock.
- A cloud of gas and particles from an explosive eruption will collapse, and rush down the slopes of the volcano as a deadly pyroclastic flow.

Key vocabulary

volcano, magma, lava, viscous, vent, magma chamber, volcanic gas, pyroclastic flow, mudflow, crater (see the glossary at the end of this book)

Skills practised in 'Your turn'

- Geography skills: making and labelling a larger copy of a diagram; analysing photos
- Literacy skills: writing an 'eye-witness' e-mail about an explosive eruption
- Thinking skills: finding explanations; arranging eruption products in order of danger

Unit outcomes

By the end of this unit, most pupils should be able to:

- define the terms given in 'Key vocabulary' above
- draw a labelled cross-section showing the structure of a volcano
- explain why some eruptions are explosive, and others are 'runny'
- list the products from eruptions, and say what damage they do

Resources

For starter **1**: a bottle of fizzy water and some kitchen paper or a kitchen towel

For starter **2** and plenaries **1 – 4**: see *geog.1 resources and planning OxBox CD-ROM*

For starter **3**: sugar paper and coloured marker pens

For plenary **5**: a pair of True/False cards, like referee cards, for each pupil (green for true, red for false)

Ideas for a starter

1. Shake a bottle of fizzy water vigorously. Ask: What will happen if I open the top? Why? (The gas will propel the water out of the bottle.) Open it and watch. The same thing happens in a volcanic eruption – but this time the gas is dissolved in magma. Some magma is very thick and gassy, so it explodes out.
2. With books closed, show the movie *Red hot lava*. What is this stuff? Where did it come from? Why is it like this?
3. Students work in pairs to create a spider map on sugar paper, showing what they know already about volcanoes. (They can return to their spider maps in plenary **6**.)

Ideas for plenaries

Plan plenaries for strategic points throughout the lesson, as well as at the end.

1 Show the movie *Pyroclastic flow*. Discuss it. Then show *Red hot lava* and compare the two.

2 This is an extended version of question **3** in 'Your turn'. Pupils look closely at the damage shown in the upper photo on page 133. (You could display the photo.) The first pupil points out a damaged item (such as the church roof), and suggests what may have happened to it. (It could have caught fire, or collapsed under a heavy layer of ash.) The next pupil points out something different. After a few pupils have had a go, the class may run out of fresh observations.

3 Which kind of eruption was the one in the upper photo on page 133: explosive or non-explosive? (You could display the photo.) Why do you think so?

4 To help pupils with question **5** of 'Your turn', you could display the photo and discuss it, before they start. What is going on here?

5 Call out 10 statements about eruptions, some true and some false. For example:
An eruption in one country can cause damage in countries far away.
Lava flows are much more dangerous than pyroclastic flows.
A pyroclastic flow is when water mixes with gas, ash and other materials.

Pupils raise green or red cards, or shout out *True* or *False*. Where a statement is false, ask a pupil to correct it. Where it is true, ask a pupil to explain why.

6 Pupils who did starter **3** return to their spider maps, and add anything else they have learned, in a different colour. They then come up with ways to group the information. (For example under *Cause, Materials erupted, Damage, Location …*) They could group by underlining in different colours, and add a colour key.

Further class and homework activities

Worksheets 9B, 9E, 9F and 9G on *geog.1 resources and planning OxBox CD-ROM*

Suggestions 26 and 27 on page 171 of this book

Volcano! in *geog.1, Plates, earthquakes and volcanoes*, on *geog.world CD-ROM*

The destruction of Armero in *geog.1, Plates, earthquakes and volcanoes*, on *geog.world CD-ROM*

Slow the flow! on *geog.1 resources and planning OxBox CD-ROM*

Answers to 'Your turn'

1 a Magma: melted rock below ground

b Lava: melted rock that has erupted through the Earth's surface

2 Note that the cloud above the volcano is not a pyroclastic flow – it has not started to flow down the slope yet!
Pupils could label it *cloud of erupted material* or similar.
They could list what it contains.

3 a It was probably covered in a heavy layer of ash, which caused it to collapse. (Or if it were wooden it could have burned.)

b The leaves have been removed, but the trunks still stand. They were probably destroyed by scorching hot volcanic gases.

4 There's not really a correct answer here since the order depends on the nature and intensity of an individual eruption. So expect some discussion. One possible order is shown on the right. If the danger is ranked according to the area affected, plumes of dust would go higher in the list. But one important point is that a pyroclastic flow can much more harm than a lava flow.

5 Mount Pinatubo had an explosive eruption. Students should recognise that the photo shows a pyroclastic flow approaching. (This can travel at 200 km an hour!)

pyroclastic flow: very fast; scorches, burns and smothers everything in its path

ash: can suffocate people and animals; destroys crops; causes buildings to collapse

volcanic gases: cause acid rain; can kill people, animals and plants

plumes of dust: can block out the sun, lowering temperatures around the world; can cause planes to crash

lava flow: destroys crops; can bury and burn towns and villages (but you can run out of its way)

9.8 Montserrat: living with an active volcano

help at a glance

About this unit

This unit describes how Montserrat has changed since 1995, when its volcano awoke. It also explains how the island was formed. In 'Your turn' pupils write a letter describing Plymouth, the island's ruined capital. They consider the impact of the volcano's activity on different groups of people. They make plans for future tourism on the island. And they come up with pros and cons for keeping the island running.

Key ideas

- The Caribbean is a volcanically active region, because the North American, South American and Caribbean plates meet there.
- Montserrat and other islands were in fact created by volcanic activity.
- A volcano that is becoming active usually gives out warning signs. So if scientists are monitoring it, they can warn people. People can be evacuated to a safe place.
- The volcano on Montserrat awoke in 1995. At the start of 2008 it was still showing activity – and no-one can predict how long it will remain active.

Key vocabulary

island arc, vulcanologists, monitor, pyroclastic flow, safe zone, evacuate (see the glossary at the end of this book)

Skills practised in 'Your turn'

- Geography skills: drawing a sketch map based on a photo
- Literacy skills: explaining in own words; writing a letter describing an abandoned town, with a photo as stimulus
- Thinking skills: deducing how the eruptions will have affected different groups; making plans for tourism; finding arguments for and against keeping Montserrat running, and identifying further information that would be needed, to make a final decision

Unit outcomes

By the end of this unit, most pupils should be able to:

- explain the terms given in 'Key vocabulary' above
- describe where Montserrat is, and how it was formed
- give at least four examples of the impact of the volcano's activity

Resources

For starter **1**: outline world map

For starter **3** and plenaries **4** and **5**: a class set of atlases

For starter **4** and plenaries **2** and **3**: see *geog.1 resources and planning OxBox CD-ROM*

Ideas for a starter

1. Where's the Caribbean? Without looking at any other map for help, pupils point out where they think the Caribbean is, on an outline map of the world (on the board) – or else explain without a map. A prize for the first pupil to get it correct?
2. Montserrat is in the Caribbean. How many other Caribbean islands can you name?
3. Have atlases ready on the desks. Ask the pupils 5 or 6 quiz questions about Montserrat. (They have to start by finding it in the atlas.) They could work in pairs.
4. Look for the Caribbean on the map on page 122 of *geog.1* students' book. What do you notice? Now look at the map on page 123. What do you notice? (You could display these maps. They are in the material for Unit 9.2.)

Ideas for plenaries

Plan plenaries for strategic points throughout the lesson, as well as at the end.

1 The UK and Montserrat have strong links. Can anyone tell me why? (It's a British Overseas Territory – it was previously called a colony. It was taken over by the British in 1632.)

2 Show the movie *Montserrat volcano*. Discuss it. What would you say the magma is like inside this volcano: thin and runny, or thick and gassy?

3 Ask questions about the photo of Montserrat on page 120 of *geog.1* students' book. (You could display the photo.)
- Where on the photo is the volcano? What are the clues?
- What are the fluffy white patches? (Clouds.)
- What are the wide grey areas? (The result of pyroclastic flows.)
- Some thinner lines lead to the wide grey areas. What do you think these show? (River valleys. There were many pyroclastic flows down river valleys.)
- Some pyroclastic flows flowed right into the sea and built up a fan-shaped delta. Can you see this on the photo? Where is it? (Lower right.)
- Why is the part below the red line out of bounds?
- Where is the safe zone? About what % of the island is it?
- 1 cm on this photo represents approximately 1.7 km on the ground.
- About how long is the island at its longest point, and how wide at its widest point?
- About how long would it take to cycle all around it, if you cycled at 20 km per hour? (The coastline is about 40 km long.)

4 Look in the atlas and find the island arc that Montserrat belongs to. Which other islands are part of this arc – and formed in the same way as Montserrat?

5 Which other Caribbean islands might be in danger of volcanic eruptions? Why do you think so? (The others in the island arc. Have pupils check the atlas.)

Further class and homework activities

Interactive activity for Unit 9.8 on *geog.1 resources and planning OxBox CD-ROM*

Suggestions 28 – 30 on page 171 of this book

Answers to 'Your turn'

1 The North and South American plates are pushing under the Caribbean plate. As they do so, rock melts and pushes up through the ocean floor, giving underwater volcanoes. One of these formed the island of Montserrat. The plates are still moving, and now molten rock is pushing up through the Montserrat volcano again.

2 Pupils need to understand that Plymouth was burned and buried by several pyroclastic flows, and heavy ash falls, over a long period.

3 a Many farms in the southern part of the island were destroyed by pyroclastic flows, mudflows and ash showers. The farmers can't return to their land because the area is out of bounds. Even in the 'safe' north, ash showers and dust are a nuisance for farmers. (But in the long run volcanic ash, dust and lava make soil fertile.)

b Many hotels were destroyed (eg in Plymouth). The eruptions kept tourists away, and ruined most of the hotel business. For a while, visiting journalists and scientists may have helped business. But overall, it will take a long time for tourism to recover, especially while much of the island still out of bounds.
So hotel owners have probably turned to other occupations.

c Taxi drivers will have little or no work, since tourism is dead, and many of the roads have been destroyed. The safe area is not large so local people might not bother with taxis.

4 c Possible activities: taking boat and helicopter trips around the island to see the damage; guided walks along the edge of the safe area; volcano-viewing through binoculars or a telescope, from a safe vantage point. Maybe the Montserrat Volcano Observatory would allow visits? Then there is swimming and other water sports, and boat trips to neighbouring islands.

d Masks and hard hats available for all tourists, to protect against ashfalls. Keep in close touch with the vulcanologists who are monitoring the volcano. Carry first-aid kits. Tell tourists in advance what they should do in an emergency. Make it clear that the south is out-of-bounds.

e Before-and-after photos? lumps of lava with writing on? phials of ash? volcano videos?

5 a & b Pupils need to think about social issues, not just money. Is it right to force people to leave their country?

c You'd need data about Montserrat's future needs, and whether it can ever support itself; opinions from vulcanologists about the volcano's future activity; and, most important, the opinions of people still living there. They must have a say in any plans.

9.9 Coping with earthquakes and eruptions

help at a glance

About this unit

This unit looks at our responses to the disasters caused by earthquakes and eruptions. In 'Your turn' pupils match definitions to terms, group responses in different ways, and explore the link between a country's wealth and its ability to cope with disasters.

Key ideas

- Our responses to disasters – whether these are the result of earthquakes, eruptions, floods, hurricanes, or other natural hazards – tend to follow a pattern.
- In the short term we rush to help the survivors. Help may arrive from governments, aid agencies, and individuals around the world, as well as from local communities.
- In the long term we try to prevent similar disasters. We can't eliminate natural hazards, but we can set up monitoring and warning systems, try to find reliable ways to predict hazardous events, and take other steps to protect ourselves.
- The wealthier a country, the more effective it's likely to be, in responding to disasters.

Skills practised

- Literacy skills: using the glossary; matching terms to definitions; writing to a word limit
- Numeracy skills: comparing some development indicators for different countries
- Thinking skills: grouping responses in different ways; coming up with reasons and explanations; understanding the implications of some development indicators

Key vocabulary

short-term, long-term, aid agencies, emergency, local, national, international (see the glossary at the end of this book)

Unit outcomes

By the end of this unit, most pupils should be able to:

- explain the terms given in 'Key vocabulary' above
- give three examples of short-term responses to a disaster
- give three examples of long-term responses to a disaster
- explain why poorer countries may find it harder to cope with these disasters

Resources

For starters **1 – 3** and plenaries **2** and **3**: all images from the book are on *geog.1 resources and planning OxBox CD-ROM*

Ideas for a starter

1 Turn to (or display) the photo of the earthquake survivor on page 128 of the students' book. Imagine you are this woman or one of her family. What kind of help will you and your family need straight away? What help will you need in the future? What kind of help would make you feel safer in the future, in or around that area? Write pupils' responses on the board, under the headings *short-term* and *long-term*.

Then ask: What kind of help, if any, would cost nothing to give? Who might be able to provide the help that's needed? The local community? The government? Other countries? Aid agencies? Do you think the answer will be different for different countries? For example will it be different for Pakistan and Italy? Why?

2 Display the three photos from the top row on page 136 of the students' book. What do they they show? They have something in common. What is it?

3 Display the three photos from the second row on page 136 of the students' book. What do they they show? They have something in common. What is it?

Ideas for plenaries

Plan plenaries for strategic points throughout the lesson, as well as at the end.

1. Here are three ways to help survivors of an earthquake, like the one in Balakot:
   - give them food and drinking water
   - help them to build new stronger homes
   - develop a reliable way to predict when earthquakes will occur.

   Which response do you think is the most urgent? Which will probably take longest and cost most? Which would help most people, overall?
2. Any of the starters not used already could be used as a plenary.
3. Do question **4** of 'Your turn' as a plenary. Display the photo for it. What else can you see in the photo? (A river. It is the River Indus.)
4. Earthquakes and volcanoes are hazards. What does that mean? (Potential sources of danger.) What other natural hazards can you name? (Floods, drought, hurricanes, tsunami, forest fires ...) What's the difference between hazards and disasters? (A disaster is when a hazardous event occurs, creating sudden great misfortune for people.) In what ways are our responses likely to be similar, for all these disasters?
5. Do you think we'll always have natural hazards to face? Do you think we'll always have disasters?
6. From what you learned in this chapter, which do you think might be easier to predict: earthquakes or eruptions?
7. Summarise what you learned today in 30 words. Now summarise it in 12. Now summarise it in 3.

Further class and homework activities

Interactive activity for Unit 9.9 on *geog.1 resources and planning OxBox CD-ROM*

Interactive quiz for Chapter 9 on *geog.1 resources and planning OxBox CD-ROM*

Worksheets 9H and 9I on *geog.1 resources and planning OxBox CD-ROM*

Why live in a danger zone? on *geog.1 resources and planning OxBox CD-ROM*

Suggestions 31 – 34 on page 171 of this book

Assessment materials for Chapter 9 on *geog.1 assessment file & OxBox CD-ROM*

Review 'Your goals for this chapter' on page 119 of *geog.1* students' book

Answers to 'Your turn'

1 A = short-term, B = long-term, C = emergency, D = monitor, E = predict, F = geologists, G = aid agencies

2 Responses to the earthquake disaster ...

short-term: A, G, H, J

long-term: B, C, D, E, F, I

3 a local: D, G

b national: B, C, F

c international: A, E, H, I, J

4 The photo should give pupils some idea of the mountainous terrain in northern Pakistan. Many smaller villages are not marked. There are only steep tracks to most villages (and many of these were destroyed by landslides, in the earthquake). Bitter cold, and heavy snow, added greatly to the survivors' problems – and to the difficulties in getting help to them. Often, the only way was by helicopter.

5 a USA

b i USA: most money for delivering good training programmes; highest ratio of TVs on which to show programmes

i USA: best motorway network for moving supplies and helpers around, and moving injured people to hospital; highest ratio of doctors, most money for medical supplies and emergency services

iii USA: as in **ii**.

6 If 'coping well' means rescuing people, and providing help for survivors, and repairing damage, this is true. Wealthier countries generally have a good infrastructure for warning people of danger and getting help to victims; and better equipment and facilities; and more money to spend on training people, and on repairs.

However, poorer countries may show enormous resilience in coping with disaster. For example, think of the millions of people in Bangladesh who cope with severe flooding nearly every year.

9 Further suggestions for class and homework

Most of these suggestions are addressed to your pupils. Where research or further resources are needed, the internet will almost certainly provide the answer. (Eg *google* and choose *Web* or *Images*.)

A slice through the Earth

1 Earth driller You have been ordered by a government to invent a secret machine that can drill a tunnel to the Earth's centre. Describe all the technical problems you will face, going from the crust to the centre. Then see if you can come up with an annotated sketch for your machine! ***

2 Journey to the centre of the Earth (Simpler than **1**.) Design a machine that will drill to the centre of the Earth, taking *you* along for the trip. Label all its specialist features. *

3 Why is it so hot inside the Earth? Find the answer to this question, using books or the internet. ***

4 Capture that heat! Design a system for using the heat inside the Earth to heat homes and/or cook food, all over the world. **/***

5 Ocean mountains and trenches There are many mountains and deep valleys under the oceans. Look in books or on the internet to find out the names and locations of the highest ocean mountains and deepest ocean trenches. Mark them on an outline world map. **

Our cracked Earth

6 The pattern of earthquakes and volcanoes: a writing exercise Pupils write a piece describing the pattern of earthquakes and volcanoes around the world. And then they write an improved version.

a First pupils take five minutes to write a description of the pattern, using the map on page 122 of *geog.1* students' book, or a similar map in an atlas, without much guidance.

b Now the class brainstorms criteria for a good piece of geographical writing. For example *accurate, use correct geographical terms, give some details about places.* The class agrees on a set of criteria, and notes it down.

c Pupils now self-mark what they have written and give it a score out of 10. The teacher could ask some pupils to read theirs aloud, and comment on the score.

d Finally pupils rewrite, using the agreed criteria. This time it will take longer. They use geographical terms – for example *southern hemisphere, Pacific Ocean*. They can include negatives such as: *There are no volcanoes down the east coast of North America.* Encourage pupils to look at a political map of the world in order to give more detail. **/***

7 A supercontinent breaks up A map of the world 300 million years ago would have looked very different from today's map. Then the land formed one big supercontinent, which we call Pangaea. (There were several others too, before it.) Tell the class about Pangaea, and how plate movements led to its break-up. Find an animation to show them. (The internet has many examples. Look for one at the right level.) Then find out how the Earth may look 50 million years from now, at www.scotese.com/future.htm. */**/***

8 Travelling by plate Britain once sat near the equator. We have fossils to prove it! So how did it get to be where it is today? Find out about Pangaea, and how and when it broke up, and how the land that we now live on moved north. Explain what made it move, and add some drawings. ***

9 Countries on the edge Use a world map and plate map to name 15 countries that lie on, or close to, plate edges. *

10 The dinosaurs' world Go to www.scotese.com/K/t.htm to see how the world map may have looked at the time the dinosaurs died out. How has it changed since then? **

How are the plates moving?

11 Draw diagrams showing plate movements From what you remember in class, draw a set of diagrams showing:
- two plates moving apart under the ocean
- an oceanic plate pushing into a continental plate
- a continental plate sliding past another continental plate

Add text explaining what is happening in each diagram. Each time say whether you get earthquakes, volcanoes or both. **

12 Predicting where the trenches are When two plates push into each other under the ocean, one is dragged under the other, or subducted, at an ocean trench.

a Using the map on page 123 of *geog.1* students' book, predict where you are likely to find ocean trenches.

b Then find a map of the ocean floor and check whether you were correct. **/***

13 Ocean trenches What are they like? What kinds of creatures live in them? Find out and tell the class. You could take the Mariana trench, the deepest one, as your example. ***

14 Demonstrate how fold mountains are formed Fold mountains are formed when two continental plates push into each other, squeezing and folding rock upwards. Think of a way to demonstrate this using a suitable material. (Dough?) Make sure it works, and then show the class. *

15 The world's great fold mountains The world has many great ranges of fold mountains. Find out where they are. Then mark and label them on an outline map of the world. **/***

Earthquakes

16 The San Andreas fault Most earthquakes are the result of sudden rock movements along faults. The San Andreas fault is one of the world's most famous ones. Find out about it, and write an article about it for a geography magazine.
- Include a map to show where it is.
- Name the plates that grind along at this fault.
- Say whether there are any earthquakes or volcanoes.
- Include some annotated photos or drawings if you can. ***

17 Which country had an earthquake today? Try an internet search by typing in *earthquakes today*. See if you can download a map, or else mark the earthquake sites on an outline map of the world. ***

Earthquake in Pakistan

18 What's happened to the people of Balakot? See if you can find out what has happened to the people of Balakot and the surrounding villages, since the earthquake in 2005. What about all the people who lost their homes? And how is the new town coming along? Write a report for the class. ***

19 Design a quake-resistant building Pupils explore ways to make a building quake-resistant. Could you cooperate with the design & technology department for this? ***

20 Quake-resistant building Find out what's being done to make buildings quake-resistant. The dome homes in Indonesia are one example. (See page 136 of the students' book.) Try an internet search. Draw sketches and label the special features of buildings you find. ***

21 Why is Italy prone to earthquakes? Find out, and write your answer like a unit in *geog.1* students' book. Add a plate map. What about some earthquake photos? **/***

22 Duck, cover, hold! Carry out an internet search to learn about the earthquake drill taught in North America. Produce a leaflet to teach eight-year-olds the drill. (With drawings?) *

23 Out in an earthquake? What should you do? Do a search on the internet, typing in for example *earthquake safety outdoors.* Using any tips you find, design a set of cards telling people outside, or in cars, how to protect themselves in an earthquake. Use drawings – and as few words as possible! **

Tsunami!

24 Saved by a schoolgirl A British schoolgirl called Tilly Smith, then aged ten, was on holiday in Thailand in December 2004. She saw the tsunami approach. She knew what it was. What happened next? Do an internet search, and write a newspaper report. It MUST be in your own words. Add a map? */**/**

25 A tsunami warning system for the Indian Ocean Is it in place yet? Find out, and tell the class. If it is, here's a challenge: see if you can explain in simple words how it works. **

Volcanoes

26 Make a volcano You will need strips torn from newspaper (about 4 cm by 15 cm), a thick paste made from flour and water, and a small plastic juice bottle as base. Dip the strips in the paste and wrap them around the bottle to build up a volcano shape. (Don't block the neck of the bottle.) You could add one or two secondary vents. When your volcano is dry, paint it with water-based paint and then coat it with varnish. *

27 Make your volcano erupt You will need two teaspoonfuls of baking soda, red food colouring or powdered paint, half a cup of vinegar, a few drops of washing-up liquid, a funnel, and a tray (or a flat surface outdoors). Spoon the baking soda carefully into the bottle. Mix the vinegar, detergent and colouring, and pour the mixture into the bottle through a funnel. Stand back and watch the eruption! *

Montserrat: a volcano awakens

28 History of Montserrat Find out more about the history of Montserrat, from 1600 to today, and write it up as brief notes on a timeline. **/***

29 Montserrat today Use the internet to find out about the current level of activity of the Montserrat volcano. Give the information in the form of a bulletin for Radio Montserrat. **

30 Monitor eruptions around the world Use the Volcano World website: volcano.und/nodak.edu/ to find out which volcanoes have been active in the last four weeks. Mark them on an outline map of the world. **

Coping with earthquakes and eruptions

31 Earthquakes and the aid agencies Using reports on the Pakistan earthquake of 2005 (or a more recent earthquake) as an example, find out:
- which agencies provide aid to earthquake victims
- what kind of aid they provide
- where they get the money and materials from. ***

These websites may be useful: oxfam.org.uk ifrc.org/news oneworld.org christian-aid.org.uk dfid.gov.uk

32 Launch an appeal for disaster victims It is December 2004. You have a 40-second TV slot to launch an appeal for help, for the survivors of the tsunami around the Indian Ocean. Write a script to fit exactly 40 seconds. Draw a storyboard to go with it, showing the images you will broadcast. **

33 Predicting earthquakes If we could reliably predict earthquakes, hundreds of thousands of lives would be saved. But how good are the experts at predicting them? Work with a partner or small group to find out. A good start: type *predicting earthquakes* into a search engine. ***

34 Play Taboo Divide the class into paired teams to play this game – perhaps 4 or 5 in a team. There are two parts to the game. Each team follows the instructions below.

a First, choose the taboo words.

– Choose 6 key words on earthquakes or volcanoes (or both). Make a card for each.

– At the top write the key word, and in a different colour add five words that you'd really really want to use, if you were explaining the key word to someone else. (These become the taboo words.)

b Now play the game.

– Swap all your cards with another team – but not your opposing team. (No team should have the cards it prepared.)

– Now, play the game with your opposing team.

Each team takes turns. To play, a pupil chooses a card, hidden from the rest of his or her team, and then gives verbal clues, *but without using any of the taboo words*, to help the rest of the team guess the key word. The team has just one minute to guess, but can make any number of guesses in that time.

– Meanwhile the opposing team must keep an eye on the clock *and* make sure that no taboo words are used. (So the opposing team must see the chosen card.)

c Then the teams reverse roles. **

Glossary

A

abrasion – the scratching and scraping of a river bed and banks by the stones and sand in the river.

active volcano – a volcano that has erupted recently and is likely to do so again.

aerial photo – a photo taken from above (for example from an aircraft or hot-air balloon); it can be a vertical aerial view (from directly above) or an oblique view (from an angle).

aid – help given by one country to another.

aftershocks – small tremors that follow an earthquake. They can continue for hours or even weeks, while the rocks settle into a new position.

aid agency – a non-governmental organisation that helps people in poorer countries, or in emergencies; Oxfam and the Red Cross are examples.

altitude – height of a place above sea level.

annotations – notes added to a sketch map, pointing out important or interesting features.

asylum seeker – a person who flees to another country for safety, and asks to be allowed to stay there.

atmosphere – the layer of gas around the Earth.

attrition – how rocks and stones get worn away by knocking against each other, in rivers (and in the sea).

B

bedload – stones and other materials that roll or bounce along a river bed. (It is too heavy to be carried along.)

bedrock – the solid rock below the soil.

biological weathering – where plant roots grow into cracks in rock and make them widen. This helps to break the rock down.

brownfield site – a site that was already built on, and is being redeveloped.

built environment – the built things that surround us. These include streets, shops and housing.

business park – an area set up as a place for modern businesses.

C

capital city – the main city in a country. Paris is the capital of France. The capital city is usually the largest city – but not always.

catchment area – the area from which a school draws its pupils, or a shopping centre draws its customers; or another term for a river's drainage basin.

central business district (CBD) – the area at the centre of a town or city where you find the main shops and offices.

channel – the trench in which a river flows.

chemical weathering – the breaking down of rock by chemical reaction with air or water. For example rain attacks and dissolves limestone.

city – a large settlement. Cities offer more services than towns do.

climate – the 'average' weather in a place (what it's usually like).

cloud – a collection of tiny water droplets high in the air. When the droplets join to form larger drops, it rains.

Commonwealth of countries – a 'club' of 53 countries, including the UK, with strong historical links; 51 of them were Britiish colonies.

commute – to travel to another place to your work (for example live in Aylesbury and commute to London.

comparison goods – goods like clothes, shoes, and furniture, where you like to see a choice before you buy.

condense – to change from gas to liquid. Water vapour condenses to water when it's cooled.

confluence – the point where two rivers join.

congestion – overcrowding in a town or city; and traffic jams.

consumers – people who buy and use goods and services.

contaminated – contains harmful things; for example, contaminated soil has absorbed harmful chemicals or organisms.

contour line – line on a map joining places that are the same height above sea level.

conurbation – a continuous built-up area formed when towns and cities spread so much that they join up.

convection current – a current of material, for example air, water, or soft rock, that flows upwards because it is warmer than its surroundings.

convenience goods – low-cost goods like milk, newspapers and sweets that you buy in the nearest convenient place.

core – the innermost layer of the Earth. It is mainly iron plus a little nickel.

corner shop – a small shop in a residential area, selling things like food and newspapers. It may be owned and run by a local family.

crater – the hollow at the mouth of a volcano. Lakes often form in craters.

crust – the thin outer layer of the Earth, made of rock. We live on the crust.

D

dam – a wall built across a river to control the flow of water. Dams are used to prevent flooding, or provide hydroelectricity, or both.

defence forces – the army, navy, air force; they defend the country from attack.

delta – a flat area at the mouth of a river, made of sediment deposited by the river.

department store – a large shop selling a wide range of goods, from perfume to furniture. It usually takes up at least two floors.

deposit – to set down, or drop; a river deposits sand and other material as it slows down and loses energy.

derelict – run-down and abandoned. For example a derelict house.

detached house – it stands alone, not joined on to other houses.

developed country – one with a good standard of living – good houses, schools, roads and so on.

developers – companies that buy land and put up buildings, then rent them out or sell them.

development – a housing estate or shopping plaza or other group of buildings, built as one project.

disaster relief – help given to the survivors of a disaster. It is usually in the form of food, water, shelter, medicine and clothing.

dormant volcano – a 'sleeping' volcano. It has not erupted for many years, but may erupt again one day.

dormitory town – people live there but travel somewhere else to work.

drainage basin – the land around a river, from which rainwater drains into the river. (It is also called the river basin or catchment area.) Heavy rain in the drainage basin can lead to flooding.

dwelling – a building to live in (like a house or flat).

E

earthquake – a shaking in the Earth's crust set off by a sudden rock movement (when rock that was under strain gives way).

economic – about money and business.

economic activity – work you earn money from.

economic migrants – people who move to a new place to find work, and to improve their standard of living.

embankment – a river bank that has been built up to stop the river flooding.

emergency services – services such as police, ambulance and fire brigade that help when people are in danger, for example during a flood.

emigrant – a person who leaves his or her own country to settle in another country.

Environment Agency – the body that looks after rivers and the environment in England and Wales. It issues flood warnings and has a Floodline you can ring.

environmental – to do with our surroundings and how we look after them (air, rivers, wildlife and so on).

environmental geography – about how we interact with and affect the natural environment.

epicentre – the point on the ground directly above the focus (centre) of an earthquake.

equator – an imaginary line around the centre of the Earth, from which latitude is measured. (London is 51.5° north of the equator.)

erosion – when a river picks up particles of rock and soil from its bed and banks. It carries them along and eventually deposits them again.

estuary – the mouth of a large river, which is affected by the tides. As the tide rises, sea water flows into the estuary and mixes with the river water.

euro – a currency used in common by several EU countries

European Union – a 'club' of European countries that trade freely with each other, and share many laws and aims; 27 countries have joined it, including the UK.

evacuate – to move people from a dangerous place to a safe one (for example when a volcanic eruption is expected).

evaporation – the change from liquid to gas.

extinct volcano – a volcano that has not erupted for thousands of years and is not likely to erupt again.

F

fault – a break in layers of rock, showing where a mass of rock has dropped down, or slid up, or slipped sideways.

flash flood – a sudden flood, usually caused by a very heavy burst of rain.

flood – an overflow of water from the river.

flood defences – built to stop rivers flooding, or protect us from floods. For example embankments along rivers, and flood walls around buildings.

flood plain – flat land around a river that gets flooded when the river overflows.

focus – the centre of an earthquake. It is the exact point where rock moved, setting off the quake. It could be far below the ground.

fold mountain – a mountain formed when land gets folded upwards because tectonic plates are pushing into each other.

foreshocks – small tremors that occur before an earthquake. They could start weeks before it. They can act as a warning.

fossil fuels – coal, oil, natural gas.

fumarole – a vent or opening in or around a volcano, that gives out steam and hot gases. Dormant volcanoes often have active fumaroles.

function – an activity in a settlement; for example its main function could be as a port or seaside resort; but it will offer other functions too, such as shopping, and financial services.

G

GDP – see gross domestic product.

GDP per capita – the GDP divided by the population. It gives you an idea of how well off the people in a country are, on average. It is given in US dollars (PPP) so countries can be compared fairly. (PPP stands for purchasing power parity.)

geologist – a person who studies rocks.

geology – the study of rocks.

geothermal energy – energy from hot rock; water is pumped down to the rock and turned into steam, which can then be used to heat homes or make electricity.

geyser – a burst of boiling water and steam from the ground. It is caused by hot rock below the surface making groundwater boil.

glacier – a river of ice.

gorge – a narrow valley with steep sides.

global warming – average temperatures around the world are rising; experts say this is largely due to carbon dioxide from burning fossil fuels.

granite – a hard rock formed when melted rock (magma) cools and hardens underground. So granite is an igneous rock.

gravity – an attractive force between two bodies, that depends on their mass; for example the force between the Earth and the sun, that keeps the Earth in its orbit around the sun; gravity makes things we throw in the air fall back to the Earth again.

green belt – an area of open land around a city, which is protected from development, to stop the city spreading further.

greenfield site – a site that has not been built on before.

grid lines – lines we draw on a map, to make it easier to find places; we number the lines, or label the rows and columns of the grid with letters and numbers; then we can find or refer to places use grid references.

grid reference – a set of numbers, or numbers and letters, that helps you find a place on a map.

gross domestic product – the total value of the goods and services produced in a country in a year. It is given in US dollars (PPP) so countries can be compared fairly. (PPP stands for purchasing power parity.)

groundwater – rainwater that has soaked down through the ground and filled up the cracks in the rock below.

H

hamlet – a very small settlement with only small number of houses. Many hamlets have no shop of any kind, and not even a pub.

hazard – a source of potential danger.

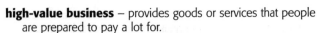

high-value business – provides goods or services that people are prepared to pay a lot for.

housing estate – a cluster of homes that have been planned and built together, as one project.

human geography – to do with how and where we live, the settlements we live in, how we earn a living, and so on.

hydraulic action – the action of water pressure in breaking up a river bank. In a fast flowing river, the water is forced into cracks in the bank.

hydroelectricity – electricity generated by using rivers to spin turbines. The turbines are usually built into the walls of dams.

hydrograph – a graph to show how the flow of water in a river changes over time, for example during a flood.

hydrological cycle – see water cycle.

hydrology – the study of the water cycle or any part of it.

I

igneous rock – the type of rock formed when melted rock (magma) cools and hardens into crystals. Granite is an example.

image – a photo or drawing of something.

immigrant – a person who moves here from another country, to live.

impermeable – does not let water pass through. Granite is impermeable.

industrial area – an area where you find factories and industrial estates.

Industrial Revolution – the period of history (around the 18th century when many new machines were invented and many factories built).

industry – a branch of manufacturing or trade, such as the car industry or the building industry.

infiltration – the soaking of rainwater into the ground.

infrastructure – the basic services in a country, such as roads, railways, water supply, telephone system.

insulated – surrounded or covered with something that prevents heat loss (or that stops sound or an electric current getting through).

insurance – you pay a fee to insure an item; then if it gets lost or damaged, the insurance company gives you money to repair or replace it.

interception – the capture of rainwater by leaves. Some evaporates again and the rest trickles to the ground.

interdependence – how countries, depend on each other.

international – to do with more than one country.

internet – the network of millions of computers around the world, all linked together. A lot of shopping is done over the internet.

invader – someone who enters a country to attack it.

irrigate – to water crops (and not leave it up to the rain)

isobar – a line on a weather map joining places with the same air pressure.

isotherm – line on a map joining places that are at the same temperature.

L

landfill site – a site set aside for dumping rubbish.

landform – a feature formed by erosion or deposition (for example a V-shaped valley).

land use – what a piece of land is used for. (It could be used for shops, homes or schools, for example.) There is often conflict over land use.

landslide – when land slides down a slope. It could be caused by an earthquake, or a long period of heavy rain. A landslide can take roads, homes and people with it.

landslip – another word for landslide.

latitude – how far a place is north or south of the equator, in degrees.

lava – melted rock that erupts from a volcano.

leeward – sheltered from the wind.

lithosphere – the hard outer part of the Earth's surface. It is broken into large pieces called plates that are slowly moving around.

local – to do with the area around you.

location – where something is.

long profile – a cross section along a river bed showing how it slopes from the source to the sea.

long-term – for the years ahead, stretching into the future.

longitude – how far a place is east or west of the prime meridian, in degrees.

low-level job – does not need much skill, and is not well paid.

M

magma – melted rock below the Earth's surface. When it reaches the surface it is called lava.

magnitude of an earthquake – how much energy it releases. This is measured on the Richter scale.

mantle – the middle layer of the Earth, between the crust and the core.

manufacturing – making goods in factories.

market town – a town that grew because of its market (like Aylesbury did); today it may have some industry too.

meander – a bend in a river.

media – forms of communication, such as TV, radio, newspapers, the internet.

mental map – a map you create and carry in your head; it is really a sequence of images, like a movie; it helps you find your way around.

merchandise – goods for sale.

migrant – a person who moves to another part of the country or another country, often just to work for a while.

model – a simplified picture of a system, that shows its overall properties and what the patterns are.

monsoon – the season in south-east Asia when warm moist winds blow in from the sea, bringing lots of rain.

mouth – the end point of a river, where it enters the sea or a lake.

mudflow – a river of mud. It can form when material from an erupting volcano mixes with ice or water, or when heavy rain washes loose earth away. (They are also called lahars.)

N

natural – to do with, or produced by, nature – not made by humans.

natural environment – the air, rivers, mountains, and other natural things around us.

natural hazard – a natural source of potential danger. Earthquakes and volcanic eruptions are natural hazards.

national – to do with the whole country (eg the national anthem).

NGO (non-governmental organisation) – a not-for-profit organisation, such as Oxfam, that helps people and is independent of the government.

North Atlantic Drift – a warm current in the Atlantic Ocean; it keeps the weather on the west coast of Britain mild in winter.

O

Ordnance Survey – the official government agency that produces maps of the UK; you can buy OS maps for every part of the UK.

OS map – a map of an area produced by the Ordnance Survey, a government body. It uses OS symbols to show features such as car parks and churches.

out-of-town development – a development such as a new shopping centre that is built outside of the town.

out-of-town shopping centre – a shopping centre built outside a town or city, with a wide range of shops, and large car parks; it will have restaurants, and perhaps other services such as banks, a medical centre, and a cinema.

oxbow lake – a lake formed when a loop in a river is cut off by floods.

P

peninsula – a piece of land almost surrounded by water.

permeable – lets water soak through.

persecute – to punish or treat cruelly (for example because of race or religion).

physical geography – is about the natural features around us: mountains, rivers, the oceans, glaciers, deserts, water, climate and so on.

physical weathering – where rock is broken into smaller pieces by the action of heat, cold and ice. (But it is not chemically changed.)

plan – a map of a small area (such as a room) drawn to scale.

plates – the Earth's surface is broken into large slabs. The slabs are called tectonic plates, or just plates.

plunge pool – a deep pool at the base of a waterfall.

population – the number of people living in a place.

population density – the average number of people per square kilometre. Population density is high in urban areas and low in rural areas.

porous – has tiny holes that let water through. Gritstone is a porous rock.

pothole – a hole down through rock, caused by weathering and erosion. You find potholes in limestone areas.

precipitation – water falling from the sky (as rain, hail, sleet or snow).

prevailing winds – the ones that blow most often; in the UK they are south west winds (blowing from the south west).

primary sector – the part of the economy where people take things from the Earth and sea (farming, fishing, mining).

prime meridian – an imaginary line around the Earth, through the north and south poles, from which longitude is measured. (It's also called the Greenwich meridian.)

profit – the money you get paid for something, minus your expenses in providing or making the thing.

pyroclastic flow – a scorching hot avalanche of gas, ash, cinders and rocks that rushes down the slopes of a volcano after an explosive eruption.

Q

quake-proof – short for earthquake-proof: designed so that it can cope with being shaken in an earthquake.

quaternary sector – the part of the economy where people do high-tech research (for example into genes).

R

rain shadow – area sheltered from the rain by a hill or mountain.

recycle – to use again; for example to turn waste paper into pulp, and back into new paper, or to melt down old bottles to make new ones.

redevelop – to rebuild on a site that has already been in use.

refugee – a person who has been forced to flee from danger (for example from war).

regenerate – redevelop a run-down area and bring it back to life again.

relief – the height of the land. A relief map shows mountains, hills and low land.

reservoir – a structure where water is stored for our water supply. Reservoirs look like lakes (and some are made from lakes).

residential area – an area of a town or city that is mainly housing (rather than shops or offices).

Richter scale – a scale for measuring the amount of energy given out in an earthquake.

Ring of Fire – the ring of volcanoes around the Pacific Ocean.

run off – rainwater that runs across the surface of the ground and drains into the river.

rural area – an area of countryside, where people live on farms and in villages.

S

saltation – the bouncing movement of sand and small stones along a river bed.

saturated – soil is saturated when it is so full of water that no more can soak in.

scale – the ratio of the distance on a map to the real distance.

secondary sector – the part of the economy where people make or manufacture things (such as cars or furniture).

sediment – a layer of material (stones, sand and mud) deposited by a river.

sedimentary rock – forms when sediment is compressed over millions of years. Limestone is an example. Different types of sediment give different rock.

seismic wave – wave of energy given out in an earthquake; it shakes everything.

seismometer – an instrument for recording vibrations during an earthquake.

semi-detached house – it is joined to one other house.

service – something set up to meet people's needs. For example a shop, a school, a library, the postal service.

service provider – the company that gives you access to the internet; you usually have to pay a monthly fee.

settlement – a place where people live. It could be a hamlet, village, town or city.

settlement function – the main activity of a settlement. For example it could be a port or seaside resort or industrial town.

settlement hierarchy – settlements in order of size, with the largest one first. (The capital city is usually at the top of the hierarchy.)

settler – a person who settles in a place where no-one has lived before.

sewage works – where all the waste liquid from our homes is cleaned up, before it is put back into the river.

shopping centre – has many shops under one roof. Shopping centres are often several storeys high and include cafés, restaurants and a post office.

shopping parade – a short block of shops in a residential area in the suburbs. It might include a post office and hair salon, for example.

short-term – just for the days and weeks (and perhaps months) ahead.

silt – fine particles of soil carried by rivers.

site – the land a settlement is built on.

situation – the position of a settlement in relation to things like rivers, hills and other settlements.

sketch map – a simple map to show what a place is like, or how to get there; it is not drawn to scale.

social – about society and our way of life.

soil – a mixture of clay, sand and the remains of dead plants. It forms when rock is broken down by weathering.

solution – the dissolving of minerals from a river bed and banks, by the water.

source – the starting point of a river.

southern hemisphere – the half of the world south of the equator.

species – a species consists of a group of related organisms that are capable of interbreeding; we belong to the species Homo sapiens.

sphere of influence – area around a settlement (or shop, or other service) where its effect is felt. London has a very large sphere of influence.

spot height – a dot and number on an OS map, showing the height of that place above sea level (in metres).

spring – a flow of fresh water from the ground.

suburbs – areas that are mainly residential, some distance from the CBD; the inner suburbs are closer to the centre, while the outer suburbs are on the edge of the town or city

supermarket – a shop selling food, drinks and household goods (mainly convenience goods, but sometimes more expensive goods such as microwave cookers) that you pick from shelves, put in a basket or trolley, and bring to the check-out

suspension – small particles of rock and soil carried along in the river. They make the water look cloudy or muddy.

sustainable development – brings economic, social and environmental benefits, and can be carried on into the future, without doing harm

T

tectonic plates – the Earth's surface is broken into large slabs. The slabs are called tectonic plates (or just plates).

terraced house – a house joined on to other houses, forming a row of houses.

tertiary sector – the part of the economy where people provide services (for example techers, doctors, taxi drivers).

throughflow – the flow of rainwater sideways through the soil, towards the river.

TNC (transnational corporation) – a big company that has branches in different countries; Nike is a TNC.

town – a quite large and densely populated settlement. It may offer a good range of services – but not as many as a city does.

traction – the rolling movement of rocks and stones along a river bed.

transpiration – the loss of water through the leaves of a plant. The roots take in water from the soil to replace it.

transport – the carrying away of eroded material by rivers.

treaty – a binding agreement between countries

trench – a deep V-shaped valley in the ocean floor.

tributary – a river that flows into a larger one.

tropics – the part of the Earth that lies between the Tropic of Cancer (23.5 °N) and the Tropic of Capricorn (23.5 °S).

tsunami – a huge wave caused by an underwater earthquake.

U

urban area – a built-up area, such as part of a city. It's the opposite of rural.

urban regeneration – when a run-down urban area is redeveloped and brought to life again.

U-shaped valley – a valley shaped like the letter U, carved out by a glacier.

V

vale – a very broad open valley.

valley – an area of low land, with higher land on each side. It may have a river flowing through it.

vent – a hole through which lava erupts, on a volcano.

venue – a place where an event is held; for example Wembley stadium.

village – a small settlement with only a small range of services. For example many small villages have only one or two shops.

volcano – where melted rock comes out through the Earth's surface. Many volcanoes are cone-shaped mountains, with an opening (vent) in the top.

V-shaped valley – a valley shaped like the letter V, carved out by a river.

vulcanologist – a volcano scientist.

W

water cycle – the non-stop cycle in which water is evaporated from the sea into the air, falls as rain, and returns to the sea in rivers.

water table – the upper surface of groundwater. The water table rises and falls depending on how much rain there is.

water vapour – water in gas form.

waterfall – where a river or stream flows over a steep drop.

watershed – an imaginary line separating one river drainage basin from the next.

weather – the state of the atmosphere – for example how warm or wet or windy it is.

weathering – the breaking down of rock. It's caused mainly by the weather.

windward – facing into the wind.